Home Life

the low-carb bible

A three-stage plan for permanent weight loss

linda gassenheimer

Kyle Cathie Limited

To Harold – for his love of good food and his enthusiastic support and advice.

Published in Great Britain 2005 by
Kyle Cathie Limited
122 Arlington Road
London NW1 7HP
www.kylecathie.com
general.enquiries@kyle-cathie.com

First published in USA as *Low-carb Meals in Minutes* and *More Low-carb Meals in Mintues*
by Bay Books, San Francisco, USA, and in Great Britain as *Low-carb Meals in Minutes* and *Low-carb Diet for LIfe*.

ISBN 1 85626 574 9

Text © 2000, 2003, 2005 Linda Gassenheimer
Photography © 2001, 2003 Juliet Piddington

Senior Editor: Helen Woodhall
Editor of The Low-carb Bible: Stephanie Horner
Anglicisation: Delora Jones
Designer: Mark Buckingham
Production: Sha Huxtable and Alice Holloway

Linda Gassenheimer is hereby identified as the author of this work
in accordance with Section 77 of the Copyright, Designs and Patents Act 1988.

A Cataloguing In Publication record for this title is available from the British Library.

Colour separations by Scanhouse Ltd.
Printed and bound by Kyodo

contents

introduction

Why are millions of people giving up their bagels, sandwiches and pasta meals? After unsuccessful attempts at weight loss from low-fat, high-carb diets, they're finally getting the results they want from a low-carb lifestyle.

My experience began nine years ago. My husband told me he was going to try a low-carbohydrate diet. My first reaction was, 'Why? We have always eaten well-balanced meals, and most diets are just fads.' But he was determined. He had never had a weight problem before, but he found the few pounds gained during a holiday weren't coming off. In addition, he had just come from the cardiologist, where he learned his triglycerides were at an all-time high and his cholesterol was creeping into an area of concern.

As I watched him struggle to put together low-carb meals, I realised that this was going to be a challenge for both of us. Bagels for breakfast and cans of sugary soft drinks after tennis were out. No more baked potato with his steak. And what could he substitute for crackers and crisps with drinks?

I read all of the available books on the subject and set out to create low-carb recipes and menus that suited our fast-paced lives. As I became more involved, I worked with several cardiologists, endocrinologists and nutritionists working in the field. What I found was that the doctors and nutritionists could readily explain why this approach worked, but they could not tell me how to adapt it to my busy life. In fact, when I attended medical lectures, the reception for the diet was highly enthusiastic, but the questions at the end – even from the doctors in the audience – were 'How do I do it? What do I eat?' I began writing articles, giving lectures and teaching cooking classes. As I heard from readers and worked with participants in my classes, I was astounded by their weight-loss results. However, they were starved for additional recipes, techniques and guidelines.

I was lost when I first tried to make low-carbohydrate meals. I had to fundamentally rethink my approach to shopping and cooking. I started by restocking the pantry and refrigerator. The changes were dramatic.

off the list were:

- Low-fat processed foods, such as fat-free biscuits, cakes and other sugary desserts.
- Fat-free mayonnaise, salad dressings, cream cheese and soured cream.
- Condiments, sauces and salsas where sugar is one of the first five ingredients.
- Pancakes, bagels and waffles.
- Jams and jellies.
- Pizza and platefuls of pasta as a main course.
- Garnished baked potato as a meal.
- Sugary soft drinks and fruit juices.
- Crisps, pretzels and popcorn.

on the list were:

- Eggs, as many as four a week. We hadn't eaten them for breakfast in 10 years.
- Egg substitute (which is basically egg whites), as a good source of protein.
- A well-stocked vegetable drawer: lettuce cucumbers, celery, peppers, mushrooms, tomatoes.
- Low-fat deli meats, such as turkey breast, chicken, ham and lean roast beef.
- Brown rice and wholemeal pasta, in place of the lower fibre, less nutritious white varieties.
- High-fibre, whole-grain breads that are relatively low in carbohydrate.
- No-sugar-added tomato sauce and salad dressings.
- Real mayonnaise made with soya bean or olive oil
- High-fibre, no-sugar-added, bran breakfast cereal.
- Olive and rapeseed oil.
- Walnuts, pecans, almonds and peanuts.
- Eight glasses or 1.8 litres (3 pints) of water a day.

With this list of dos and don'ts, I created recipes that are fast, fun and delicious. My husband's response was enthusiastic: he lowered his cholesterol and triglyceride counts to healthy levels, lost his extra weight and has kept it off for five years.

Why is this lifestyle becoming mainstream? What are the principles behind it, and why is it working for so many people?

The theory behind low-carbohydrate, high-protein diets is this: eating lots of carbohydrates could over-stimulate insulin production, causing peaks and valleys in blood sugar levels that might, in turn, create hunger pangs. On the other hand, protein is digested more slowly, promoting more even blood sugar levels. Eating more protein, fewer carbs and more mono-unsaturated fat promotes weight loss by decreasing fat storage, increasing fat burning and delaying the onset of hunger pangs.

Several cardiologists steered me away from diets that call for high levels of saturated fat. My experience has also been that many diets are based on gimmicks. My husband and I, as well as my readers, like to go out and enjoy our meals. We don't want to be oddities at the dinner table, especially in business situations. We want to be part of the mainstream, and we've found that special timing and food combination requirements are unnecessary. They're difficult to follow and stick to over a long period, and they're not necessary for a successful low-carb lifestyle.

So how do you get started? *The Low-Carb Bible* follows my 'Dinner in Minutes' promise: attractive, delicious, fun, healthy, complete meals that are quick and easy to make.

The menus are designed to fit our fast-paced lives. After many years of juggling my family, career and a desire for good food, I've learned to use classic techniques and familiar combinations to produce delicious results while cutting cooking time.

For many days of the week we eat breakfast on the run, if at all, and lunch at our desks or at a fast food restaurant, while dinner is takeaway, home-delivered or restaurant fare. So, I've included some recipes based on assembling prepared foods, as well as a guide to eating out and ordering in.

You will find a wide variety of meals that sample many ethnic flavours. Wherever I travel throughout the world, I go to street markets with chefs, taste their foods and bring back their flavours to add to the repertoire of simple, low-carb recipes.

The Low Carb Bible covers all aspects of food, from purchasing to preparing ingredients. It streamlines the organisation of your kitchen. An efficient kitchen with equipment in easy reach, uncluttered work surfaces and a clean sink can save you 10–15 minutes of preparation time. The recipes use staples you will keep in your store cupboard and a few products you can readily buy with one-stop shopping in your local supermarket, and there's no need to think about how to cook a dish or what goes with it. Lastly, presentation is as important as preparation. If a dish doesn't look attractive, nothing else matters.

Consider 'Dinner in Minutes' an approach you can use for everyday meals, or dressed up for parties and special events. Each recipe works as a blueprint you can adapt, within the blueprint guidelines, to suit both your taste and the occasion. This flexible approach lets you choose whatever is in season, on sale or just fits your mood:

- You can buy the freshest looking fish available rather than the variety called for in a recipe.
- You can use the best sirloin or fillet steak, or more economical cuts like flank and skirt steaks.
- Branching out to use the freshest and best ingredients, like a gourmet infused olive oil or aged balsamic vinegar, will add even more flavour.

shopping list

Each recipe contains a shopping list based on how most people buy food.

- The shopping list saves you both time and money since you buy only what you need.
- Ingredients are listed by supermarket sections to help you navigate the aisles with ease.
- I've included tips on how to get in and out of the supermarket fast and how to take advantage of today's timesaving prepared foods.
- Quick shopping is as important as quick cooking. You won't have to think about how many mushrooms to buy. I've given you the amount.

- The staples list helps you organise your cupboards, so that they are not filled with extraneous items. You will already have many of the ingredients for the recipes and will only need to buy a few fresh items.

helpful hints and countdown

Each meal contains helpful hints on shopping, preparation, cooking and substitutions, as well as a countdown for getting the whole meal on the table at the same time.

- You can hit the kitchen on the run without having to plan or think about each step.
- In my home the dinner preparation starts the minute I turn on the light in the kitchen, and it does not end until the plates are brought to the table.
- The helpful hints tell you what to buy, how to buy it and what you can substitute. They include tips on the best preparation method and quick-cooking techniques, as well as time-saving clean-up tips.

Low-carbohydrate programmes are normally divided into three phases: an initial phase of significant carbohydrate reduction, an intermediate phase for reintroduction of carbs and a maintenance phase of balanced eating.

3-step low-carb eating plan

1 quick start: reducing carbohydrate intake for maximum weight loss

The first step to successful eating in this plan calls for a reduction of carbohydrates. While differences exist, most proponents of lower carb levels advise an intake of about 30–40 grams of carbs a day. My Quick Start section maintains that level through healthy dishes using vegetables and lean proteins. My students tell me breakfast is the greatest challenge to adapting to low-carb eating. The 14-day menu plans give you a variety of easy recipes – some simple ones for breakfast on the run, and others that can be completed in 15–20 minutes. Salads and wraps fit the bill for lunches. Try the Mozzarella Tomato Tower or Smoked Trout Salad. Many are available on restaurant menus, and you can use the recipes for proportion guidelines. Dinner can be Pecan-Crusted Fish or Pacific Rim Pork, both taking only minutes to make.

2 which carbs: reintroducing carbs while continuing to lose weight

Two things usually happen at this point. You're losing weight and feel good, so you stay on the first phase until you get bored, or tempted. Or, you think, 'Great, I've lost weight! Now I can have the foods I love and forget about the carb restrictions.' The Which Carbs 14-day menu plan will help you sail through the second phase without having to question what you're eating. I reintroduce carbohydrates in the form of high-fibre, low-simple sugar carbohydrates. Bran breakfast cereal helps start the day the low-carb way. Add to this dishes like Cheddar Scramble or Raspberry Smoothie. Cajun Prawn Salad or Turkey and Tzatziki Sandwich are two tasty lunches. How does Pesto Chicken or Seared Sesame Tuna sound for dinner?

3 right carbs: permanent level with great food for a healthy lifestyle

So, what should you eat to maintain your weight loss? Right Carbs has the answers. Vietnamese Pancakes, Prawn Caesar Wrap and Chicken with Parmesan and Tomato Sauce are a breakfast, lunch and dinner that are quick to make, fit the guidelines and, most important of all, taste fabulous!

Does it mean you can't have desserts? No. Some meals include a dessert, often based on fresh fruit or yoghurt, which completes the nutritional composition of the meal. In addition, I have created a guilt-free Desserts chapter to satisfy your sweet tooth. When you want to take the time to make a special dessert, try Strawberry Pecan Whip or Mocha Fudge Soufflé.

So how does my husband handle holidays and blow-out weekends? No need to worry here. Remember, balance is the key. We have found that you can splurge on special occasions without negative effects when you return to eating the Right Carbs. In other words, the low-carbohydrate approach is forgiving. Following the programme, even with some deviations, will produce a good result. My husband found that returning to the Right Carbs is easy because it takes so little effort and the menus are so appealing. Any time you want to restart weight loss, you can go back to Quick Start for a week or two and work yourself back up to Right Carbs.

The 14-day menu plans at the start of each of the three sections are organised to provide a day-to-day guide to low-carb eating. The breakfasts, lunches and dinners are presented as entire meals. While you can mix and match if you prefer a different side dish, the meals have been created to achieve the nutritional priorities of that phase. By all means, if you don't like or can't eat a particular food, simply replace that meal with another from the same section. Regardless of the section, feel free to substitute fish or chicken for each other.

Regulating your intake of tea and coffee is important on the low-carb diet. One cup of either with each meal is fine – preferably decaffeinated. If you are drinking more than this, it really should be decaff. For the Quick Start programme, omit the skimmed milk if you can; once you move on to Which Carbs and Right Carbs, adding skimmed milk is OK. As for alcohol, limit yourself to 1 glass of wine or 1 measure of spirits a day.

The Low-Carb Bible is for all of you who want to eat healthily and be able to fit a low-carbohydrate weight-loss programme into your time-starved lives. The low-carb lifestyle has certainly changed our lives. My husband and I no longer think about what is and isn't low-carb – we just consider it good food that fits into our busy schedule.

Before starting a programme of this type, it is always best to check with your doctor first. This is especially true if you are taking any medication under a doctor's care – particularly if being treated for diabetes. It might be interesting to look at your cholesterol and related blood tests before and after to compare your results.

My goal in sharing these recipes with you is to help you enjoy good food for good health. My husband and I love good food. Now, with these recipes, we can live to eat and eat to live. *Bon appétit.*

smart shopping the low-carb way

When I was the Executive Director of a gourmet grocery chain, I used to hear people say, 'I hate shopping. I'd cook more if I had the ingredients at home.' Here are some tips that will help get you in and out of the shops quickly.

some advice

The adage of 'don't go shopping on an empty stomach' is true. If I go to the shops when I'm tired and hungry, I just get to a starving point and eat anything offered to me. Go after a meal, or have a snack before you go. This will help you concentrate on what you should be buying instead of what you shouldn't buy.

Try to go to the supermarket when it isn't crowded or directly after a long day's work. Carry a cool box in your car so you can stop on the way to work, during lunch or at other times. Alternatively, if you have use of an office refrigerator, use it to store groceries. Here's a hint: there have been many times when I've accidentally left my shopping at work or at a friend's house. The best solution is to put your car keys in one of the bags. You won't be able to go anywhere without them.

Keep the foods from the staples list on hand. (See pages 16–17.) You will only need to pick up a few fresh items to complete your meal.

supermarket savvy
let the markets help you

Supermarkets are in a 'meals solution' revolution. They are constantly updating their selection to help us get our meals on the table fast. Use them to your advantage.

dairy

Reduced-fat cheese has come a long way. Gone is the rubbery cheese that won't melt. Many producers have used new techniques to develop lower fat cheeses that melt well.

deli

Ask for roast chicken breast only. Look for new leaner cuts of cooked meats – gammon, roast beef and ham have been made leaner without the use of high carbs.

fruit and veg

Bags of washed, ready-to-eat salads are one of the best conveniences I've seen. Read the labels. If they don't say ready-to-eat or washed, then you will need to wash the ingredients prior to using.

Many supermarkets have prepared, ready-to-eat vegetables as well as cubes of melon and pineapple – another time-saving buy.

meat

Look for lower fat or lean meats – supermarkets may have separate sections for lean meats or mark them with special labels. Of the many marinated or precooked meats available, check their sugar, salt and fat content.

salad bar

Great for picking up a quick salad or lunch and buying cut vegetables and fruits for cooking at home.

supermarket aisles

There are many items that make our lives easier, with more coming out each day. Low-fat, no-sugar-added salad dressings and tomato-based pasta sauces are a few of the products. In fact, there are so many available, it's best to try a few and, when you find one you like, buy several bottles to keep on hand. Again, the most important advice is to read the nutritional labels and ingredients lists.

how to read the labels

It's worth spending a few minutes reading food labels, as many prepared foods have added salt and sugar. However, the terms used can be confusing:

In the US, the Food Safety Act of 1990 makes it an offence to falsely describe a food's contents. Other provisions cover specific terms.

- 'Low-fat' means 3g or less per 100g/ml.
- 'Low-sodium' means 40mg or less per 100g/ml.
- 'Sugar Free' means 0.2g or less per 100g/ml.
- 'No added sugar' means no sugar, or foods composed mainly of sugar are added to the food or its ingredients.
- 'Light' or 'lite' is not covered by law. This term can be used to describe the texture of a food, or to suggest it is low in fat.

serving size

Always check the serving size on the label. It can be misleading. If the serving size is 1 tablespoon, you need to think whether that is the amount you will actually eat.

Ingredients must be listed in descending order by weight. Generally, if an ingredient is fifth or lower in the list, it has minimal amounts in each serving.

Here are some guidelines on what to look for on nutritional labels:

Oil and Vinegar Dressing, Balsamic Dressing, Vinaigrettes

The nutritional analysis for meals using one of these dressings is based on either olive oil or rapeseed oil being used. Try to stay away from non-fat dressings. In general, when they cut the fat, they add carbohydrates.

Look for:

Quantity	Calories	Carbohydrates
1 tablespoon	75	0.5–1.5g

Mayonnaise

Look for:

Soya bean oil, rapeseed oil or olive oil (Major brands are made with soya bean oil.)

Quantity	Calories	Carbohydrates
1 tablespoon	100	0g

Reduced-fat Mayonnaise

Look for:

Quantity	Calories	Carbohydrates	Fat
1 tablespoon	50	1g	5g

Caesar Dressing

Look for:

Quantity	Calories	Carbohydrates
1 tablespoon	80	0.5–1.5g

Tomato and Pasta Sauces

Select no-sugar-added, no-salt-added, or low-sodium brands. There are now many excellent ones.

Look for:

Quantity	Calories	Carbohydrates	Fibre	Sodium	Fat
225ml (8fl oz)	60–80	12–14g	2–3g	40mg	0g

Non-fat, Low-sodium Chicken Stock

Look for:

Quantity	Calories	Sodium
225ml (8 fl oz)	15	560mg

Low-Sodium Soy Sauce

Look for:

Quantity	Calories	Sodium
1 tablespoon	10	574mg

Tortilla (15cm/6in)

Look for:

Quantity	Calories	Carbohydrates
25g (1 oz)	90	16g

Wholemeal Bread

Look for:

Quantity	Calories	Carbohydrates	Fibre
1 slice	50	10g	3g

Other Breads and Rolls

Look for:

Quantity	Calories	Carbohydrates	Fibre
1 slice/1 roll	80	15g	0.7–2g

Bran Cereal*

Look for:

Quantity	Calories	Carbohydrates	Fibre
25g (1oz)	80	24g	13g

*Read labels carefully; labels say cereals are healthy, but look for the amounts of sugar, syrup or honey.

Lean Ham and Gammon

Look for:

Quantity	Calories	Sodium	Fat
25g (1oz)	37	246mg	1.4g

Reduced-Fat, Semi-Skimmed Milk Mozzarella Cheese

Look for:

Quantity	Calories	Fat	Sodium
25g (1oz)	72	4.5g	132mg

Peppers

Look for:

Quantity	Calories	Carbohydrates	Fat	Sodium
225g (8oz)	40	8g	0g	20mg

Marinated Artichoke Hearts

Look for:

Quantity	Calories	Carbohydrates	Fat	Sodium
25g (1oz)	25	2g	1.5g	90mg

Unsweetened Apple Sauce

Look for:

Quantity	Calories	Carbohydrates	Sodium
225ml (8fl oz)	100	30g	30mg

Low-Fat Frozen Yoghurt

Look for:

Quantity	Calories	Fat	Carbohydrates
115ml (4fl oz)	120	3g	20g

staples

Keep these staples permanently in stock and you'll only need to shop for a few fresh items to make quick tasty meals.

bottled or tinned goods

Dijon mustard

Fat-free, low-sodium chicken stock

Haricot, cannellini and black beans and chickpeas

Mayonnaise made with olive or soya bean oil

Low-sodium, no-sugar-added chopped tomatoes and tomato sauce

Low-sodium tomato juice

No-sugar-added oil and vinegar dressing

No-sugar-added tomato salsa

Palm hearts

Tuna packed in water

Water chestnuts

condiments

Hot pepper sauce

Low-sodium soy sauce

Worcestershire sauce

dairy

Eggs

Egg substitute (basically liquid egg whites)

Light yoghurt

Parmesan cheese

Reduced-fat Swiss, Cheddar and mozzarella cheese

Reduced-fat cottage cheese

Skimmed milk

deli

Chicken breast

Lean ham (avoid honey-smoked or sugar-glazed)

Lean gammon

Lean roast beef

Turkey breast

dry goods

Artificial sweetener, preferably granulated

High-fibre, no-sugar-added, bran breakfast cereal

Oatmeal

Salt

Wholemeal flour

Wholemeal pasta

Mushroom, Turkey and Tarragon Omelette   **p43**

Turkey Salsa Roll **p42**

freezer goods

Frozen, diced green sweet pepper

Frozen, diced onion

grains and breads

Barley

Brown rice

Lentils

Pearl barley

Multi-grain bread

100% wholemeal bread

Rye bread

Wholemeal pitta bread

Wholemeal tortillas

Wild rice

oils and vinegars

Balsamic vinegar

Distilled white vinegar

Olive oil

Olive oil spray

Rapeseed oil

Red wine vinegar

Rice vinegar

fresh produce department

Celery

Cucumbers

Garlic

Lemon

Peppers

Red onions

Yellow onions

Tomatoes

spices and herbs

Black peppercorns

Cayenne pepper

Chilli powder

Ground cinnamon

Ground cumin

Dried chives

Dried dill

Dried oregano

Dried rosemary

Dried tarragon

equipment

You really don't need a lot of special equipment to make these meals. However, the following items will speed your preparation time and make your life easier.

food processor

A food processor or hand-held blender will quickly slice, chop and blend foods together.

garlic press

Some of the newer ones allow you to crush garlic without peeling the cloves.

knives

Sharp knives are important for fast and accurate cutting. A dull knife can be dangerous. It can slip or slide when you are trying to slice. Three different types are all you really need for most cutting tasks: a 33cm (13in), 20.5cm (8in) and a serrated knife for fruits or tomatoes. Vegetable peelers are actually little knives: for easy peeling, make sure yours is sharp, and replace as soon as it starts to dull.

microwave oven

Use this fast-cooking tool. And remember, any dish that's microwave safe is dishwasher safe, too.

meat thermometer

I love the new style probe that uses a cord which is connected to a dial that sits on the worktop. It works well for items on the hob, in the oven or under the grill.

pots and pans

You can make most of the meals in this book using a medium 23–25.5cm (9–10in) non-stick frying pan, a large 3–4 litre (5–7 pint) saucepan and a wok. Nonstick frying pans are essential, as these recipes are designed for cooking with small amounts of oil. If you follow the instructions, your food will not stick.

scale

A small kitchen scale is very handy and inexpensive.

quick cooking tips and helpful hints

Each recipe has a helpful hints section. Knowing what to substitute, how best to prepare ingredients or some other shortcut can make a big difference to the time it takes you to get your meal on the table.

chopping fresh herbs

To quickly chop herbs, dry and snip the leaves right off the stem with scissors.

crisp stir-fry

For crisp, not steamed, stir-fried vegetables, start with a very hot wok or frying pan. Let the vegetables sit a minute before tossing to allow the wok to regain its heat.

dried spices and herbs

If using dried spices, make sure they are less than 6 months old. To bring out the flavour of dried herbs, chop them with fresh parsley. The juice from the parsley will help release the flavour of the herbs.

electric cooking

To get a quick high/low response from electric rings, heat two rings, one on medium-high and the other on low. Move the pan back and forth between them.

fluffy rice

I like to cook my rice like pasta, using a pot of boiling water that's large enough for the rice to roll freely. Use this method or follow the directions on the packet of rice.

food processor

To use the food processor for a recipe without having to stop to wash the bowl, first chop the dry ingredients (such as nuts), and then the wet ones (such as onion). You won't have to stop in the middle of preparing the ingredients.

fresh ginger

To chop fresh ginger quickly, cut it into small cubes and press through a garlic press with large holes. If using a press with small holes, just capture the juice that is squeezed out; it will give enough flavour for the recipe.

parmesan cheese

Buy good quality Parmesan and grate it by hand or in a food processor. Freeze extra for use later – simply spoon out what you need and leave the rest frozen.

peeling prawns

Buying peeled prawns saves time otherwise spent shelling them yourself.

timely stir-fry

To keep from looking back at a recipe as you stir-fry the ingredients, line them up on a cutting board or plate in the order of use. You will know which ingredient comes next.

washing herbs

To wash watercress, rocket, parsley or basil quickly, place the bunch, head first, into a bowl of water. Leave for a minute, then lift out and shake dry. The dirt and sand will be left behind. Repeat if necessary.

low-carb food guidelines

After you've cooked several recipes in this book, you will begin to understand the types of ingredients and proportions that are part of a low-carb lifestyle. Use these foods to help you create your own menus.

Vegetables are an important part of a healthy eating lifestyle. You may find it hard to believe that vegetables have carbohydrates, some more than others. Here's a list of low-carb vegetables, versus those with high carbs to be eaten in smaller quantities.

eat as many of these vegetables as you like:

Alfalfa sprouts

Artichokes

Asparagus

Aubergine

Bok choy

Broccoli

Brussels sprouts

Cabbage

Cauliflower

Celery

Courgettes

Cucumber

Green beans

Herbs, all types

Kale

Leeks

Lettuce, all types

Mange tout

Mixed salad leaves

Mushrooms, all types

Onions/spring onions

Okra

Peppers (sweet peppers and all hot peppers)

Radishes

Spinach

Swedes

Swiss chard

Tomatoes

Turnips

Yellow courgettes

eat these vegetables in measured amounts (about 75g/3oz per serving):

Beetroot

Carrots

Hard squash, such as acorn or butternut

Potatoes

Sweetcorn

fruits

Fruits are often high in carbohydrates, and they should be avoided during the Quick Start phase. They are reintroduced in the Which Carbs and Right Carbs stages. The amounts given below are guidelines for how much should be eaten at a serving:

Apple (1 small)

Apricots (4)

Apricots, dried (7 halves)

Banana (½)

Berries: strawberries, raspberries and blueberries (110g/4oz)

Cantaloupe (¼ whole cantaloupe)

Cherries (12 cherries)

Grapes (about 12)

Grapefruit (½)

Honeydew (¼ whole honeydew)

Kiwi (1)

Lemon juice (50ml/2fl oz)

Lime juice (50ml/2fl oz)

Nectarine (1)

Orange (1)

Tangerine (1)

Mango (½)

Peach (1)

Pear (1)

Pineapple (2 rings or 60g/2½oz)

Plums (2)

Watermelon (175g/6oz)

meats, poultry and seafood

Here's a list of the leaner cuts:

beef

Fillet

Sirloin and minced sirloin

Silverside

Topside

pork

Fillet

Lean gammon

Lean ham (no honey-baked or sugar-glazed)

veal

Escalope

Leg fillet

Loin chop

lamb

Leg (preferred)

Chops with visible fat removed

poultry (skinless)

Chicken breast

Chicken legs

Turkey breast and low-fat turkey sausage

Poussins

Spring chicken

seafood

All types of shellfish. Tuna, salmon, sardines, mackerel, halibut and trout are high in omega-3 fatty acids. Try to eat one of these on a regular basis.

tips for eating out

One of the biggest challenges to eating a healthy diet is that many of our meals are prepared outside the home. We eat out, order in and eat on the run. Use the recipes in this book as a guide to eating out, and you will be able to order from the menu with confidence. Here are some additional hints and tips to eat well:

- Avoid all deep-fried foods.

- Avoid sugary drinks. Opt for water, unsweetened iced tea or diet soft drinks.

- Plain, soft tacos or tortilla-filled wraps are fine as long as they aren't filled with rice and beans.

- Roasted or grilled meats are best. Make sure you include vegetables with your meal and avoid sugar-based sauces, especially barbecue sauce and most glazes.

- Many meals are loaded with carbs. If possible, order two vegetables instead of a starch.

- Ask for your salad dressing on the side. You'll be surprised at how far 1 tablespoon of dressing will go, or just dip your salad into the dressing.

- If you order dessert, share it with the table or make sure you don't have a starch during dinner. Better still, order a fresh fruit salad or berries.

- Have a low-carb snack (vegetables, a few nuts, a slice of low-fat cheese) before you go out to eat. This will help you avoid the basket of bread while you're waiting for your meal.

- Don't go out for drinks on an empty stomach. One drink will make you hungry, and you'll eat the first thing you can find. Have a healthy snack before you go out. If you think it will be a long night, start with sparkling water with a piece of lemon or lime or a diet soft drink first.

- Fast food can be fine. Order grilled chicken or fish and discard the bread or eat half a roll only. Stay away from baked potatoes, chips and crisps.

- Chinese food can be loaded with sugar. Order stir-fried meats and vegetables or skewered meats, and avoid soups with fried wontons, egg rolls, ribs in thick sauce and noodles. Some restaurants now offer brown rice as an alternative to white.

- Italian food doesn't have to mean a plate of pasta. Order an antipasto platter or any of the meats, salads or vegetables.

- French food can be very healthy. Order clear soups, salads, vegetables, meats or seafood, but avoid heavy sauces and bread.

- Japanese sushi is based on rice – very often

with sugar added to it. Try miso soup or any of the cooked meats and vegetables instead.

● Mexican food can be high in saturated fat and carbohydrates. Fajitas (1 tortilla) with garnishes, grilled meats and salads are fine. Avoid rice, refried beans and nachos.

sizing it up*

Watch portion size when eating out. Here's a guide to help you size up what you should be eating.

75g (3oz) cooked meat, poultry, or fish	a deck of cards
35g (1½oz) cheese	6 dice
1 tortilla	an 18cm- (7in-) plate
1 muffin	a large egg
1 teaspoon butter	a thumb tip
2 tablespoons peanut butter	a golf ball

*Food Insight News published by IFIC (International Food Information Council)

Snacks are important little meals that will help you through the day, especially during the Quick Start phase. They can prevent that sinking feeling at 4 or 5 p.m. when your energy is low, or the mid-morning, is-it-time-for-lunch clock watching.

Knowing what to snack on and how to have it handy can help prevent raids on the vending machine to satiate sweet cravings. Here are some ideas:

● If you've had an extra large salad for lunch, take some back to the office or home and use the remainder as an afternoon snack.

● 25g (1oz) low-fat cheese

● 50ml (2fl oz) low-fat cottage cheese

● 25g (1oz) nuts, such as almonds, pecans and walnuts. Keep portion-sized packets of nuts in your drawer at work, handbag or brief case.

● 50g (2oz) deli meats, such as lean ham, turkey, chicken or roast beef

● 1 hard-boiled egg. Keep a few hard-boiled eggs on hand for snacks. They need to be refrigerated.

● 25g (1oz) sunflower seeds

● 6 olives

● Raw vegetables (cucumber, celery sticks, broccoli or cauliflower florets, sliced pepper)

quick start

To start you off cutting carbs, I have devised two-week menu plans. Follow one of the two provided here, or pick and choose dishes between them for extra variety.

When I give cooking classes and present these meals, the reaction is always one of surprise: 'You mean I can eat all of that?' Knowing the quantities of each type of food you can eat will help you to build your own recipes to fit your lifestyle.

I have organised the menus into a meal-at-a-glance chart with some easy and quick meals mid-week and those that take a little more time for the weekends. They are arranged to give variety throughout the day and over the days of the week.

Breakfast

There's plenty of variety in these breakfasts to fit all tastes, from Microwave Marinara Scramble to Turkey Salsa Roll. Pick the ones you like and use them for this initial Quick Start two-week period.

Mid-Morning Snack

When you first start reducing your carbohydrate intake, you will find you need to eat a mid-morning snack. I've included a section with some suggestions. (See page 23.)

Lunch

There's a lunch for any occasion here – quick-take lunches that can be eaten at home or taken with you, more elaborate lunches for when you have more time or friends come round.

Enjoy Spanish Tuna-Stuffed Tomatoes and Nutty Chicken Minestrone. Both these meals can be made at home and taken to work. They are commonly found on lunch menus. If you are eating out, use these recipes as a guide for the portion size you should eat.

I've got into the habit of ordering my salads with the dressing on the side. Most salads come swimming in dressing. I find that 1 tablespoon of dressing gently coats the salad without overpowering it. So, I prefer to add the dressing to the salad myself. (See pages 22–23 for more tips on eating out.)

Mid-Afternoon Snack

When you first start reducing carbs, you will need to eat a mid-afternoon snack. (See page 23 for some healthy low-carb options.)

Dinner

Do you feel like eating Italian, French, Greek or American food tonight? There's something from each ethnic group – Steak au Poivre, Marsala Chicken, Roasted Salmon and Herb Sauce, Greek Prawns with Feta Cheese, and Chicken Burgers with Warm Mushroom Salad are some of the tempting meals you'll want to try. For those days during the week when you are really pressed for time, select Jamaican Jerk Pork or Savoury Sage Chicken from the Super Speed Suppers section of the book. For weekends, when you have more time and want something special, try the Dijon Chicken with Crunchy Couscous or Garlic-Stuffed Steak from the Weekends section of the book.

How low is low carb? It's important to reduce carbohydrate intake low enough for a period of time so that you eliminate the peaks of insulin secretion. Following one of my Quick Start 14-Day Menu Plans, you will consume an average of 30–40 grams of carbohydrates per day. Carbohydrate percentage is based on carbohydrates less fibre consumed, which is the normal way of calculating carbohydrate consumption. The balance of these meals is 11 per cent of calories from carbs, 38 per cent of calories from lean protein, and 36 per cent of calories from mono-unsaturated and polyunsaturated fats and 11 per cent of calories from saturated fat.

To achieve the correct balance, I have structured the recipes as complete meals. Whatever meal you pick, it's best to stay with the entire menu given.

quick start 14-day menu plan (1)

week 1	breakfast	lunch	dinner
sunday	Smoked Salmon Pinwheels 31	Mozzarella Tomato Tower 48	Spicy Prawns with Roasted Asparagus 71
monday	Devilish Eggs 38	Turkey Bundles 47	Asian Ginger Salmon 77
tuesday	Swiss Scramble 39	Tuna Salad Wraps 50	Glazed Balsamic Chicken 75
wednesday	Cheesy Fried Eggs 32	Smoked Trout Salad 51	Tex-Mex Meat Loaf . . .73
thursday	Sautéed Ham and Tomatoes 33	Roast Beef and Watercress Wraps 52	Marsala Chicken 86
friday	Florentine Eggs and Ham 34	Grilled Cheddar and Chicken Salad 54	Sirloin Burger with Fresh Slaw 82
saturday	Sausage and Vegetable Stir Fry 35	Portobello Stuffed with Smoked Trout and Sun-dried Tomatoes . . .55	Pacific Rim Pork 79

week 2	breakfast	lunch	dinner
sunday	Pepper and Turkey Omelette 36	Salmon Balsamico 49	Veal Escalopes with Garlic Greens 81
monday	Smoked Chicken and Cheddar Grill 37	Turkey Bundles 47	Pecan-crusted Fish with Vegetable Creole 74
tuesday	Devilish Eggs 38	Greek Salad 53	Glazed Balsamic Chicken 75
wednesday	Swiss Scramble 39	Grilled Cheddar and Chicken Salad 54	Salsa-baked Snapper 70
thursday	Sautéed Ham and Tomatoes 33	Smoked Trout Salad . . .51	Rosemary-roasted Pork 83
friday	Cheesy Fried Eggs 32	Roast Beef and Watercress Wrap 52	Herb-stuffed Chicken 85
saturday	Cheddar and Sausage Frittata 40	Portobellos Stuffed with Smoked Trout and Sun-dried Tomatoes 55	Steak au Poivre 90

quick start 14-day menu plan (2)

week 1	breakfast	lunch	dinner
sunday	Bacon and Cheese Crêpes 41	Mozzarella Tomato Tower...........................48	Dijon Chicken with Crunchy Couscous 249
monday	Microwave Eggs Parmesan....................44	Chicken with Dill Mustard.....................56	Greek Prawns with Feta Cheese 233
tuesday	Mushroom, Turkey and Tarragon Omelette........43	Cheese and Chicken Bundles.....................57	Hot Pepper Prawns.......63
wednesday	Turkey Salsa Roll...........42	Nutty Chicken Minestrone 58	Mediterranean Baked Fish.............................64
thursday	Microwave Marinara Scramble.....................45	Spanish Tuna-Stuffed Tomatoes.....................59	Savoury Sage Chicken.....................235
friday	Sautéed Ham and Tomatoes.....................33	Crunchy Oriental Chicken Salad.............................60	Jamaican Jerk Pork........234
saturday	Cheddar and Sausage Frittata..........................40	Crab Gratin...................61	Chicken Burgers with Warm Mushroom Salad..........68

week 2	breakfast	lunch	dinner
sunday	Bacon and Cheese Crêpes 41	Mozzarella Tomato Tower.........................48	Garlic Stuffed-Steak 250
monday	Microwave Eggs Parmesan...................44	Chicken with Dill Mustard.....................56	Crab Cakes and Slaw....................69
tuesday	Mushroom, Turkey and Tarragon Omelette........43	Cheese and Chicken Bundles.....................57	Pork Escalopes with Spinach and Mushrooms.................88
wednesday	Turkey Salsa Roll...........42	Nutty Chicken Minestrone..................58	Roasted Salmon and Herb Sauce.........................89
thursday	Microwave Marinara Scramble.....................45	Spanish Tuna-Stuffed Tomatoes.....................59	Tuscan Chicken............66
friday	Sautéed Ham and Tomatoes.....................33	Crunchy Oriental Chicken Salad...........................60	Savoury Sage Chicken......................235
saturday	Cheddar and Sausage Frittata........................40	Crab Gratin...................61	Veal Saltimbocca...........252

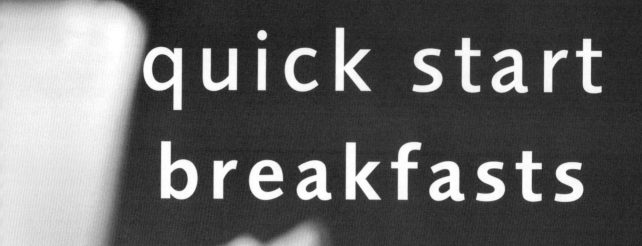

quick start breakfasts

smoked salmon pinwheels

Smoked salmon spread with cream cheese makes an elegant, quick breakfast for midweek or the weekend.

smoked salmon pinwheels

350g (12oz) smoked salmon
50g (2oz) low-fat cream cheese
1 tablespoon skimmed milk
1 medium cucumber, sliced
2 medium tomatoes, sliced
Salt and freshly ground black pepper to taste

Place salmon on a cutting board. Soften cream cheese with skimmed milk and mix until smooth. Spread on salmon. Roll up, slice crosswise into 1cm (½in) pinwheels, and place on 2 plates. Season the cucumber and tomato slices with salt and pepper and divide between the plates. *Makes 2 servings.*

One serving: 324 calories, 37g protein, 11g carbohydrate, 14g fat (6g saturated), 61mg cholesterol, 1468mg sodium, 1g fibre

countdown

- *Slice cucumber and tomatoes.*
- *Complete recipe.*

shopping list

DAIRY
   1 small packet low-fat cream cheese (50g/2oz needed)
FISH
   350g (12oz) sliced smoked salmon
FRUIT AND VEG
   1 medium cucumber
   2 medium tomatoes
STAPLES
   Skimmed milk
   Salt
   Black peppercorns

cheesy fried eggs

Eggs sunny side up are an American tradition. Here's a variation on the theme.

cheesy fried eggs

2 handfuls washed, ready-to-eat lettuce leaves

Half a cucumber, peeled and sliced

2 teaspoons olive oil

2 large eggs

Salt and freshly ground black pepper to taste

75g (3oz) sliced reduced-fat Swiss or Gruyère cheese (about 4 slices)

Place the lettuce on a plate and microwave on high for 1 minute. Divide the lettuce and cucumber between 2 plates, and heat the olive oil in a medium-sized non-stick frying pan over a medium-high heat. Break the eggs into the pan, and sprinkle with salt and pepper to taste. Cover and cook for 2 minutes. Remove the lid and place the cheese over the egg yolks. Cover and cook 1 minute. Serve the eggs on the cooked lettuce.

Makes 2 servings.

One serving: 265 calories, 23g protein, 8g carbohydrate, 17g fat (6g saturated), 236mg cholesterol, 147mg sodium, 1g fibre

helpful hints

- If you like your egg yolk cooked through, flip the egg over in the pan before adding the cheese.
- To determine the weight of each slice of cheese, divide the packet weight by the number of slices.

countdown

- Microwave lettuce.
- Slice cucumber.
- Cook egg.

shopping list

DAIRY

1 packet sliced reduced-fat Swiss or Gruyère cheese (75g/3oz needed)

FRUIT AND VEG

1 packet washed, ready-to-eat lettuce

Half a cucumber

STAPLES

Olive oil

Eggs

Salt

Black peppercorns

smoked salmon pinwheels   p31

florentine eggs and ham　p34

sautéed ham and tomatoes

This is a quick, 5-minute breakfast that can be made in a frying pan, grill pan or microwave oven.

sautéed ham and tomatoes

225g (8oz) sliced lean ham
2 small tomatoes, sliced
2 teaspoons olive oil
Salt and freshly ground black
*   pepper to taste*

Sauté the ham in a medium-sized non-stick frying pan over a medium-high heat for 2 minutes, or until the ham begins to brown. Place the tomatoes on 2 plates and drizzle with olive oil. Sprinkle with salt and pepper to taste. Divide the ham between the plates and serve.
Makes 2 servings.

One serving: 305 calories, 30g protein, 12g carbohydrate, 16g fat (5g saturated), 136mg cholesterol, 797mg sodium, 3g fibre

helpful hint

● *Look for low-fat ham. Stay away from honey-baked ham.*

countdown

● *Preheat grill (if using).*
● *Cook ham.*
● *Assemble dish.*

shopping list

DELI
    225g (8oz) sliced lean ham
FRUIT AND VEG
    2 small tomatoes
STAPLES
    Olive oil
    Salt
    Black peppercorns

florentine eggs and ham

Cooking the washed, ready-to-eat spinach in a microwave makes this a 15-minute breakfast.

florentine eggs and ham

florentine eggs and ham

275g (10oz) washed, ready-to-eat fresh spinach

2 tablespoons freshly grated Parmesan cheese

Salt and freshly ground black pepper to taste

225g (8oz) sliced lean ham (about 8 slices), cut into strips

1 tablespoon distilled white vinegar

2 eggs

Place the spinach in a microwave-safe bowl and microwave on high for 5 minutes. Sprinkle with the Parmesan cheese and season with salt and pepper to taste. Chop the cooked spinach into bite-sized pieces and divide between 2 plates.

Set a medium-sized non-stick frying pan over a medium heat. Add the ham and sauté for 2 minutes, or until slightly browned. Divide evenly over the beds of spinach.

Next, add the vinegar to a pan of simmering water and create a whirlpool in its centre. Drop an egg into the whirlpool, turn off the heat and leave covered for 4 minutes, or until set. Repeat with the second egg. Serve the eggs over the ham and spinach.

Makes 2 servings.

One serving: 337 calories, 37g protein, 10g carbohydrate, 19g fat (5g saturated), 270mg cholesterol, 1501mg sodium, 7g fibre

helpful hints

● Buy good quality Parmesan cheese and grate it yourself. Freeze extra for quick use later – simply spoon out what you need and leave the rest frozen.

● If you prefer fried eggs add the olive oil to the same pan. Break the eggs into the pan and fry until set, about 1 minute. Using a spatula, gently turn the eggs over. Sprinkle with salt and pepper to taste.

countdown

● Make spinach.
● Make ham and eggs.

shopping list

DELI
    225g (8oz) sliced lean ham

FRUIT AND VEG
    1 bag washed, ready-to-eat fresh spinach (275g/10oz needed)

STAPLES
    Eggs
    Parmesan cheese
    Olive oil
    Salt
    Black peppercorns

sausage and vegetable stir fry

Here's a tasty breakfast made without eggs. If you can find them, keep frozen, diced onions and green pepper to use when really pressed for time. The flavour and texture are slightly different, but the results are good and save chopping time.

sausage and vegetable stir fry

275g (10oz) washed, ready-to-eat fresh spinach

Salt and freshly ground black pepper to taste

2 teaspoons olive oil

2 low-fat turkey sausages (175g/6oz), cut into 1cm (½in) slices

4 slices yellow onion

1 medium-sized green pepper, seeded and sliced

6 button mushrooms, sliced

Place the spinach in a microwave-safe bowl and microwave on high for 5 minutes. Add salt and pepper to taste. Divide the spinach between 2 plates. Heat the olive oil in a non-stick frying pan over a medium-high heat. Add sausages, onion, pepper and mushrooms. Sauté for 5 minutes or until sausages are cooked through. Season with salt and pepper to taste. Spoon over spinach. Makes 2 servings.

One serving: 271 calories, 22g protein, 18g carbohydrate, 13g fat (3g saturated), 45mg cholesterol, 715mg sodium, 7g fibre

helpful hints

● *To determine the weight of each sausage, divide the packet weight by the number of sausages.*

● *To save time, buy sliced mushrooms.*

● *If using whole mushrooms, clean them with a damp paper towel.*

countdown

● *Microwave spinach.*

● *Sauté sausage and vegetables.*

shopping list

MEAT
  1 small packet low-fat turkey sausages (175g/6oz needed)

FRUIT AND VEG
  1 small bag washed, ready-to-eat fresh spinach
  1 medium-sized green pepper
  1 small packet button mushrooms

STAPLES
  Yellow onion
  Olive oil
  Salt
  Black peppercorns

pepper and turkey omelette

Colourful peppers flavour this tasty omelette – and it takes only 20 minutes from start to finish. The recipe can easily be doubled, saving half for the next day. Simply rewarm in a microwave for about 2 minutes on high.

pepper and turkey omelette

225ml (8fl oz) egg substitute
25g (1oz) chopped fresh parsley
Salt and freshly ground black
    pepper to taste
2 teaspoons olive oil
1 medium-sized red pepper, sliced
1 medium-sized yellow pepper,
    sliced
175g (6oz) sliced smoked turkey
    breast, diced

Preheat the grill. Combine the egg substitute and parsley. Add salt and pepper to taste. Place a medium-sized non-stick frying pan over a medium-high heat and add the oil. Sauté the peppers for 5 minutes. Add the egg mixture and turkey and allow to set for 2 minutes. Place under the grill for 3 minutes. Remove from the grill, cut in half, slide out of the pan and serve hot. *Makes 2 servings.*

One serving: 289 calories, 39g protein,
13g carbohydrate, 8g fat (2g saturated),
60mg cholesterol, 295mg sodium, 0g fibre

helpful hints

- To speed cooking the peppers, place them in a microwave-safe bowl and microwave on high for 2 minutes and then sauté them with the turkey for a few seconds before adding the eggs.
- Any mixture of peppers can be used for a colourful effect: red, yellow, green, orange or purple.
- 2 whole eggs and 6 egg whites can be used instead of the egg substitute.

countdown

- Preheat grill.
- Prepare ingredients.
- Make omelette.

shopping list

DELI
    175g (6oz) sliced smoked
    turkey breast
FRUIT AND VEG
    1 small bunch fresh parsley
    1 medium-sized red pepper
    1 medium-sized yellow
    pepper
STAPLES
    Egg substitute
    Olive oil
    Salt
    Black peppercorns

smoked chicken and cheddar grill

This is an on-the-go breakfast that can be made in 5 minutes. Any type of lean or low-fat cooked meat can be used.

smoked chicken and cheddar grill

2 large cucumbers, peeled and sliced on the diagonal

2 tablespoons mayonnaise made with soya bean or olive oil

175g (6oz) sliced roasted chicken breast

Salt and freshly ground black pepper to taste

35g (1½oz) sliced reduced-fat Cheddar cheese (about 2 slices)

Preheat the grill. Place the cucumbers on a foil-lined baking tray and spread the slices with mayonnaise. Top with the chicken slices and season with salt and pepper to taste. Tear the cheese into pieces to cover the chicken. Place under the grill for 1 minute or until the cheese melts. Divide between 2 plates and serve.
Makes 2 servings.

One serving: 351 calories, 34g protein, 9g carbohydrate, 20g fat (5g saturated), 92mg cholesterol, 329mg sodium, 2g fibre

helpful hints

● *Slice the cucumber on the diagonal for a larger surface area and oval-shaped slice.*

● *To determine the weight of each slice of cheese, divide the packet weight by the number of slices.*

countdown

● *Preheat grill.*
● *Complete recipe.*

shopping list

DAIRY
1 packet sliced reduced-fat Cheddar cheese (35g/1½oz) needed

DELI
175g (6oz) sliced roasted chicken breast

FRUIT AND VEG
2 large cucumbers

STAPLES
Mayonnaise made with soya bean or olive oil
Salt
Black peppercorns

devilish eggs

Devilled eggs are a classic comfort food. They can be made ahead, stored in the refrigerator and are easily carried with you for a breakfast or lunch on the run. In fact, it's a good idea to keep a few hard-boiled eggs on hand for quick meals or snacks.

devilish eggs

6 eggs (only 2 yolks used)

2 tablespoons mayonnaise made with soya bean or olive oil

2 teaspoons Dijon mustard

Large pinch of cayenne pepper

2 tablespoons snipped fresh chives

Salt and freshly ground black pepper to taste

8 celery stalks, cut into 10cm (4in) pieces

Place the eggs in a small saucepan and cover with cold water. Set over a medium-high heat and bring to a boil. Reduce the heat to low and gently simmer for 12 minutes. Drain, and then fill the pan with cold water. When the eggs are cool to the touch, peel and cut in half lengthwise. Remove and discard the yolks from 4 of the eggs. Set the egg whites on 2 plates. Place the remaining 2 whole eggs in the bowl of a food processor or mash with a fork in a mixing bowl. Add the mayonnaise, mustard, cayenne pepper and chives. Season with salt and pepper to taste. Process until smooth. Fill the egg whites with the mixture. Serve with celery.

Makes 2 servings.

One serving: 251 calories, 16g protein, 14g carbohydrate, 18g fat (3g saturated), 218mg cholesterol, 653mg sodium, 4g fibre

helpful hint

- *The easiest way to chop fresh chives is to cut them with scissors.*

countdown

- *Hard boil the eggs.*
- *Prepare the filling.*

shopping list

FRUIT AND VEG

  1 small bunch fresh chives or 1 jar dried

STAPLES

  Celery

  Eggs

  Mayonnaise

  Dijon mustard

  Cayenne pepper

  Salt

  Black peppercorns

swiss scramble

This breakfast can be made in 15 minutes or less. Swiss cheese, sweet peppers and spring onions add flavour and colour to the light eggs.

swiss scramble

2 teaspoons olive oil

2 medium-sized green peppers, sliced

2 whole eggs

6 egg whites

150g (5oz) spring onions, sliced

75g (3oz) sliced reduced-fat Swiss or gruyère cheese (about 4 slices), torn into small pieces

Salt and freshly ground black pepper to taste

Heat the oil in a medium-sized non-stick frying pan. Add the peppers and sauté for 3 minutes. Combine the whole eggs, egg whites, spring onions and cheese in a medium-sized bowl and season with salt and pepper to taste. Add to the frying pan and scramble for 2 minutes, or until cooked to desired doneness. Spoon onto 2 plates and serve.
Makes 2 servings.

One serving: 346 calories, 35g protein, 15g carbohydrate, 17g fat (6g saturated), 236mg cholesterol, 311mg sodium, 0g fibre

helpful hints

● *225ml (8fl oz) egg substitute can be used instead of whole eggs.*

● *Any type of reduced-fat cheese can be used.*

● *To determine the weight of each slice of cheese, divide the packet weight by the number of slices.*

countdown

● *Prepare all ingredients.*

● *Make spinach.*

● *Make eggs.*

shopping list

DAIRY

  1 packet sliced reduced-fat Swiss or Gruyère cheese (75g/3oz needed)

FRUIT AND VEG

  2 medium-sized green peppers

  1 bunch spring onions

STAPLES

  Olive oil

  Eggs

  Salt

  Black peppercorns

cheddar and sausage frittata

helpful hints

- 2 whole eggs plus 6 egg whites can be used instead of the egg substitute.
- To determine the weight of each sausage, divide the packet weight by the number of sausages.
- Use a pan with an ovenproof handle to put in the oven.

countdown

- Preheat oven 200°C/400°F/gas mark 6.
- Prepare ingredients.
- Make frittata.

shopping list

DAIRY
 1 small packet grated, reduced-fat Cheddar cheese (50g/2oz needed)
MEAT
 1 packet low-fat turkey sausages (175g/6oz needed)
GROCERY
 1 tin water chestnuts
FRUIT AND VEG
 1 medium-sized red pepper
 1 small bunch rocket
STAPLES
 Olive oil
 Egg substitute
 Red onion
 Celery
 Salt
 Black peppercorns

A frittata is a little like a crustless quiche and takes about 10 minutes to cook. It's great for breakfast, and when cooled and cut into squares, it makes great canapés or snacks.

cheddar and sausage frittata

2 teaspoons olive oil

225g (8oz) red onion, sliced

1 medium-sized red pepper, sliced

2 celery stalks, sliced

2 low-fat turkey sausages, cut into 1cm (½in) slices

175g (6oz) tinned water chestnuts, drained and sliced

225ml (8fl oz) egg substitute

50g (2oz) rocket, washed and sliced

50g (2oz) grated, reduced-fat Cheddar cheese

Salt and freshly ground black pepper to taste

Preheat the oven to 200°C/400°F/gas mark 6. Heat the olive oil in a medium-sized non-stick frying pan over a medium-high heat. Sauté the onion, pepper, celery, sausages and water chestnuts over a high heat for 3 minutes. Combine the egg substitute, rocket and cheese in a medium-sized bowl and season with salt and pepper to taste. Reduce the heat to medium and pour the egg mixture into the pan. Swirl in the pan to cover the vegetables. Allow to set for 3 minutes. Transfer to the oven for 7 minutes, or until the eggs set to the desired consistency. Cut the frittata in half, slide out of the pan onto 2 plates and serve.

Makes 2 servings.

One serving: 396 calories, 36g protein, 20g carbohydrate, 19g fat (7g saturated), 65mg cholesterol, 1088mg sodium, 3g fibre

bacon and cheese crêpes

Making eggs into thin crêpes is the secret to this dish. Be sure to use a good non-stick frying pan for best results.

bacon and cheese crêpes

225ml (8fl oz) egg substitute

Freshly ground black pepper

Olive oil spray

175g (6oz) lean gammon, cut into 2.5cm (1in) strips

75g (3oz) grated semi-skimmed milk mozzarella cheese

1 medium tomato, sliced

Pre-heat grill. Mix egg substitute with pepper to taste. Heat a medium non-stick frying pan on medium-high heat. Spray with olive oil spray and pour half the egg substitute into frying pan and spread to make a thin layer. Leave to cook for 2 minutes. Turn over for 1 minute. Remove from heat to a foil-lined baking tray. Repeat with second half of egg mixture. Sprinkle bacon and cheese over crêpes. Fold over once and place under grill about 25cm (10in) from heat. Grill for 2 minutes or until cheese melts. Carefully slide on to a plate, place sliced tomatoes on the side and serve.

Makes 2 servings.

Per serving: 335 calories, 43.2 grams protein, 7.0 grams carbohydrate, 14.2 grams fat (7.5 saturated), 73 milligrams cholesterol, 1227 milligrams sodium, 0 grams fibre

helpful hint

● Make these crêpes ahead, and fill and warm in a microwave oven when needed.

countdown

● Pre-heat grill.
● Make egg base.
● Complete recipe.

shopping list

DAIRY

1 packet grated semi-skimmed milk mozzarella cheese

DELI

175g (6oz) lean gammon

FRUIT AND VEG

1 medium tomato

STAPLES

Egg substitute

Olive oil spray

Black peppercorns

turkey salsa roll

Sliced turkey roll stuffed with Cheddar cheese and topped with salsa is a breakfast that can be made ahead and warmed in 1 minute in a microwave oven before eating.

turkey salsa roll

225g (8oz) sliced, smoked turkey breast
50g (2oz) grated reduced-fat Cheddar cheese
225ml (8fl oz) no-sugar-added tomato salsa

Place turkey slices on the work surface or a plate and sprinkle each slice with cheese. Roll up slices and divide between 2 plates. Microwave each plate on high for 1 minute or until cheese melts. If not using a microwave oven, place turkey rolls on a foil-lined baking sheet under a grill for 1 minute. Remove plates from microwave and spoon salsa over the top.
Makes 2 servings.

Per serving: 310 calories, 44.0 grams protein, 10.4 grams carbohydrate, 8.5 grams fat (4.2 saturated), 90 milligrams cholesterol, 1036 milligrams sodium, 4.0 grams fibre

helpful hints

● To help the morning rush, stuff the turkey the night before and warm just before eating.

countdown

● Prepare ingredients.
● Complete dish.

shopping list

DAIRY
1 small packet grated reduced-fat Cheddar cheese
DELI
225g (8oz) sliced, smoked turkey breast
STAPLES
1 small jar no-sugar-added tomato salsa

mushroom, turkey and tarragon omelette

Omelettes take only minutes to make. A perfect omelette is golden on the top with a delicate creamy centre. The secret is to cook it over medium-high heat for only a couple of minutes.

mushroom, turkey and tarragon omelette

4 egg whites

2 large whole eggs

110g (4oz) smoked turkey breast, cut into 25cm (1in) cubes

1 teaspoon dried tarragon

Salt and freshly ground black pepper

Olive oil spray

110g (4oz) thinly sliced portobello mushrooms

1 medium tomato, cut into 25cm (1in) pieces

Place eggs and egg whites in a bowl and stir in turkey, tarragon and salt and pepper to taste. Heat a medium non-stick frying pan over medium-high heat and spray with olive oil. Sauté mushrooms and tomatoes for 2 minutes and remove. Pour in the egg mixture. Let the eggs set for about 30 seconds. Tip the pan and lightly move the eggs so that they set completely. Cook for 1½ minutes or until eggs are set. Cook a few seconds longer for firmer eggs.

Place the mushrooms and tomatoes on half the omelette and fold the omelette in half. Slide out of the pan by tipping the pan and holding a plate vertically against the side of the pan. Turn pan and plate to invert the omelette on to the plate. Cut in half and serve on 2 plates.
Makes 2 servings.

Per serving: 228 calories, 31.5 grams protein, 4.7 grams carbohydrate, 9.3 grams fat (2.5 saturated), 253 milligrams cholesterol, 215 milligrams sodium, 0 grams fibre

helpful hints

● *Any herb can be used.*

● *Dried tarragon is called for in the recipe. If using dried herbs, make sure the jar is less than 6 months old.*

● *For best results, use a good-quality non-stick pan.*

countdown

● *Prepare ingredients.*

● *Complete omelette.*

shopping list

DELI

110g (4oz) smoked turkey breast

FRUIT AND VEG

110g (4oz) portobello mushrooms

1 medium tomato

STAPLES

Eggs (6 needed)

Olive oil spray

Dried tarragon

Salt

Black peppercorns

microwave eggs parmesan

Here is another quick microwave breakfast. The timing of this dish depends on the power of your microwave oven. Also, some like their eggs dry, others wet. Select the timing according to your preference. Remember the eggs will continue to cook for about 1 minute after they are removed from the oven.

helpful hints

- Buy good-quality Parmesan cheese and grate it yourself or chop it in the food processor. Freeze extra for quick use. You can quickly spoon out what you need and leave the rest frozen.

countdown

- Make eggs.
- Arrange salad on 2 plates.

shopping list

DELI
110g (4oz) smoked turkey
FRUIT AND VEG
1 medium tomato
1 small head romaine lettuce
STAPLES
Eggs (6 needed)
Parmesan cheese
Salt
Black peppercorns

microwave eggs parmesan

4 egg whites
2 large eggs
110g (4oz) smoked turkey, cut into small cubes
2 tablespoons grated Parmesan cheese
Salt and freshly ground black pepper
Several romaine lettuce leaves
1 medium tomato, sliced

Place 2 egg whites and 1 whole egg in a microwave-safe bowl about 18cm (7in) in diameter. Add 2 tablespoons turkey, 1 tablespoon Parmesan cheese and salt and pepper to taste. Whisk with a fork. Microwave on high for 1 minute. Stir and microwave for 30 seconds and stir. For drier eggs, microwave 30 seconds more. Arrange lettuce leaves on 2 plates and place tomato slices on top. Spoon eggs on to plate. Using the same bowl, repeat for second serving.
Makes 2 servings.

Per serving: 255 calories, 35.3 grams protein, 4.5 grams carbohydrate, 10.9 grams fat (4.0 saturated), 260 milligrams cholesterol, 394 milligrams sodium, 0.2 grams fibre

microwave marinara scramble

This breakfast takes just minutes to make in a microwave oven. A rich, thick marinara sauce gives these scrambled eggs a taste of Naples.

The timing of this dish depends on the power of your microwave oven. Also, some like their eggs dry, others wet. Select the timing according to your preference. Remember the eggs will continue to cook for about 1 minute after they are removed from the oven.

microwave marinara scramble

150g (5oz) washed, ready-to-eat
  baby spinach

110g (4oz) lean ham, cut into
  2.5cm (1in) pieces

225ml (8fl oz) egg substitute

50ml (2fl oz) low-salt, no-sugar-
  added marinara sauce

Salt and freshly ground black
  pepper

6 tablespoons grated semi-
  skimmed milk mozzarella
  cheese

Place spinach and ham in a microwave-safe bowl and microwave on high for 2 minutes. Divide between 2 plates.

Combine egg substitute and marinara sauce together in a microwave-safe bowl. Season with salt and pepper to taste. Cover with clingfilm or a plate. Microwave on high for 4 minutes. Stir and divide in half. Place each portion on top of the spinach and ham. Sprinkle 2 tablespoons mozzarella cheese on top of each portion. *Makes 2 servings.*

Per serving: 250 calories, 33.6 grams protein,
10.6 grams carbohydrate, 8.6 grams fat
(4.0 saturated), 43 milligrams cholesterol,
1127 milligrams sodium, 3.6 grams fibre

helpful hints

● *If you don't have a microwave oven, sauté the spinach for 1 minute in a small frying pan and remove to a plate. Scramble the eggs in the same pan.*

● *If baby spinach is unavailable, use any type of spinach or lettuce.*

countdown

● *Microwave spinach.*

● *Microwave scrambled eggs.*

shopping list

DAIRY
  1 small packet grated semi-skimmed milk mozzarella cheese

DELI
  110g (4oz) lean ham

GROCERY
  1 small jar low-salt, no-sugar-added marinara sauce

FRUIT AND VEG
  1 bag washed, ready-to-eat baby spinach (150g/5oz needed)

STAPLES
  Egg substitute (225ml/8fl oz needed)
  Salt
  Black peppercorns

quick start
lunches

turkey bundles

For the times when you don't have time to make a lunch, here is a dish you can make and eat in minutes.

turkey bundles

350g (12oz) roasted sliced turkey breast

18 to 20 leaves romaine or other lettuce

100g (3½oz) coleslaw

2 small tomatoes, sliced

Place a slice of turkey on a lettuce leaf. Add a spoonful of coleslaw and a slice of tomato. Fold the lettuce. Continue with additional lettuce leaves until all the turkey is used.

Makes 2 servings.

> One serving: 398 calories, 52g protein, 16g carbohydrate, 12g fat (3g saturated), 125mg cholesterol, 269mg sodium, 2g fibre

helpful hints

● *Check the ingredients of shop-bought coleslaw, as some prepared versions have added sugar.*

● *Drain the coleslaw before use.*

shopping list

DELI

350g (12oz) roasted sliced turkey breast

100g (3½oz) coleslaw

FRUIT AND VEG

1 head romaine or other lettuce

2 small tomatoes

mozzarella tomato tower

This tower is made by alternating tomato slices, mozzarella and fresh basil until the tomato is re-formed. It's a modern version of a tomato-mozzarella plate that's fun to serve and delicious, too.

mozzarella tomato tower

4 teaspoons olive oil

2 medium tomatoes, cut into 1cm (½in) slices

Salt and freshly ground black pepper to taste

225g (8oz) reduced-fat mozzarella cheese, sliced

150g (5oz) washed, ready-to-eat mixed salad leaves

2 tablespoons pine nuts

20 leaves fresh basil

2 tablespoons no-sugar-added oil and vinegar dressing

Drizzle 2 teaspoons of the olive oil over the tomato slices, and season with salt and pepper to taste. Drizzle the remaining 2 teaspoons of olive oil over the cheese, tossing to coat well. Divide the salad leaves between 2 plates. Sprinkle with the pine nuts. Place the stem slices of the tomatoes in the centre of the salad, skin side down. Sprinkle a little mozzarella on top of each. Place a few basil leaves on the mozzarella. Continue layering the tomato slices, mozzarella and basil leaves until the tomatoes are rebuilt, ending with a sprinkling of mozzarella on top. Gently press the slices together with the palm of your hand. Drizzle the tomatoes and salad leaves with the dressing and serve.
Makes 2 servings.

One serving: 427 calories, 35g protein, 12g carbohydrate, 24g fat (6g saturated), 16mg cholesterol, 971mg sodium, 4g fibre

helpful hint

- Yellow tomatoes make an attractive alternative to red ones.

countdown

- Prepare ingredients.
- Assemble salad.

shopping list

DAIRY

2 balls reduced-fat mozzarella cheese (225g/8oz needed)

GROCERY

1 small packet pine nuts

FRUIT AND VEG

2 medium tomatoes

1 small bunch fresh basil

1 bag washed, ready-to-eat mixed salad leaves

STAPLES

Olive oil

No-sugar-added oil and vinegar dressing

Salt

Black peppercorns

mozzarella tomato tower **p48**

salmon balsamico p49

salmon balsamico

Rich, flavourful salmon is easy to cook and very filling. The smooth, rich texture goes well with cool, crunchy salad leaves and vegetables.

salmon balsamico

2 teaspoons olive oil
225g (8oz) salmon fillet
Salt and freshly ground black pepper to taste
225g (8oz) sweet potatoes, peeled and cut into 1cm (½in) cubes
125ml (4fl oz) balsamic vinegar
150g (5oz) washed, ready-to-eat mixed salad leaves
2 tablespoons no-sugar-added oil and vinegar dressing

Heat the oil in a small non-stick frying pan over a medium-high heat. Rinse salmon and pat dry with kitchen paper. Sauté the salmon for 3 minutes, then turn and brown for 3 more minutes, or longer if the salmon is more than 2.5cm (1in) thick. Sprinkle the cooked salmon with salt and pepper to taste and set aside.

Fill another pan with water and bring to the boil. Add the sweet potato and cook for 5 minutes, then drain. Add the vinegar and sweet potatoes to the salmon, return to the heat and reduce for about 1 minute, or until the liquid is syrupy. Divide the salad leaves between 2 plates and toss with the salad dressing. Place the salmon on top of the salad leaves. Spoon the glaze and sweet potato cubes on top and serve.
Makes 2 servings.

One serving: 365 calories, 30g protein, 16g carbohydrate, 20g fat (3g saturated), 80mg cholesterol, 158mg sodium, 6g fibre

helpful hint
● *Any type of fish fillet can be used.*

countdown
● *Sauté salmon.*
● *Assemble salad.*

shopping list
FISH
225g (8oz) salmon fillet
FRUIT AND VEG
225g (8oz) sweet potatoes
1 bag washed, ready-to-eat mixed salad leaves
STAPLES
Olive oil
No-sugar-added oil and vinegar dressing
Balsamic vinegar
Salt
Black peppercorns

tuna salad wraps

You can find almost any type of food in wraps these days, including a whole dinner. I've used large lettuce leaves for the wrap in this recipe. ● These wraps are really portable and will last at least a day in the refrigerator. I take them out when we go sailing. They are great for a day outside – easy to serve and very delicious.

tuna salad wraps

12 or 14 large romaine lettuce
    leaves, washed and dried
500g (18oz) tinned tuna packed in
    water, rinsed and drained
50ml (2fl oz) mayonnaise made
    from soya bean or olive oil
25g (1oz) snipped chives
110g (4oz) red onion, diced
Salt and freshly ground black
    pepper to taste
12 x 30.5 x 10cm (11 x 4 in)
    rectangles foil, parchment paper
    or greaseproof paper
110g (4oz) fresh basil leaves,
    washed and dried
350g (12oz) alfalfa sprouts, tops
    only

Crush the stems of the lettuce leaves so they lie flat. In a small mixing bowl, break the tuna up with a fork and stir in the mayonnaise, chives and onion. Add salt and pepper to taste. Spread the foil pieces on the work surface. Place a romaine leaf on each square. Spoon some of the tuna salad on each leaf and top with the basil. Spoon the remaining tuna salad on top and sprinkle with alfalfa sprouts. Roll up each leaf like a cigar, and wrap tightly in the foil. Seal the ends and slice in half crosswise. Use immediately or place in plastic bags and refrigerate until needed.
Makes 2 servings.

One serving: 421 calories, 37g protein,
12g carbohydrate, 25g fat (3g saturated),
66mg cholesterol, 738mg sodium, 1g fibre

helpful hints

● Use the tuna salad recipe given or use shop-bought tuna salad. If the shop-bought version is dripping in mayonnaise, drain it before using. Be sure to check the ingredients list of shop-bought tuna salad, as some have sugar added.
● The easiest way to snip chives is with scissors.

countdown

● Cut foil squares.
● Make tuna salad.
● Assemble wraps.

shopping list

GROCERY
    500g (18oz) tinned tuna
        packed in water
FRUIT AND VEG
    1 head romaine lettuce
    1 small bunch chives
    1 small bunch basil
    350g (12oz) containers alfalfa
        sprouts
STAPLES
    Red onion
    Mayonnaise made from soya
        bean or olive oil
    Foil
    Salt
    Black peppercorns

smoked trout salad

It takes only a few minutes to put this tasty lunch together. A good quality smoked trout needs very little added to it to make a great meal.

smoked trout salad

*175g (6oz) washed, ready-to-eat
   mixed salad leaves*
350g (12oz) smoked trout
25g (1oz) walnut pieces
2 teaspoons olive oil
*Salt and freshly ground black
   pepper to taste*

Place the salad leaves on individual dishes. Flake trout into 1cm (½in) pieces and place on top of the salad leaves. Sprinkle with the walnuts and drizzle with the oil. Season with salt and pepper to taste and serve.
Makes 2 servings.

One serving: 342 calories, 31g protein,
5g carbohydrate, 22g fat (4g saturated),
77mg cholesterol, 60mg sodium, 2g fibre

helpful hints

- *Any type of smoked fish can be used.*
- *Any type of lettuce can be used.*

countdown

- *Prepare ingredients.*
- *Assemble salad.*

shopping list

FISH
   350g (12oz) smoked trout
GROCERY
   *1 small packet walnut pieces
   (25g/1oz needed)*
FRUIT AND VEG
   *1 bag washed, ready-to-eat
   mixed salad leaves*
STAPLES
   Olive oil
   Salt
   Black peppercorns

roast beef and watercress wraps

Rocket and horseradish give these roast beef wraps a spicy bite. Watercress adds a little crunch. Wraps are great finger food. This recipe uses large lettuce leaves instead of tortillas to wrap around the filling.

roast beef and watercress wraps

12 large round lettuce leaves, washed and dried

12 x 30.5 x 10cm (11 x 4in) rectangles foil, parchment paper or greaseproof paper

2 tablespoons mayonnaise made with soya bean or olive oil

2 tablespoons horseradish

350g (12oz) sliced lean roast beef

110g (4oz) fresh rocket, washed and dried

12 small sprigs watercress, washed and dried

Crush the stems of the lettuce leaves so they lie flat. Place the foil pieces on the work surface. Place one lettuce leaf on each piece of foil. Combine the mayonnaise and horseradish in a small bowl and spread on the leaves. Place one layer of roast beef on each leaf. Top with some rocket and a sprig of watercress. Roll up each leaf like a cigar, then wrap tightly in the foil. Seal the ends and slice in half crosswise to serve. *Makes 2 servings.*

One serving: 466 calories, 52g protein, 7g carbohydrate, 24g fat (6g saturated), 144mg cholesterol, 235mg sodium, 1g fibre

helpful hints

- These travel well. Make them ahead, store in a plastic bag and refrigerate until needed.
- Any type of lettuce can be used. Large leaves are needed.

countdown

- Cut foil squares.
- Assemble recipe.

shopping list

DELI

350g (12oz) thinly sliced lean roast beef

GROCERY

1 jar horseradish

FRUIT AND VEG

1 head round lettuce

1 small bunch rocket

1 small bunch watercress

STAPLES

Mayonnaise made with soya bean or olive oil

Foil

greek salad

With the help of the supermarket deli, you can make this salad in less than 5 minutes. A traditional Greek salad has olives, feta cheese, radishes and good olive oil. You can also add sweet peppers, capers and anchovies, all of which can be found on the supermarket shelves. Use this recipe as the base and build your own salad with other fresh vegetables.

greek salad

2 tablespoons no-sugar-added oil and vinegar dressing

2 teaspoons dried oregano or 2 tablespoons fresh

225g (8oz) washed, ready-to-eat lettuce leaves

1 medium cucumber, peeled and sliced

12 black olives, chopped (preferably kalamata)

8 radishes, sliced

8 spring onions, sliced

35g (1½oz) drained capers

225g (8oz) medium-sliced lean turkey breast

75g (3oz) reduced-fat feta cheese, crumbled

Freshly ground black pepper to taste

Combine the oil and vinegar dressing and oregano together in a salad bowl. Add the lettuce, cucumber, olives, radishes, spring onions and capers. Toss well. Slice the turkey breast into 1cm (½in) strips. Sprinkle on top of the salad with the crumbled feta cheese. Add pepper to taste. Divide between 2 plates and serve.

Makes 2 servings.

One serving: 455 calories, 41g protein, 15g carbohydrate, 25g fat (9g saturated), 118mg cholesterol, 1639mg sodium, 2g fibre

helpful hints

● Use dried oregano in this recipe for speed but make sure it is less than six months old. Fresh oregano (available in most supermarkets) adds a sweeter flavour to the salad. Use it if you have time.

● Any type of washed, ready-to-eat lettuce can be used.

countdown

● Make salad dressing.
● Make salad.

shopping list

DAIRY
1 packet reduced-fat feta cheese (75g/3oz needed)

DELI
225g (8oz) medium-sliced lean turkey breast

GROCERY
1 jar capers
1 packet black olives (preferably kalamata)

FRUIT AND VEG
1 bag washed, ready-to-eat lettuce leaves
1 medium cucumber
1 small bunch radishes
1 bunch spring onions (8 needed)

STAPLES
No-sugar-added oil and vinegar dressing
Dried oregano
Black peppercorns

grilled cheddar and chicken salad

This lunch can be made in 5 minutes by using either leftover chicken or roasted skinless chicken from the supermarket, but read the labels carefully to make sure there are no hidden carbs. Buy the original flavour rather than the honey-baked or barbecued variety. ● The cheese melts, providing a warm covering for the cool salad.

grilled cheddar and chicken salad

2 tablespoons mayonnaise made
with olive or soya bean oil
2 tablespoons warm water
2 tablespoons Dijon mustard
225g (8oz) roasted chicken breast,
chopped
1 medium-sized green pepper,
seeded and chopped
110g (4oz) yellow onion, diced
25g (1oz) chopped fresh parsley
Salt and freshly ground black
pepper to taste
2 large tomatoes, sliced
2 slices reduced-fat, mature
Cheddar cheese (35g/1½oz)

Preheat the grill. Combine the mayonnaise, water and mustard in a medium-sized bowl. Add the chicken, pepper, onion and parsley. Add salt and pepper to taste and toss well. Place the tomato slices on an ovenproof dish or on a foil-lined baking tray and season with a little salt and pepper. Spread with chicken salad and tear cheese slices into small pieces to fit over the chicken salad. Grill for 2 minutes, or until the cheese melts, and serve.

Makes 2 servings.

One serving: 434 calories, 46g protein, 14g carbohydrate, 22g fat (6g saturated), 116mg cholesterol, 723mg sodium, 0g fibre

helpful hints

- Chop all ingredients in a food processor.
- To determine the weight of each slice of cheese, divide the packet weight by the number of slices.

countdown

- Preheat grill.
- Make chicken salad.
- Complete recipe.

shopping list

DAIRY
1 packet sliced, reduced-fat, mature Cheddar cheese (35g/1½oz needed)
DELI
225g/8oz roasted chicken breast
FRUIT AND VEG
1 medium-sized green pepper
1 small bunch fresh parsley
2 large tomatoes
STAPLES
Yellow onion
Mayonnaise made with olive or soya bean oil
Dijon mustard
Salt
Black peppercorns

portobellos stuffed with smoked trout and sun-dried tomatoes

Large portobello mushroom caps have an earthy flavour and meaty texture. They can be roasted, grilled or sautéed. This dish can be eaten warm or at room temperature, and it only takes about 15 minutes to make. ● Curly endive has lacy, green-trimmed leaves, but any type of lettuce can be used for this recipe.

portobellos stuffed with smoked trout and sun-dried tomatoes

Olive oil spray

4 large portobello mushroom caps, washed (225g/8oz)

Salt and freshly ground black pepper to taste

2 tablespoons mayonnaise made with olive or soya bean oil

1 tablespoon freshly squeezed lemon juice (about ½ lemon)

50ml (2fl oz) horseradish

225g (8oz) smoked trout or other smoked fish

175g (6oz) sun-dried tomatoes, drained and diced

Several leaves curly endive

Preheat the oven to 230°C/450°F/gas mark 8. Line a baking tray with foil and spray with olive oil. Place the mushrooms on the tray and spray both sides with olive oil until lightly coated. Bake for 5 minutes; turn and bake for 5 more minutes. Remove from the oven, and add salt and pepper to taste.

Combine the mayonnaise, lemon juice and horseradish in a medium-sized mixing bowl. Flake the smoked trout into the mayonnaise mixture. Stir in the sun-dried tomatoes, blending well. Season with salt and pepper to taste. Spoon the mixture into the mushroom caps. Divide the lettuce between 2 plates, top with the stuffed mushroom caps and serve.

Makes 2 servings.

One serving: 476 calories, 33g protein, 17g carbohydrate, 30g fat (5g saturated), 82mg cholesterol, 179mg sodium, 4g fibre

helpful hints

- To clean whole mushrooms, wipe them gently with damp kitchen paper.
- The smoked fish filling can be mixed in a food processor.

countdown

- Preheat oven to 230°C/450°F/gas mark 8.
- Roast mushrooms.
- Assemble dish.

shopping list

FISH

225g (8oz) smoked trout or other smoked fish

GROCERY

1 jar horseradish

1 jar sun-dried tomatoes

FRUIT AND VEG

4 large portobello mushrooms (225g/8oz)

1 lemon

1 head curly endive

STAPLES

Olive oil spray

Mayonnaise made with olive or soya bean oil

Salt

Black peppercorns

chicken with dill mustard

This lunch of sliced chicken breast topped with a dill mustard sauce and crunchy sliced celery requires no cooking and can be assembled the night before. It's also a good recipe for leftover chicken.

chicken with dill mustard

350g (12oz) thick-sliced (about
   0.5cm/¼in) deli chicken breast
3 tablespoons Dijon mustard
1½ tablespoons mayonnaise
1½ teaspoons dried dill
12 medium celery stalks, thinly
   sliced

Divide chicken between 2 plates. Mix mustard, mayonnaise and dill together and spread half the mixture over the chicken. Place celery slices on top and cover with remaining sauce.
Makes 2 servings.

Per serving: 440 calories, 57.9 grams protein, 19.4 grams carbohydrate, 18.5 grams fat (2.9 saturated), 148 milligrams cholesterol, 1146 milligrams sodium, 6.0 grams fibre

helpful hints

● *Dried dill is called for in the recipe. If using dried herbs, make sure the jar is less than 6 months old.*

countdown

● *Prepare ingredients.*
● *Complete dish.*

shopping list

DELI
   350g (12oz) thick-sliced
      (about 0.5cm/¼in) deli
      chicken breast
STAPLES
   Celery (12 stalks needed)
   Dijon mustard
   Dried dill
   Mayonnaise

cheese and chicken bundles

Roasted chicken, blue cheese, walnuts and yoghurt blend together to make a tasty spread that is rolled into lettuce leaves. These little bundles can be made ahead and taken to eat on the run.

cheese and chicken bundles

50g (2oz) blue cheese, crumbled
50ml (2fl oz) non-fat natural
  yoghurt
2 tablespoons walnut pieces
225g (8oz) roasted chicken strips
Several romaine lettuce leaves
  (about 6)
4 medium celery stalks

Place blue cheese, yoghurt, walnuts and chicken in the bowl of a food processor fitted with a chopping blade. Process to a spreadable consistency. Place lettuce leaves on work surface or a board and spread chicken mixture on leaves. Roll up lengthways and wrap in foil or greaseproof paper. Cut celery stalks into 5cm (2in) pieces and serve on the side.
Makes 2 servings.

Per serving: 411 calories, 46.9 grams protein, 13.3 grams carbohydrate, 21.3 grams fat (7.2 saturated), 118 milligrams cholesterol, 652 milligrams sodium, 3.2 grams fibre

helpful hints

- Any large lettuce leaves can be used.
- Buy plain roasted chicken strips. Stay away from honey roasted or barbecue chicken.

countdown

- Prepare ingredients.
- Make bundles.

shopping list

FRUIT AND VEG
  1 small head romaine lettuce
DAIRY
  1 small pot non-fat natural
    yoghurt
  1 small packet blue cheese
DELI
  1 packet roasted chicken
    strips (225g/8oz needed)
GROCERY
  1 small packet walnut pieces
STAPLES
  Celery

nutty chicken minestrone

This minestrone is a refreshing blend of flavours using fresh vegetables, chicken and pistachio nuts combined with the perfume of fresh basil. Minestra is Italian for soup. Minestrone is a thick soup that can be made in 20 minutes using bought cooked chicken breasts. Leftover chicken can be used for this recipe. Look for shelled pistachio nuts. They are now available in most supermarkets.

nutty chicken minestrone

helpful hints

- Walnuts, pecans or almonds can be substituted for pistachio nuts.
- Buy good-quality Parmesan cheese and grate it yourself or chop it in the food processor. Freeze extra for quick use. You can spoon out what you need and leave the rest frozen.
- Grated carrots are available in the fruit and veg section of the supermarket.

countdown

- Prepare ingredients.
- Make soup.

shopping list

FRUIT AND VEG
1 small pack grated carrots
1 bag washed, ready-to-eat spinach
1 medium tomato
1 small bunch basil

MEAT
225g (8oz) roasted chicken strips or pieces

GROCERY
1 small packet shelled pistachio nuts

STAPLES
Olive oil
Parmesan cheese
Fat-free, low-sodium chicken stock (350ml/12fl oz needed)
Celery
Salt
Black peppercorns

2 teaspoons olive oil
50g (2oz) grated carrots
1/2 celery stalk, sliced
1 medium tomato, diced
350ml (12fl oz) fat-free, low-sodium chicken stock
350ml (12fl oz) water
225g (8oz) roasted, ready-to-eat chicken strips
Salt and freshly ground black pepper
110g (4oz) washed, ready-to-eat spinach
15g (1/2oz) fresh basil
2 tablespoons freshly grated Parmesan cheese
2 tablespoons coarsely chopped pistachio nuts

Heat the oil in a large saucepan on medium-high heat. Add the carrot and celery. Sauté for 5 minutes. Do not brown the vegetables. Stir the vegetables gently, being careful not to break them up. Add the tomato, chicken stock and water. The liquid should cover the vegetables. Add more water, if needed. Bring to a simmer and partially cover with a lid, leaving space for steam to escape. Simmer for 10 minutes. Add the chicken and simmer for 5 more minutes. Add salt and pepper to taste. Remove from heat. Stir in the spinach and basil. Leave to stand for 1 minute. Spoon into 2 soup bowls. Sprinkle each bowl with Parmesan cheese and pistachio nuts. *Makes 2 servings.*

Per serving: 379 calories, 46.6 grams protein, 10.1 grams carbohydrate, 18.4 grams fat (4.3 saturated), 103 milligrams cholesterol, 731 milligrams sodium, 1.3 grams fibre

spanish tuna-stuffed tomatoes

Olives, pimientos and almonds mix with tuna to make a Spanish tuna salad. This is also a good recipe for leftover chicken or other seafood.

spanish tuna-stuffed tomatoes

2 large tomatoes

2 tablespoons mayonnaise

Freshly ground black pepper

250g (9oz) tinned tuna packed in water, drained

6 stoned green olives, sliced

225g (8oz) sliced sweet pimiento, drained

2½ tablespoons flaked almonds (25g/1oz)

Several lettuce leaves, washed and torn into bite-sized pieces

Cut tomatoes in half, scoop out pulp and seeds, and take a thin slice off the rounded bottom of each half. This will help the tomatoes sit straight on the plate. Set the tomato halves aside. Mix mayonnaise with black pepper to taste. Add the tuna, olives, pimiento and almonds. Mix to combine. Taste for seasoning and add more, if necessary.

Place the lettuce on 2 plates and the tomato halves on the lettuce. Fill the tomatoes with the tuna salad. Serve extra salad on the lettuce. *Makes 2 servings.*

Per serving: 404 calories, 39.2 grams protein, 12.6 grams carbohydrate, 22.5 grams fat (2.3 saturated), 61 milligrams cholesterol, 945 milligrams sodium, 0.2 grams fibre

helpful hints

- *Use good-quality, water-packed, tinned tuna.*
- *To help the tomato halves sit straight, cut a thin slice from the rounded ends.*
- *Any type of lettuce can be used.*

countdown

- *Prepare ingredients.*
- *Make recipe.*

shopping list

FRUIT AND VEG

2 large tomatoes

1 small head lettuce

GROCERY

250g (9oz) tinned tuna packed in water

1 jar stoned green olives (6 needed)

1 small jar sweet pimientos

1 small packet flaked almonds (25g/1oz needed)

STAPLES

Mayonnaise

Black peppercorns

crunchy oriental chicken salad

Roasted or rotisserie chicken takes on a new dimension in this quick salad. Adding ginger and soy sauce to a bottled oil and vinegar dressing gives it an Oriental flavour.

crunchy oriental chicken salad

225g (8oz) roasted, ready-to-eat chicken pieces

175g (6oz) drained, sliced water chestnuts

4 spring onions, sliced

3 tablespoons olive oil and vinegar dressing

2 teaspoons low-sodium soy sauce

½ teaspoon ground ginger

150g (5oz) washed, ready-to-eat mixed gourmet salad leaves

Place chicken pieces, water chestnuts and spring onions in a large bowl. Mix dressing, soy sauce and ginger together and pour over chicken. Toss well. Divide salad leaves between 2 plates and spoon chicken salad on top.
Makes 2 servings.

Per serving: 378 calories, 38.7 grams protein, 17.3 grams carbohydrate, 18.1 grams fat (3.1 saturated), 96 milligrams cholesterol, 437 milligrams sodium, 4.6 grams fibre

crab gratin

Good-quality crabmeat is the secret to this quick lunch. Fresh crabmeat from the seafood counter would be best; but if this is difficult to find, use pasteurised crabmeat.

crab gratin

3 tablespoons mayonnaise

2 tablespoons lemon juice or water

350g (12oz) crabmeat

Salt and freshly ground black pepper

2 large tomatoes, cut into 1cm (½in) slices

25g (1oz) grated reduced-fat Cheddar cheese

Pre-heat grill. Mix mayonnaise and lemon juice together in a small bowl. Add crabmeat and flake with a fork as it's mixed with the mayonnaise. Add salt and pepper to taste. Place tomato slices on foil-lined baking tray. Spoon crab over tomatoes and sprinkle cheese on top. Place under grill for 2–3 minutes or until cheese melts. Remove to 2 plates and serve.

Makes 2 servings.

Per serving: 382 calories, 37.1 grams protein, 9.1 grams carbohydrate, 21.2 grams fat (4.5 saturated), 149 milligrams cholesterol, 746 milligrams sodium, 0 grams fibre

helpful hints

● *Frozen crab can be used. The flavour will be fine; the crabmeat will be soft.*

● *Pasteurised crabmeat can be found in the refrigerated section of the seafood department.*

countdown

● *Pre-heat grill.*

● *Prepare ingredients.*

● *Make gratin.*

shopping list

FRUIT AND VEG

2 large tomatoes

DAIRY

1 small packet grated reduced-fat Cheddar cheese

SEAFOOD

350g (12oz) crabmeat

STAPLES

Lemon

Mayonnaise

Salt

Black peppercorns

quick start
dinners

hot pepper prawns

Hot, spicy prawns with lots of garlic are a popular Spanish tapas dish. The prawn dish is normally served on its own for tapas; but by adding a quick salad, it becomes an entire meal. Chicory is a small cigar-shaped head of lettuce that is creamy white. It has tightly packed leaves and can be cleaned by wiping the outer leaves with damp kitchen paper. The leaves will turn brown if soaked in water.

hot pepper prawns

275g (10oz) washed, ready-to-eat spinach

6 garlic cloves, crushed

Salt and freshly ground black pepper

1 tablespoon olive oil

Pinch crushed chilli flakes

350g (12oz) prawns, peeled

2 tablespoons chopped fresh parsley

Place spinach and 3 crushed garlic cloves in a large microwave-safe bowl. Microwave on high for 3 minutes. Add salt and pepper to taste. Toss well. Divide between 2 plates. Heat a medium non-stick frying pan on medium-high heat. Add olive oil and chilli flakes. When oil is hot, add prawns and remaining 3 crushed garlic cloves. Toss prawns in oil for 2–3 minutes or until prawns are no longer translucent. Remove from heat and sprinkle with parsley and salt and pepper to taste. Spoon over spinach including pan juices.

Makes 2 servings.

Per serving: 299 calories, 41.4 grams protein, 11.5 grams carbohydrate, 10.7 grams fat (1.5 saturated), 260 milligrams cholesterol, 426 milligrams sodium, 7.2 grams fibre

red pepper and chicory salad

2 medium heads chicory

1 medium red pepper, sliced into 2.5cm (1in) strips

2 tablespoons olive oil and vinegar dressing

Salt and freshly ground black pepper

Wipe chicory with damp kitchen paper. Cut off about 1cm (1/2in) from the bottom or flat end and discard. Cut chicory into 1cm (1/2in) slices and place in a small bowl. Add red pepper strips to bowl. Drizzle with dressing and add salt and pepper to taste. Toss well.

Makes 2 servings.

Per serving: 253 calories, 1.3 grams protein, 7.1 grams carbohydrate, 25.2 grams fat (4.4 saturated), 0 milligrams cholesterol, 239 milligrams sodium, 0 grams fibre

helpful hints

- *Shelled prawns are available at most supermarket seafood counters. The slightly higher cost is worth the time saved.*
- *A quick way to chop parsley is to wash, dry and snip the leaves with scissors right off the stem.*
- *Any type of lettuce can be used for the salad.*

countdown

- *Make salad.*
- *Prepare prawns.*

shopping list

SEAFOOD

  350g (12oz) shelled prawns

GROCERY

  1 small jar crushed chilli flakes

FRUIT AND VEG

  1 bag washed, ready-to-eat spinach (275g/10oz needed)

  1 medium red pepper

  1 small bunch parsley

  2 medium heads chicory

STAPLES

  Olive oil

  Garlic

  Olive oil and vinegar dressing

  Salt

  Black peppercorns

mediterranean baked fish

helpful hints

- *Any type of mild white fish fillet can be used in this recipe. Bake about 10 minutes per 2.5cm (1in) of thickness.*
- *Grate the courgettes in a food processor using a julienne cutting blade or use a grater with 0.5cm (¼in) holes.*

countdown

- *Pre-heat oven to 200ºC/400ºF/gas mark 6.*
- *Make fish.*
- *While fish bakes, make courgettes.*
- *Assemble salad.*

Try a taste of the Mediterranean with this baked snapper topped with pinenuts, olives and pimiento. An Italian friend does great courgettes with a hint of melted cheese on top. She told me her secret: grate the courgettes, using a grater with large holes. They cook faster and taste better. I created this quick courgette gratin with memories of her wonderful dish.

mediterranean baked fish

350g (12oz) snapper fillets
Salt and freshly ground black pepper
2 teaspoons olive oil
2 tablespoons pinenuts
6 stoned green olives, cut in half
110g (4oz) sliced sweet pepper, drained

Pre-heat oven to 200ºC/400ºF/gas mark 6. Line a baking tray with foil. Rinse fish and pat dry with kitchen paper. Sprinkle fish with salt and pepper to taste. Place on prepared baking tray and drizzle oil on top. Bake for 10 minutes. Spoon pinenuts, olives and peppers over fish. Return to oven for 10 minutes.
Makes 2 servings.

Per serving: 255 calories, 33.2 grams protein, 2.2 grams carbohydrate, 8.0 grams fat (1.2 saturated), 62 milligrams cholesterol, 373 milligrams sodium, 0 grams fibre

green salad

150g (5oz) washed, ready-to-eat lettuce
2 tablespoons olive oil and vinegar dressing

Place lettuce in a large bowl and toss with dressing.
Makes 2 servings.

Per serving: 84 calories, 0.6 grams protein, 1.9 grams carbohydrate, 8.5 grams fat (1.3 saturated), 0 milligrams cholesterol, 81 milligrams sodium, 0.3 grams fibre

Crab Cakes and Slaw | **p69**

courgette gratin

450g (1lb) courgettes, grated

2 tablespoons grated Parmesan
cheese

Salt and freshly ground black
pepper

2 teaspoons olive oil

Place courgettes in a microwave-safe bowl.
Microwave on high for 2 minutes. If you do not
have a microwave oven, bring a small saucepan
of water to the boil and add the courgettes.
Drain as soon as the water comes back to the
boil. Spoon half the courgettes into a shallow
ovenproof dish. Sprinkle 1 tablespoon Parmesan
cheese and salt and pepper to taste on top.
Cover with remaining courgettes and finish with
Parmesan cheese and salt and pepper to taste.
Drizzle olive oil on top. Place in oven with fish
for 5 minutes or until cheese melts.

Makes 2 servings.

Per serving: 129 calories, 7.9 grams protein,
8.0 grams carbohydrate, 8.4 grams fat (2.8 saturated),
9 milligrams cholesterol, 219 milligrams sodium,
1.2 grams fibre

shopping list

FRUIT AND VEG

450g (1lb) courgettes

1 bag washed, ready-to-eat
lettuce

SEAFOOD

350g (12oz) snapper fillets

GROCERY

1 small packet pinenuts
(15g/^{1}/$_2$oz needed)

1 small jar stoned green
olives

1 small jar sweet peppers

STAPLES

Olive oil

Olive oil and vinegar dressing

Parmesan cheese

Salt

Black peppercorns

tuscan chicken

A fresh tomato-basil relish tops this simple chicken dish. The broccoli takes only minutes to cook in a microwave oven. It's topped with toasted almonds.

helpful hints

- *Any type of ripe tomato can be used for the relish.*
- *Fresh parsley or coriander can be used instead of basil.*
- *A quick way to chop basil is to wash, dry then snip the leaves with scissors off the stem.*
- *To save washing an extra pan, sauté the almonds for a few minutes in a large frying pan, then remove them and use the same pan to cook the chicken.*

countdown

- *Make tomato relish.*
- *Sauté almonds.*
- *Prepare chicken.*
- *Make broccoli..*

tuscan chicken

1 large plum tomato, diced
2 tablespoons diced red onion
50g (2oz) sliced sweet peppers, drained
15g (1/2oz) snipped fresh basil leaves
1/2 tablespoon balsamic vinegar
Salt and freshly ground black pepper
350g (12oz) boneless, skinless chicken breasts
Olive oil spray

Mix tomatoes, onion, sweet peppers and basil together in a small bowl. Add vinegar and toss to mix. Add salt and pepper to taste. Set aside. Place chicken between two pieces of greaseproof paper or foil and flatten with a kitchen mallet or the bottom of a heavy pan to 1cm (1/2in) thick. Heat a large non-stick frying pan on medium-high heat and spray with olive oil spray. Add chicken and sauté 3 minutes per side. Season to taste on the cooked sides. Divide between 2 dinner plates and spoon the tomato relish on top.
Makes 2 servings.

Per serving: 307 calories, 54.6 grams protein,
4.2 grams carbohydrate, 9.0 grams fat (2.1 saturated),
144 milligrams cholesterol, 131 milligrams sodium,
0 grams fibre

toasted almond broccoli

40g (1¹/₂oz) flaked almonds
225g (8oz) broccoli florets
2 teaspoons olive oil
Salt and freshly ground black
  pepper

Heat a non-stick frying pan on medium heat and add the almonds. (This can be done in the same pan to be used for the chicken.) Sauté for 1 minute or until almonds are golden, not brown. Remove and set aside. Place broccoli in a microwave-safe bowl and microwave on high for 4 minutes. Remove and add oil and salt and pepper to taste. Toss well. Sprinkle almonds on top.

Makes 2 servings.

Per serving: 213 calories, 9.7 grams protein, 13.4 grams carbohydrate, 16.2 grams fat (1.4 saturated), 0 milligrams cholesterol, 40 milligrams sodium, 4.9 grams fibre

shopping list

FRUIT AND VEG
  1 large plum tomato
  1 small bunch basil
  225g (8oz) broccoli florets
MEAT
  350g (12oz) boneless,
    skinless chicken breasts
GROCERY
  1 small jar sweet peppers
  40g (1¹/₂oz) flaked almonds
STAPLES
  Red onion
  Olive oil spray
  Olive oil
  Balsamic vinegar
  Salt
  Black peppercorns

chicken burgers with warm mushroom salad

These burgers are tasty and juicy and take only a few minutes to make. Prepared pesto sauce gives the burgers a taste of Italy and keeps the meat juicy.

chicken burgers

350g (12oz) chicken mince

2 tablespoons prepared pesto sauce

1/2 teaspoon freshly ground black pepper

Dash of salt

Olive oil spray

1 medium tomato, coarsely chopped

Several basil leaves, cut into bite-sized pieces

1 spring onion, sliced

Salt and freshly ground black pepper

Mix chicken, pesto, black pepper and salt together in a small bowl. Shape into burgers about 9–10cm (3 1/2–4in) in diameter and 1cm (1/2in) thick. Heat a medium-sized non-stick frying pan on medium-high heat. Spray with olive oil spray and sauté burgers 5 minutes on each side. Remove to 2 dinner plates.

Toss tomato, basil and spring onion together, and add salt and pepper to taste. Spoon over cooked burgers.

Makes 2 servings.

Per serving: 381 calories, 56.6 grams protein, 7.0 grams carbohydrate, 15.0 grams fat (3.9 saturated), 149 milligrams cholesterol, 410 milligrams sodium, 0.8 grams fibre

warm mushroom salad

Olive oil spray

225g (8oz) sliced portobello mushrooms

2 garlic cloves, crushed

Salt and freshly ground black pepper

2 tablespoons olive oil and vinegar dressing

Several radicchio leaves

Heat a non-stick frying pan on medium-high heat and spray with olive oil. Add mushrooms and garlic. Sauté for 5 minutes. Add salt and pepper to taste. Remove to a small bowl. Add dressing and toss well. Place radicchio leaves on 2 dinner plates. Spoon mushrooms on to leaves.

Makes 2 servings.

Per serving: 127 calories, 1.9 grams protein, 5.4 grams carbohydrate, 10.2 grams fat (1.6 saturated), 0 milligrams cholesterol, 80 milligrams sodium, 0.2 grams fibre

helpful hints

● Parsley or coriander can be used instead of basil in the burgers.

● Only 2 tablespoons pesto are needed for the burgers. Extra pesto sauce can be frozen.

● To save washing up, cook the mushrooms , then remove and use the same pan for the burgers.

● A quick way to chop basil is to wash, dry, then snip the leaves with scissors off the stem.

countdown

● Sauté mushrooms and remove from frying pan.

● Prepare chicken burgers while mushrooms cook.

● Prepare tomato topping for chicken.

● Cook chicken burgers.

shopping list

FRUIT AND VEG

1 medium tomato

1 small bunch fresh basil

1 small bunch spring onions

225g (8oz) portobello mushrooms

1 small head radicchio

MEAT

350g (12oz) chicken mince

GROCERY

1 small jar prepared pesto sauce

STAPLES

Olive oil spray

Garlic

Olive oil and vinegar dressing

Salt

crab cakes and slaw

Crab cakes are very popular. Nearly every restaurant seems to have its own version, but the base usually has Worcestershire sauce, hot pepper sauce and onions or spring onions. Fresh crabmeat is best for this recipe. If difficult to find, use pasteurised crabmeat.
Homemade coleslaw is a breeze with a ready-to-eat, sliced coleslaw mix from the fruit and veg department.

crab cakes

450g (1lb) fresh or pasteurised
    crabmeat
2 tablespoons reduced-fat
    mayonnaise
2 tablespoons Worcestershire
    sauce
Several drops hot pepper sauce
4 spring onions, sliced
2 tablespoons Dijon mustard
2 egg whites
3 tablespoons plain breadcrumbs
Salt and freshly ground black
    pepper
2 tablespoons olive oil

Drain crabmeat. Flake meat with a fork while looking for any shell or cartilage that might remain. Mix the mayonnaise, Worcestershire sauce, hot pepper sauce, spring onions, mustard, egg whites and breadcrumbs together in a medium-sized bowl. Add salt and pepper to taste. Stir in crabmeat. Shape into 6 cakes about 7.5cm (3in) in diameter. Heat olive oil in a medium-sized non-stick frying pan on medium heat. Add crab cakes and cook for 5 minutes. Do not move crab cakes during this time. Carefully turn and cook for 5 minutes more. Serve crab cakes with coleslaw.
Makes 2 servings.

Per serving: 435 calories, 46.0 grams protein,
5.5 grams carbohydrate, 22.0 grams fat
(3.4 saturated), 182 milligrams cholesterol,
1572 milligrams sodium, 0 grams fibre

slaw

2 tablespoons reduced-fat
    mayonnaise
½ cup distilled white vinegar
Artificial sweetener equivalent to
    2 teaspoons sugar
Salt and freshly ground black
    pepper
225g (8oz) ready-to-eat coleslaw
    mix

Mix mayonnaise, vinegar and artificial sweetener together in a medium-sized bowl. Add salt and pepper to taste. Add coleslaw mix and toss well. Add more salt and pepper, if needed. Place on 2 plates.
Makes 2 servings.

Per serving: 94 calories, 2.0 grams protein,
11.1 grams carbohydrate, 5.4 grams fat
(1.0 saturated), 5 milligrams cholesterol,
139 milligrams sodium, 2.0 grams fibre

helpful hints

● *Frozen crabmeat can be used. The flavour will be fine; the texture will be softer than fresh crabmeat.*
● *Pasteurised crabmeat can be found in the seafood department.*
● *Different types of cabbage, ready-cut, can be found in the fruit and veg section of the supermarket. Use whichever you like.*

countdown

● *Make slaw.*
● *Make crab cakes.*

shopping list

FRUIT AND VEG
    1 pack coleslaw mix
    1 small bunch spring onions
SEAFOOD
    450g (1lb) fresh or
        pasteurised crabmeat
GROCERY
    1 small container plain
        breadcrumbs
STAPLES
    Reduced-fat mayonnaise
    Worcestershire sauce
    Hot pepper sauce
    Dijon mustard
    Eggs (2 needed)
    Olive oil
    Distilled white vinegar
    Artificial sweetener
    Salt
    Black peppercorns

salsa-baked snapper

This is a great meal for those evenings you need to get a tasty dinner on the table in 15 minutes. Fresh fish is the original fast food. Simply cover the fish with salsa, grill and serve.

salsa-baked snapper

Olive oil spray
350g (12oz) snapper fillet
Salt and freshly ground black pepper to taste
225ml (8fl oz) no-sugar-added tomato salsa

Preheat the oven to 200°C/400°F/gas mark 6. Line a baking tray with foil and spray with olive oil. Place the fish on the baking sheet, spray with olive oil and season with salt and pepper to taste. Bake for 10 minutes. Spoon the salsa over the fish and bake for 5 more minutes before serving.
Makes 2 servings.

One serving: 244 calories, 39g protein, 10g carbohydrate, 4g fat (1g saturated), 62mg cholesterol, 872mg sodium, 4g fibre

courgette parmesan

225g (8oz) courgettes, sliced
4 teaspoons olive oil
Salt and freshly ground black pepper to taste
2 tablespoons freshly grated Parmesan cheese

Place the courgettes in a microwave-safe bowl and heat on high for 5 minutes. Alternatively, bring a medium saucepan of water to a boil and add the courgettes. Boil for 3 minutes and drain. Toss with the olive oil and season with salt and pepper to taste. Sprinkle with Parmesan cheese and serve.
Makes 2 servings.

One serving: 123 calories, 4g protein, 4g carbohydrate, 11g fat (2g saturated), 4mg cholesterol, 110mg sodium, 1g fibre

italian greens

2 tablespoons no-sugar-added oil and vinegar dressing
2 teaspoons dried oregano
150g (5oz) washed, ready-to-eat, Italian-style salad leaves

Spoon the dressing into a salad bowl and stir in the oregano. Add the salad, toss well and serve.
Makes 2 servings.

One serving: 88 calories, 1g protein, 3g carbohydrate, 9g fat (1g saturated), 0mg cholesterol, 81mg sodium, 1g fibre

spicy prawns with roasted asparagus

When I made this dish for my husband, he couldn't believe it took only 5 minutes to make the sauce. The secret is red vermouth. It adds spice and depth to fresh tomatoes and goes perfectly with the prawns. ● *Roasting intensifies the flavour of fresh vegetables. The roasted asparagus takes only 15 minutes and goes perfectly with the simple leafy salad over leaf.*

spicy prawns

2 teaspoons olive oil
6 medium-sized garlic cloves,
   crushed
125ml (4fl oz) red vermouth
275g (10oz) diced tomatoes
350g (12oz) large raw prawns,
   peeled and deveined
25g (1oz) chopped fresh parsley
Several drops hot pepper sauce
Salt and freshly ground black
   pepper to taste

Heat the olive oil in a medium-sized non-stick frying pan over a medium-high heat. Sauté the garlic for a few seconds, then add the red vermouth and tomatoes. Cook for 5 minutes. Add the prawns and parsley and cook for 2–3 minutes until the prawns are pink. Season with hot pepper sauce, salt and pepper to taste. Divide between 2 plates and serve.
Makes 2 servings.

> One serving: 297 calories, 37g protein, 10g carbohydrate, 8g fat (1g saturated), 260mg cholesterol, 282mg sodium, 0g fibre

roasted asparagus

225g (8oz) fresh asparagus
2 teaspoons olive oil
Salt and freshly ground black
   pepper to taste

Preheat the oven to 200°C/400°F/gas mark 6. Cut or snap off any fibrous stem on the asparagus and discard. Slice the remaining asparagus into 5cm (2in) pieces. Line a baking tray with foil and spoon the oil onto the foil. Sprinkle the oil with salt and pepper to taste. Add the asparagus and roll in oil, making sure all the spears are coated with the oil and seasoning. Spread the asparagus into a single layer and roast in the oven for 5 minutes. Roll the asparagus in the oil to recoat and roast, 10 more minutes for thick spears and 5 more minutes for thin ones. Remove from the oven and serve with the prawns.
Makes 2 servings.

> One serving: 55 calories, 2g protein, 3g carbohydrate, 5g fat (1g saturated), 0mg cholesterol, 3mg sodium, 2g fibre

helpful hints

● *To save roasting time, the asparagus can be cooked in a microwave oven on high: 3 minutes for thin asparagus and 5 minutes for thick spears.*

● *Buy peeled prawns – it is well worth the time otherwise spent peeling them yourself.*

countdown

● *Preheat oven 200°C/400°F/gas mark 6.*
● *Start asparagus.*
● *Make prawns.*
● *Make Italian greens.*

shopping list

TO BUY:
   350g (12oz) large raw
      prawns
   1 small bottle red vermouth
   1 small bunch fresh parsley
   1 medium tomato
   225g (8oz) asparagus
   1 bag washed, ready-to-eat,
      Italian-style salad leaves
STAPLES
   Olive oil
   No-sugar-added oil and
      vinegar dressing
   Garlic
   Hot pepper sauce
   Salt
   Black peppercorns

spicy prawns with roasted asparagus continued

green salad

150g (5oz) washed, ready-to-eat, Italian-style salad leaves

2 tablespoons no-sugar-added oil and vinegar dressing

Salt and freshly ground black pepper to taste

Place the salad in a small bowl and drizzle with the dressing. Season with salt and pepper to taste. Toss well and serve.

Makes 2 servings.

One serving: 84 calories, 1g protein, 2g carbohydrate, 8g fat (1g saturated), 0mg cholesterol, 81mg sodium, 0g fibre

tex-mex meat loaf

This moist, well-seasoned meat loaf smothered in spicy salsa makes a great, homely meal. By forming the meat into small loaves instead of one large loaf, it takes only 20 minutes to cook, rather than the usual 45–60 minutes.● The heat circulates more quickly around the loaves. I The cooked loaves will keep a day in the refrigerator. If you have time, double the recipe and form 4 loaves. Save the other two for another quick meal.

tex-mex meat loaf

Olive oil spray
50g (2oz) red onion, thinly sliced
110g (4oz) mushrooms, thinly sliced
275g (10oz) minced veal
2 egg whites
Salt and freshly ground black pepper to taste

Preheat the oven to 200°C/400°F/gas mark 6. Line a baking tray with foil and spray with olive oil. Heat a non-stick frying pan over a medium-high heat and spray with olive oil. Add the onion and mushrooms and sauté for 5 minutes. Combine the vegetables with the minced veal and egg whites in a medium-sized mixing bowl. Add salt and pepper to taste. Place the meat directly on the foil-lined baking tray and shape into 2 loaves about 15 x 8cm (6 x 3in) each. Bake for 20 minutes.

spicy salsa

1 large tomato, diced
25g (1oz) chopped fresh coriander
1 small jalapeño pepper, seeded and chopped
½ teaspoon ground cumin
1 tablespoon freshly squeezed lime juice

While the loaves bake, combine the diced tomato, coriander, jalapeño, cumin and lime juice in a small bowl. Season with salt and pepper to taste. Spoon the salsa over the baked meat loaves and serve on 2 plates with the avocado.
Makes 2 servings.

One serving: 407 calories, 45g protein, 13g carbohydrate, 17g fat (10g saturated), 125mg cholesterol, 164mg sodium, 2g fibre

sliced avocado

½ small avocado, stoned, peeled and sliced
1 tablespoon no-sugar-added oil and vinegar dressing
Salt and freshly ground black pepper to taste

Arrange the avocado slices next to the meat loaves and drizzle with dressing. Season with salt and pepper to taste. Serve with the meat loaf. Makes 2 servings.

One serving: 114 calories, 1g protein, 3g carbohydrate, 12g fat (2g saturated), 0mg cholesterol, 43mg sodium, 2g fibre

helpful hint

● Use the salsa recipe given or purchase a no-sugar-added version.

countdown

● Preheat oven to 200°C/400°F/gas mark 6.
● Make meat loaf.
● Prepare avocado.

shopping list

MEAT
275g (10oz) minced veal
GROCERY
1 small jalapeño pepper
FRUIT AND VEG
1 small avocado
1 small packet sliced mushrooms (50g/2oz needed)
2 limes
1 large tomato
1 small bunch coriander
STAPLES
Olive oil spray
Red onion
Eggs
No-sugar-added oil and vinegar dressing
Ground cumin
Salt
Black peppercorns

pecan-crusted fish with vegetable creole

Pecan-flavoured fish and vegetable creole are updated versions of Southern American comfort foods. ● *To cook fish fast, preheat the baking tray in the oven. The hot tray will help to cook the fish on the underside without having to turn the fish.*

pecan-crusted fish

1/4 teaspoon salt
1/4 teaspoon freshly ground black pepper
1/4 teaspoon cayenne pepper
2 egg whites, lightly beaten
50g (2oz) pecans, finely chopped
350g (12oz) fish fillet
2 teaspoons olive oil
Olive oil spray

Preheat the oven to 200°C/400°F/gas mark 6. Line a baking tray with foil and place in the oven to heat. Combine the salt, black pepper and cayenne on a plate. Line up the spice mixture, the beaten egg whites and the pecans in a row on the work surface for easy coating of the fish. First, roll the fish in the spice mixture, coating both sides. Next, dip the fish into the egg whites and then roll in the pecans.

Heat the olive oil in a non-stick frying pan over a medium-high heat. When the oil is hot, brown the fish for 2 minutes. Turn and brown the other side for 1 minute. Remove the baking tray from the oven and spray with olive oil. Place the fish on the tray and return the tray to the oven for 5 minutes to finish cooking. Serve with the creole. *Makes 2 servings.*

One serving: 399 calories, 39g protein, 4g carbohydrate, 26g fat (3g saturated), 62mg cholesterol, 412mg sodium, 3g fibre

vegetable creole

2 teaspoons olive oil
110g (4oz) yellow onion, sliced
1 medium-sized green pepper, sliced
1 courgette, sliced
4 medium-sized garlic cloves, crushed
450g (1lb) tinned no-sugar-added, diced tomatoes
1 tablespoon Worcestershire sauce
2g (1/16oz) artificial sweetener

Heat the olive oil in a non-stick frying pan over a medium-high heat. Add the onion, pepper, courgette and garlic and sauté for 5 minutes. Lower the heat to medium. Add the tomatoes, Worcestershire sauce and artificial sweetener. Cover with a lid and cook for 5 minutes. Serve hot with the fish. *Makes 2 servings.*

One serving: 156 calories, 6g protein, 22g carbohydrate, 5g fat (1g saturated), 0mg cholesterol, 378mg sodium, 7g fibre

glazed balsamic chicken

Balsamic vinegar makes a zesty glaze for chicken – and adds very few calories in the process.
● *Roasting or grilling intensifies the flavour of vegetables. The courgettes are left to cook while you prepare the chicken and mange tout.*

glazed balsamic chicken

Olive oil spray
350g (12oz) boneless, skinless chicken breast
Salt and freshly ground black pepper to taste
125ml (4fl oz) good quality balsamic vinegar
25g (1oz) pine nuts
1 tablespoon Dijon mustard

Heat a medium-sized non-stick frying pan over a medium-high heat and spray with olive oil. Brown the chicken for 3 minutes, turn and cook for another 3 minutes. Remove from the heat, cover with a lid and let sit for 3 minutes. Remove the chicken to a plate, season with salt and pepper to taste and cover with a plate or foil to keep warm. In the same pan, add the vinegar and pine nuts. Cook over a medium-high heat to reduce, about 30 seconds, or until about half the amount of liquid remains. Add the mustard and mix well to make a smooth glaze. Return the chicken to the pan, turning to coat both sides with the glaze. Cook for another minute, then divide between 2 plates to serve and spoon any remaining glaze on top.
Makes 2 servings.

One serving: 378 calories, 54g protein, 4g carbohydrate, 11g fat (2g saturated), 144mg cholesterol, 306mg sodium, 0g fibre

helpful hint

● *To save cleaning time, sauté the chicken and remove to a plate. Cover with another plate or foil to keep warm. Use the same pan to sauté the mange tout.*
● *If yellow courgettes are unavailable, use green ones instead.*

countdown

● *Preheat grill.*
● *Start courgettes.*
● *Make chicken.*
● *Sauté mange tout.*

shopping list

MEAT
  350g (12oz) boneless, skinless chicken breast
GROCERY
  1 small packet pine nuts
FRUIT AND VEG
  225g (8oz) mange tout
  225g (8oz) yellow courgettes
  1 medium-sized red pepper
STAPLES
  Olive oil
  Olive oil spray
  Balsamic vinegar
  Dijon mustard
  Garlic
  Salt
  Black peppercorns

glazed balsamic chicken

continued

grilled courgettes

Olive oil spray

2 teaspoons olive oil

2 medium-sized garlic cloves, crushed

1 tablespoon water

225g (8oz) yellow courgettes, cut into 2.5cm (1in) slices

1 medium-sized red pepper, cut into 2.5cm (1in) pieces

Salt and freshly ground black pepper to taste

Preheat the grill. Line a baking sheet with foil and spray with olive oil. Place the foil-lined sheet under the grill 12.5cm (5in) from the heat. Combine the olive oil with garlic and water in a small mixing bowl. Remove the baking sheet from the grill and place the vegetables on the sheet. Spoon half of the olive oil mixture over the vegetables and toss well. Spread the vegetables out to form a single layer. Grill for 10 minutes. Turn the vegetables over and spoon with the remaining olive oil mixture. Grill for another 10 minutes. The courgettes should be cooked through, but not black. Sprinkle with salt and pepper to taste. Serve with the chicken. *Makes 2 servings.*

One serving: 104 calories, 3g protein, 11g carbohydrate, 7g fat (1g saturated), 0mg cholesterol, 4mg sodium, 1g fibre

mange tout

2 teaspoons olive oil

225g (8oz) mange tout, trimmed

Salt and freshly ground black pepper to taste

Heat the olive oil in a non-stick frying pan over a medium-high heat. Add the mange tout and sauté for 2 minutes, tossing continuously. Season with salt and pepper to taste. Serve with the chicken. *Makes 2 servings.*

One serving: 66 calories, 2g protein, 5g carbohydrate, 5g fat (1g saturated), 0mg cholesterol, 3mg sodium, 2g fibre

asian ginger salmon

This is a very simple 15-minute dinner. It's a basic recipe that you can use as a blueprint to make other similar dinners. Boneless, skinless chicken breast can be used instead of salmon, cauliflower instead of broccoli and yellow beans instead of green.

asian ginger salmon

Olive oil spray
350g (12oz) salmon fillet
Salt and freshly ground black pepper to taste
2 tablespoons low-sodium soy sauce
2 tablespoons water
2 tablespoons chopped fresh ginger

Heat a non-stick frying pan over a medium-high heat and spray with olive oil. Add the salmon and brown for 2 minutes. Turn, season the cooked side, then brown the second side for 2 minutes. Lower the heat and sauté for 5 minutes. Combine the soy sauce, water and ginger in a small bowl. Remove the salmon from the pan, add the soy sauce mixture to the pan and cook for several seconds. Divide the salmon between 2 plates and spoon the sauce over the salmon.
Makes 2 servings.

One serving: 310 calories, 43g protein, 2g carbohydrate, 12g fat (3g saturated), 120mg cholesterol, 714mg sodium, 0g fibre

sesame broccoli

110g (4oz) broccoli florets
2 teaspoons olive oil
25g (1oz) sesame seeds
Salt and freshly ground black pepper to taste

Place the broccoli in a microwave-safe bowl and microwave on high for 5 minutes. Alternatively, bring a pot of water to the boil and add the broccoli. Boil for 2 minutes and then drain. Heat the oil in a non-stick frying pan over a medium-high heat. Sauté the broccoli and sesame seeds for 3 to 4 minutes, or until the sesame seeds are golden and the broccoli is bright green, but crisp. Season with salt and pepper to taste. Serve with the salmon.
Makes 2 servings.

One serving: 158 calories, 7g protein, 6g carbohydrate, 14g fat (2g saturated), 0mg cholesterol, 79mg sodium, 2g fibre

helpful hints

● Broccoli and beans can be microwaved at the same time for 3 minutes on high.
● To save washing an extra pan, prepare the salmon and cover with foil to keep warm. Use same pan to sauté the broccoli.
● A washed, ready-to-eat salad can be substituted for one of the vegetables.
● To chop fresh ginger quickly, cut it into small cubes and press through a garlic press with large holes. If using a press with small holes, just capture the juice that is squeezed out; it will give enough flavour for the recipe.

countdown

● Make salmon.
● Make broccoli.
● Make beans.

shopping list

FISH
  350g (12oz) salmon fillet
GROCERY
  1 small packet sesame seeds
FRUIT AND VEG
  225g (8oz) French beans
  110g (4oz) broccoli florets
  1 small piece fresh ginger

asian ginger salmon continued

green bean salad

STAPLES
Olive oil
Olive oil spray
No-sugar-added olive oil and
  vinegar dressing
Low-sodium soy sauce
Salt
Black peppercorns

225g (8oz) French beans, trimmed
  and cut in half
2 tablespoons no-sugar-added
  olive oil and vinegar dressing
Salt and freshly ground black
  pepper to taste

Place the beans in a microwave-safe bowl and microwave on high for 3 minutes. Alternatively, bring a pot of water to the boil and add the beans. Boil for 2 minutes, and then drain. Toss the cooked beans with the salad dressing. Season with salt and pepper to taste and serve. *Makes 2 servings.*

One serving: 119 calories, 2g protein,
10g carbohydrate, 9g fat (1g saturated),
0mg cholesterol, 79mg sodium, 2g fibre

pacific rim pork

Spicy, Pacific Rim flavours add zest to this easy-to-prepare dinner. ● The pickled vegetable salad makes a great snack. Make extra and store in a plastic bag. Serve it on its own, or add it to chicken or tuna salads.

pacific rim pork

350g (12oz) pork tenderloin,
    visible fat removed

For marinade:
50ml (2fl oz) low-salt soy sauce
50ml (2fl oz) distilled white
    vinegar
4 medium-sized garlic cloves,
    crushed
4 teaspoons Dijon mustard
2 teaspoons ground ginger
Dash of freshly ground black
    pepper

Preheat the grill and place the rack on the top rung of the oven. Line a baking sheet with foil. Cut the pork almost in half lengthwise and open like a book. Do not cut all of the way through. Combine the marinade ingredients in a small bowl. Add the pork and allow to marinate for 20 minutes. Remove from the marinade and place the pork on the foil-lined baking sheet. Grill for 5 minutes, turn and grill for 3 more minutes. The pork is done when a meat thermometer inserted in the centre registers 70°C/160°F. Slice and serve with the salad and vegetables.
Makes 2 servings.

One serving: 293 calories, 50g protein, 2g carbohydrate, 8g fat (3g saturated), 159mg cholesterol, 478mg sodium, 0g fibre

pickled radish salad

225ml (8fl oz) water
150ml (5fl oz) distilled white
    vinegar
10g (½oz) artificial sweetener
1 teaspoon crushed red pepper
1 teaspoon salt
Half a cucumber, peeled and
    sliced
175g (6oz) radishes (white or red),
    peeled and sliced
2 tablespoons yellow onion,
    chopped

Mix the water, vinegar, sweetener, crushed red pepper and salt together in a medium-sized bowl. Add the cucumber, radish and onion and marinate for 15 minutes. Drain and serve.
Makes 2 servings.

One serving: 34 calories, 1g protein, 9g carbohydrate, 0g fat (0g saturated), 0mg cholesterol, 276mg sodium, 1g fibre

helpful hints

● *If possible use Daikon radish, a white, Oriental radish with a sweet, fresh flavour.*
● *To avoid having to look back at the recipe as you stir-fry, line up the ingredients on a board or plate in the order of use so you know which to add comes next.*
● *For crisp, not steamed, stir-fried vegetables, start with a very hot wok or frying pan. Let the vegetables sit for a minute before tossing to allow the wok to regain its heat.*

countdown

● *Preheat grill.*
● *Marinate pork.*
● *Make salad.*
● *Prepare stir-fry vegetable ingredients.*
● *Grill pork.*
● *While pork cooks, make stir-fry vegetables.*

shopping list

MEAT
    350g (12oz) pork tenderloin
GROCERY
    1 small jar ground ginger
    1 bottle sesame oil
FRUIT AND VEG
    1 small head Chinese
        cabbage (Chinese leaf)
    1 packet fresh bean sprouts
    1 jar crushed red pepper
    Half a cucumber
    175g (6oz) radishes

pacific rim pork continued

STAPLES

Garlic

Yellow onion

Dijon mustard

Low-sodium soy sauce

Distilled white vinegar

Artificial sweetener

Salt

Black peppercorns

ginger-garlic stir-fry vegetables

2 teaspoons sesame oil

2 teaspoons ground ginger

225g (8oz) Chinese cabbage (Chinese leaf), washed and sliced

150g (5oz) fresh bean sprouts

4 medium-sized garlic cloves, crushed

Pour the oil into a wok or non-stick frying pan and place over a high heat. When the oil begins to smoke, add the ginger, lettuce, bean sprouts and garlic. Stir-fry for 6 minutes and then serve. Makes 2 servings.

One serving: 92 calories, 4g protein, 10g carbohydrate, 5g fat (1g saturated), 0mg cholesterol, 13mg sodium, 2g fibre

veal escalopes with garlic greens

In this dish, romaine and radicchio leaves are just wilted in a pan and flavoured with garlic to form a crunchy, colourful topping for the veal escalopes. ● Veal escalopes take only a few minutes to cook. The secret to keeping them juicy is to brown them in a hot frying pan for 1 minute on each side, then remove them to a plate and cover to keep warm. Boneless, skinless chicken breasts can be substituted, though they will need to cook longer. ● Saffron is the stigmas from a saffron crocus. It is pricy because it is harvested by hand. Fortunately, a little goes a long way.

veal escalopes with garlic greens

Olive oil spray
350g (12oz) veal escalopes
  pounded to 2–3mm (¹/₈–¹/₁₆in)
  thick
Salt and freshly ground black
  pepper to taste
4 medium-sized garlic cloves,
  crushed
150g (5oz) cos and radicchio
  leaves torn into bite-sized
  pieces

Set a medium-sized non-stick frying pan over a high heat and spray with olive oil. Brown the veal for 1 minute on each side. Season the cooked sides and remove to 2 plates. Add the garlic and salad leaves to the pan. Toss for 1 minute, or until the leaves just start to wilt. Season with salt and pepper to taste. Serve the salad leaves over the veal escalopes.
Makes 2 servings.

One serving: 398 calories, 46g protein, 3g carbohydrate, 20g fat (12g saturated), 150mg cholesterol, 114mg sodium, 0g fibre

saffron cauliflower

225g (8oz) cauliflower florets
4 teaspoons olive oil
¹/₄ teaspoon saffron strands
Salt and freshly ground black
  pepper to taste

Place the cauliflower in a vegetable steamer set over boiling water. Steam for 6–7 minutes, or until tender. Alternatively, place in a microwave-safe dish – do not add water – and microwave on high for 5 minutes. Spoon the olive oil into a large serving bowl and add the saffron. Microwave on high for 10 seconds. Add the cauliflower to the oil, season with salt and pepper to taste and toss well before serving.
Makes 2 servings.

One serving: 130 calories, 4g protein, 10g carbohydrate, 9g fat (1g saturated), 0mg cholesterol, 60mg sodium, 5g fibre

helpful hints

- ● *Turmeric or bijol can be used instead of the saffron.*
- ● *Buy cauliflower already cut into florets.*
- ● *Washed, ready-to-eat salad can be used. Make sure the leaves are firm. Baby gourmet salad leaves or lamb's lettuce will be too soft to work in this recipe.*

countdown

- ● *Make cauliflower, cover to keep warm.*
- ● *Prepare veal and garlic greens.*

shopping list

MEAT
  350g (12oz) veal escalopes
GROCERY
  1 small packet saffron strands
FRUIT AND VEG
  225g (8oz) cauliflower florets
  1 small head romaine lettuce
  1 small head radicchio lettuce
STAPLES
  Olive oil
  Olive oil spray
  Garlic
  Salt
  Black peppercorns

sirloin burger with fresh slaw

In the mood for a burger? Here's a quick one made with lean sirloin and accompanied by coleslaw. Sliced, ready-to-use cabbage and carrot can be found in the fruit and veg section of the supermarket, making homemade coleslaw a breeze.

sirloin burger

50g (2oz) red onion, chopped
225g (8oz) minced lean sirloin
Salt and freshly ground black pepper to taste
Olive oil spray
35g (1½oz) sliced reduced-fat Cheddar cheese (about 2 slices)
4 teaspoons Dijon mustard

Combine the onion and minced sirloin in a medium-sized bowl. Season with salt and pepper to taste. Form into 2 patties. Set a medium-sized non-stick frying pan over medium-high heat and spray with olive oil. Cook the sirloin burgers for 5 minutes. Turn and top each burger with a slice of cheese. Continue cooking for 3 more minutes. Top the cheese with mustard and serve.
Makes 2 servings.

One serving: 338 calories, 46g protein, 2g carbohydrate, 17g fat (8g saturated), 117mg cholesterol, 496mg sodium, 0g fibre

fresh slaw

2 tablespoons mayonnaise made with soya bean or olive oil
2 tablespoons distilled white vinegar
4 teaspoons Dijon mustard
4g (⅛oz) artificial sweetener
Salt and freshly ground black pepper to taste
4 slices red onion
450g (1lb) presliced cabbage and carrot mix
2 medium tomatoes, sliced

Combine the mayonnaise, vinegar, mustard and artificial sweetener in a medium-sized bowl. Season with salt and pepper to taste. Add the cabbage, carrot and onion and toss well. Add more salt and pepper, if needed. Divide between 2 plates, and arrange the tomato slices on the side.
Makes 2 servings.

One serving: 191 calories, 5g protein, 18g carbohydrate, 12g fat (2g saturated), 5mg cholesterol, 355mg sodium, 2g fibre

rosemary-roasted pork

Northern Italy inspired this roasted pork dinner served with fennel gratin and Brussels sprouts. The secret to roasting the pork in only 15 minutes is to butterfly it by cutting it in half lengthwise. ● *Pecorino cheese is an alternative to using Parmesan cheese, but with a sharper flavour. It's made from sheep's milk and the most popular kinds are hard and perfect for grating.* ● *Fennel has a pale green bulb and stalk with feathery leaves. It has a slight anise or liquorice flavour when raw that becomes even milder when cooked.*

rosemary-roasted pork

Olive oil spray
350g (12oz) pork tenderloin
2 teaspoons olive oil
*2 tablespoons chopped fresh
    rosemary or 2 teaspoons dried*
*Salt and freshly ground black
    pepper to taste*

Preheat the oven to 200°C/400°F/gas mark 6. Line a baking tray with foil, spray with olive oil and place in the oven to heat. Remove all visible fat from the pork and cut the loin nearly in half lengthwise. Open the pork and lay flat like a book. Pound it flat with the palm of your hand or with the bottom of a pan. Rub the pork with olive oil and sprinkle with rosemary on both sides. Place the pork on the hot baking tray. Roast for 15 minutes. Remove from the oven, cover with foil and let the meat rest for 5 minutes. Season with salt and pepper to taste. Slice and serve.

Makes 2 servings.

One serving: 345 calories, 49g protein, 0g carbohydrate, 15g fat (4g saturated), 159mg cholesterol, 115mg sodium, 0g fibre

helpful hints

● *Parmesan cheese can be used instead of pecorino cheese.*
● *A quick way to chop fresh rosemary is to snip it right from the stem with scissors.*
● *Celery can be substituted for the fennel in the recipe.*

countdown

● *Preheat oven to 400°F/200°C/gas mark 6.*
● *Start pork.*
● *Make fennel.*
● *Steam Brussels sprouts.*

shopping list

DAIRY
   1 small piece pecorino cheese
MEAT
   350g (12oz) pork tenderloin
FRUIT AND VEG
   1 small bunch fresh rosemary or 1 jar dried
   1 medium bulb fennel
   110g (4oz) Brussels sprouts
STAPLES
   Olive oil spray
   Olive oil
   Salt
   Black peppercorns

rosemary-roasted pork continued

fennel gratin

4 teaspoons olive oil

half medium bulb fennel, stalks and leaves removed, thinly sliced

Salt and freshly ground black pepper to taste

2 tablespoons grated pecorino cheese

Heat the olive oil in a non-stick frying pan over a medium-high heat. Add the fennel and toss in the oil. Cover with a lid and cook for 2 minutes. Alternatively, place in a microwave-safe bowl, add the oil, and toss to coat. Cover and microwave on high for 8 minutes. Season the cooked fennel with salt and pepper to taste and toss well. Sprinkle with the cheese and place in the oven with the pork for 5 minutes, or until the cheese starts to melt. Use the same baking tray as the pork to save clean-up time. Serve with the pork. *Makes 2 servings.*

One serving: 135 calories, 2g protein, 0g carbohydrate, 11g fat (2g saturated), 4mg cholesterol, 106mg sodium, 0g fibre

brussels sprouts

110g (4oz) Brussels sprouts, damaged outer leaves removed and sprouts halved

2 teaspoons olive oil

Salt and freshly ground black pepper to taste

Place the Brussels sprouts in the basket of a vegetable steamer. Place over boiling water and steam for 6–7 minutes. Alternatively, microwave on high for 5 minutes. Transfer the cooked Brussels sprouts to a serving bowl. Add the olive oil and season with salt and pepper to taste. Toss well before serving. *Makes 2 servings.*

One serving: 60 calories, 1g protein, 4g carbohydrate, 5g fat (1g saturated), 0mg cholesterol, 12mg sodium, 1g fibre

herb-stuffed chicken

The stuffing only takes minutes to make, gives flavour to the chicken and keeps it moist during cooking. ● Small, baby turnips need only a little sautéing to bring out their sweetness.

herb-stuffed chicken

2 x 175g (6oz) boneless, skinless chicken breasts

2 tablespoons fresh tarragon or 2 teaspoons dried

2 spring onions, sliced

2 medium-sized button mushrooms

2 tablespoons fat-free plain yoghurt

Salt and freshly ground black pepper to taste

Olive oil spray

Make a horizontal slit in each chicken breast, deep enough to form a pocket the length of the breast. Chop the tarragon, spring onions and mushrooms together. Add the yoghurt and blend well. Season with salt and pepper to taste. Season the pockets of the chicken. Spoon the herb stuffing into the slit. Gently press the sides together to close the slits. Set a medium-sized non-stick frying pan over a medium-high heat, and spray with olive oil. Brown the chicken for 2 minutes on each side, seasoning each cooked side with salt and pepper. Lower the heat to medium, cover with a lid and cook for 6 more minutes. Serve hot with the vegetables. *Makes 2 servings.*

One serving: 309 calories, 55g protein, 2g carbohydrate, 10g fat (2g saturated), 144mg cholesterol, 138mg sodium, 0g fibre

pan-roasted asparagus and baby turnips

225g (8oz) fresh asparagus, trimmed

4 teaspoons olive oil

225g (8oz) baby turnips, peeled and cut into 2.5cm (1in) cubes

1 medium-sized garlic clove, crushed

Salt and freshly ground black pepper to taste

Cut the trimmed asparagus into 5cm (2in) pieces. Heat the olive oil in a medium-sized non-stick frying pan over a medium-high heat. Add the turnips and sauté for 5 minutes, turning to brown on all sides. Add the asparagus and garlic and sauté, 5 minutes for thin asparagus, 10 minutes for thick. Season with salt and pepper to taste. *Makes 2 servings.*

One serving: 134 calories, 3g protein, 12g carbohydrate, 9g fat (1g saturated), 0mg cholesterol, 90mg sodium, 5g fibre

helpful hints

● *If you use dried tarragon, check the leaves are still green. If they have started to turn brown, buy a new jar.*

● *The herbs, onions and mushrooms can be chopped in a food processor to save even more time.*

countdown

● *Prepare all ingredients.*

● *Start chicken.*

● *While chicken cooks, make asparagus and turnips.*

shopping list

DAIRY

   1 small pot fat-free plain yoghurt

MEAT

   2 x 175 (6oz) boneless, skinless chicken breasts

FRUIT AND VEG

   225g (8oz) fresh asparagus

   225g (8oz) baby turnips

   1 small bunch fresh tarragon or 1 jar dried

   1 small packet button mushrooms

   1 small bunch spring onions (2 needed)

STAPLES

   Olive oil

   Olive oil spray

   Garlic

   Salt

   Black peppercorns

marsala chicken

The rich, smoky flavour of Sicily's Marsala wine makes a quick glaze for this chicken. To help cook the chicken faster, I flatten the chicken breast to about 1cm (½in) thick. This also enlarges the surface area available to absorb the glaze.

helpful hints

- *To save cleaning a second pan, use the same one to cook the chicken and spinach.*
- *Buy an inexpensive Marsala wine for this recipe. It also goes well with veal, pork and turkey.*

countdown

- *Make salad and set aside.*
- *Make chicken.*
- *Make spinach.*

shopping list

DAIRY
1 small pot crème fraîche
MEAT
275g (10oz) boneless, skinless chicken breast
GROCERY
1 bottle medium-dry Marsala wine
FRUIT AND VEG
1 small head radicchio lettuce
1 small bunch radishes
1 bag washed, ready-to-eat fresh spinach (275g/10oz needed)
STAPLES
Olive oil
No-sugar-added oil and vinegar dressing
Garlic
Salt
Black peppercorns

marsala chicken

275g (10oz) boneless, skinless
   chicken breasts
2 teaspoons olive oil
Salt and freshly ground black
   pepper to taste
125ml (4fl oz) medium-dry
   Marsala wine
1 tablespoon crème fraîche

Remove all visible fat from the chicken. Pound with the palm of your hand to flatten to about 1cm (½in) thick. Heat the oil in a non-stick frying pan over a medium-high heat. Brown the chicken, about 2 minutes on each side. Season each cooked side with salt and pepper to taste. Add the Marsala wine to the pan and continue to cook for 2–3 minutes. Remove the chicken to 2 plates. Continue to simmer the sauce for about 1 minute to reduce. Add the crème fraîche and season with salt and pepper to taste. Spoon the sauce over the chicken and cover with foil to keep warm before serving.
Makes 2 servings.

One serving: 394 calories, 45g protein, 7g carbohydrate, 14g fat (4g saturated), 131mg cholesterol, 113mg sodium, 0g fibre

roman spinach

275g (10oz) fresh washed, ready-
   to-eat fresh spinach
2 teaspoons olive oil
4 medium-sized garlic cloves,
   crushed
Salt and freshly ground black
   pepper to taste

Place the spinach in a large saucepan (do not add water). Cover and cook for 5 minutes, tossing once or twice, then drain. Alternatively, place in a microwave-safe bowl and microwave on high for 5 minutes. Heat the olive oil in the same saucepan over a medium heat and add the garlic. Stir for about 30 seconds. Return the spinach to the pan. Season with salt and pepper to taste. Serve with the chicken.
Makes 2 servings.

One serving: 97 calories, 7g protein, 10g carbohydrate, 5g fat (1g saturated), 0mg cholesterol, 172mg sodium, 7g fibre

radicchio salad

1 small head radicchio, torn into
    bite-sized pieces

12 radishes

1 tablespoon no-sugar-added oil
    and vinegar dressing

Salt and freshly ground black
    pepper to taste

Divide the radicchio leaves between 2 plates
and grate the radishes on top. Alternatively,
grate the radishes in a food processor fitted with
a grating blade. Spoon the dressing over the
salad and season with salt and pepper to taste
before serving.

Makes 2 servings.

One serving: 103 calories, 1g protein,
6g carbohydrate, 9g fat (1g saturated),
0mg cholesterol, 96mg sodium, 1g fibre

pork escalopes with spinach and mushrooms

'Pork Escalopes with fresh sautéed tomatoes and garlic,' was the instant answer a famous TV chef gave me when I asked her what she serves her family for a quick meal.

helpful hints

- *Any type of green vegetable can be substituted for spinach.*
- *Look for shelled pistachio nuts in the supermarket.*

countdown

- *Make spinach and mushrooms.*
- *Make pork escalopes.*

shopping list

MEAT
  350g (12oz) pork fillet
GROCERY
  1 small packet shelled pistachio nuts
FRUIT AND VEG
  2 medium tomatoes
  1 bag washed, ready-to-eat spinach (275g/10oz needed)
  350g (12oz) sliced portobello mushrooms
STAPLES
  Olive oil
  Garlic
  Salt
  Black peppercorns

pork escalopes

350g (12oz) pork fillet
2 tablespoons finely chopped pistachio nuts
Salt and freshly ground black pepper
1 teaspoon olive oil
2 medium garlic cloves, crushed
2 medium tomatoes, cut into 2.5cm (1in) pieces

Remove fat from pork and cut into 2.5cm (1in) slices. Place slices between 2 pieces of clingfilm and flatten with the bottom of a heavy pan or a kitchen mallet. Place pistachio nuts on a plate and season with salt and pepper to taste. Press into pork on both sides. Heat oil in a large non-stick frying pan on medium-high heat. Brown pork for 1 minute, then turn and brown second side for 1 minute. Salt and pepper the cooked sides. Remove to a plate. Add garlic and tomatoes to the pan and cook for 3 minutes. Spoon tomatoes over pork and serve.
Makes 2 servings.

Per serving: 398 calories, 53.9 grams protein, 8.8 grams carbohydrate, 16.0 grams fat (3.9 saturated), 159 milligrams cholesterol, 126 milligrams sodium, 0 grams fibre

spinach and mushrooms

275g (10oz) washed, ready-to-eat spinach
350g (12oz) portobello mushrooms, sliced
2 teaspoons olive oil
Salt and freshly ground black pepper

Place spinach and mushrooms in a large microwave-safe bowl. Microwave on high for 5 minutes. Remove and toss well. Add olive oil and salt and pepper to taste. Toss again.
Makes 2 servings.

Per serving: 126 calories, 7.8 grams protein, 11.2 grams carbohydrate, 6.2 grams fat (0.6 saturated), 0 milligrams cholesterol, 174 milligrams sodium, 7.2 grams fibre

roasted salmon and herb sauce

Salmon, sprayed with a little olive oil and salt and pepper, takes on a buttery, creamy texture when roasted in a medium oven for 20 minutes. It is served with a herb sauce that takes only minutes in a food processor.

roasted salmon and herb sauce

2 x 175g (6oz) salmon fillets

Olive oil spray

Salt and freshly ground black pepper

40g (1½oz) rocket

50ml (2fl oz) non-fat natural yoghurt

2 teaspoons fresh lemon or lime juice

1 tablespoon mayonnaise

1 medium tomato, sliced

Pre-heat oven to 180ºC/350ºF/gas mark 4. Line a baking tray with foil. Place salmon on the tray and spray both sides of the fillet with olive oil spray. Sprinkle with salt and pepper to taste. Roast in oven for 20 minutes.

Meanwhile, remove any large stems from the rocket and place in a food processor. Add yoghurt, lemon juice and mayonnaise. Process until smooth. Add salt and pepper to taste. Spoon over roasted salmon. Place sliced tomatoes on the side.

Makes 2 servings.

> Per serving: 375 calories, 44.8 grams protein, 6.8 grams carbohydrate, 16.6 grams fat (3.5 saturated), 123 milligrams cholesterol, 180 milligrams sodium, 0 grams fibre

braised asparagus

350g (12oz) asparagus

115ml (4fl oz) water

1 teaspoon olive oil

Salt and freshly ground black pepper

Wash asparagus and cut about 2.5cm (1in) off the woody ends. Place in a large non-stick frying pan just large enough to hold them in one layer. Add the water, olive oil and salt and pepper to taste. Bring to a simmer on medium-high heat and cover with lid. Lower heat to medium-low and cook for 10 minutes. Check the water halfway through the cooking and add more if the pan is dry. Serve with the salmon.

Makes 2 servings.

> Per serving: 43 calories, 3 grams protein, 4.5 grams carbohydrate, 206 grams fat (0.4 saturated), 0 milligrams cholesterol, 138 milligrams sodium, 3.6 grams fibre

helpful hints

- *If you do not have a food processor, cut the rocket into small strips and mix with the other ingredients.*
- *If using thin asparagus, cut the braising time in half.*

countdown

- *Pre-heat oven to 180ºC/350ºF/gas mark 4.*
- *Place salmon in oven.*
- *Make asparagus.*
- *While salmon and asparagus cook, make herb sauce.*

shopping list

DAIRY

1 small pot non-fat natural yoghurt (50ml/2fl oz needed)

FISH

2 x 175g (6oz) salmon fillets

FRUIT AND VEG

350g (12oz) asparagus

1 bunch rocket (40g/1½oz needed)

1 medium tomato

STAPLES

Olive oil

Olive oil spray

Lemon

Mayonnaise

Salt

Black peppercorns

steak au poivre

Here's a meal that's perfect for those evenings when you want something a little special.
● Steak au Poivre, or black pepper steak, is a very simple, very French dish. This recipe calls for cracked or coarsely broken black peppercorns, which are available in the spice section of the supermarket. ● Crème fraîche adds a tangy flavour and creamy texture to the sauce.
● Brandy is the generic name for cognac or Armagnac. You can buy brandy in miniature bottles at many supermarkets and most off-licences. ● Palm hearts are the tender heart of the Sabal palm tree.

shopping list

DAIRY
   1 small pot crème fraîche
MEAT
   2 x 150g (5oz) beef fillets
GROCERY
   1 jar cracked black pepper
   1 small bottle brandy,
      preferably cognac
   1 jar or tin palm hearts
      (275g/10oz needed)
FRUIT AND VEG
   225g (8oz) French green
      beans (haricots verts)
   1 small head red lettuce
STAPLES
   Garlic
   Rapeseed oil
   Red wine vinegar
   Dijon mustard
   Salt
   Black peppercorns

steak au poivre

2 x 150g (5oz) fillets of beef
1 tablespoon cracked black
   pepper
4 teaspoons rapeseed oil
Salt to taste
2 tablespoons cognac
   or brandy
1 tablespoon crème fraîche

Cover the steaks with the cracked pepper, pressing it into the meat with the palm of your hand. Heat the oil in a non-stick frying pan over a medium-high heat. Brown the steaks for 4 minutes. If the steaks are browning too quickly, reduce the heat to medium. Turn and salt the cooked sides to taste. Brown the second side for 2 minutes, or until a meat thermometer registers 60°C/140°F. Remove the steaks to 2 plates.

Add the cognac to the hot pan, scraping up the brown bits as it cooks. Add the crème fraîche and mix well. Taste for salt and adjust the seasoning if necessary. Spoon the sauce on top of the steaks and serve.
Makes 2 servings.

One serving: 376 calories, 30g protein, 2g carbohydrate, 24g fat (8g saturated), 98mg cholesterol, 81mg sodium, 0g fibre

french green beans

225g (8oz) French green beans
   (haricots verts), trimmed
4 teaspoons rapeseed oil
2 medium-sized garlic cloves,
   crushed
Salt and freshly ground black
   pepper to taste

Bring a medium saucepan full of water to a boil. Add the beans. As soon as the water comes back to a boil, drain the beans. Return the beans to the pan and fill the pan with iced water to stop the cooking. Drain the beans. In the same saucepan, heat the oil over a high heat. Add the beans and garlic, and sauté for 2–3 minutes until the beans are crisp. Season with salt and pepper to taste and serve with the steak.
Makes 2 servings.

One serving: 88 calories, 3g protein,
11g carbohydrate, 5g fat (1g saturated),
0mg cholesterol, 4mg sodium, 2g fibre

palm hearts salad

1 tablespoon red wine vinegar
4 teaspoons Dijon mustard
Salt and freshly ground black
   pepper to taste
2 teaspoons rapeseed oil
275g (10oz) palm hearts, drained
   and cut into 1cm (½in) slices
Several red lettuce leaves

In a salad bowl, whisk the vinegar and mustard together until smooth. Season with salt and pepper to taste. Whisk in the oil and adjust for seasoning as necessary. Add the palm hearts to the dressing. Toss well. Place the lettuce on 2 small plates, spoon the palm hearts on top and serve.
Makes 2 servings.

One serving: 100 calories, 5g protein,
9g carbohydrate, 6g fat (1g saturated),
0mg cholesterol, 868mg sodium, 4g fibre

helpful hints

● *If pressed for time, use a bottled, no-sugar-added oil and vinegar dressing instead of the recipe provided here.*
● *Sirloin steaks can be used instead of beef fillets.*
● *Any type of lettuce leaves can be used instead of red lettuce.*
● *Artichoke hearts can be used instead of palm hearts.*
● *Ordinary green beans can be used instead of French green beans and cut in half.*
● *To save cleaning an extra pan, prepare the steaks and green beans in the same pan.*

countdown

● *Make the palm hearts salad.*
● *Blanch the green beans.*
● *Make the steak.*
● *Sauté the green beans.*

which carbs

When I teach classes, I find that this is the most important section. My students are afraid to start reintroducing carbs for fear they will negate all of the benefits they've achieved. Here's how you can prevent gaining lost weight.

The question that keeps coming up at every class is, 'How do I start to add carbohydrates to my meals?' Two things usually happen at this point. You are losing weight and feeling good, so you stay on the Quick Start phase until you get bored or have a special event. Or you think, 'Great. I've lost weight and now I can have the foods I love and forget about the carb restrictions.' But neither solution leads to a healthy lifestyle of low-carb eating.

This section shows you how to start bringing carbohydrates back into your life without gaining weight. I have carefully worked out this selection of recipes to reincorporate high-fibre, low-simple-sugar carbohydrates. They are arranged to give variety throughout the day and over the days of the week. The most important addition in this section is high-fibre cereal in the morning.

As with the other sections, I have organised the menus into two meal-at-a-glance charts, incorporating some easy and quick meals from the Super Speed Supper section to accommodate busy mid-week schedules, as well as some more elaborate recipes from the Weekend section suited to a more relaxed weekend pace.

Breakfast

You can choose from a variety of breakfasts to suit your taste. Quick ideas like the Chicory Filled with Cheese and Red Pepper be prepared in about 5 minutes from scratch – and the filling can also be made in advance. You can also enjoy Sausage and Mushroom Egg Pizzetta, or a Prawn, Pepper and Tomato Frittata. How about a Raspberry Smoothie with Toasted Walnut Oatmeal?

Lunch

Cajun Prawn Salad, Black Bean and Salsa Wraps and Chinese Chicken Salad are just some of the tempting choices from this selection. Italian Croque Monsieur gives a Latin spin to a classic French favourite, while the Hollywood Cobb Salad has been enjoyed throughout the United States for decades.

Dinner

Smothered Steak with Caramelised Onions and Stir-fry Bok Choy and Shiitake Mushrooms are two of the recipes for dinner that have been carefully planned to slowly reintroduce carbohydrates.

For those days when you are really pressed for time, select Beef Teriyaki with Chinese Noodles, Peasant Country Soup or Swordfish in Spanish Sofrito Sauce from the Super Speed Suppers section of the book.

For weekends when you have more time and want something special for your evening meal, try the Mediterranean Snapper with Provençal Salad or Chicken and Walnuts in Lettuce Puffs from the Weekends section of the book.

During the Which Carb 14-Day Menu Plan, which includes the Super Speed Suppers and Weekends meals, you will consume an average of 80–90 grams of carbohydrates per day. Carbohydrate percentage is based on carbohydrates less fibre consumed, which is the normal way of calculating carbohydrate consumption. The balance of these meals is 25 per cent of calories from carbohydrates, 38 per cent of calories from lean protein, 27 per cent of calories from mono-unsaturated and poly-unsaturated fats, and 8 per cent of calories from saturated fat.

which carbs 14-day menu plan (1)

week 1	breakfast	lunch	dinner
sunday	Tomato Frittata 99	Italian Croque Monsieur 111	Crispy Cod with Ratatouille..................129
monday	Chicory Filled with Cheese and Roasted Peppers 100	Vietnamese Crab Soup 112	Mediterranean Snapper with Provençal Salad 256–257
tuesday	Cheddar Scramble 105	Cajun Prawn Salad 113	Aubergine Parmesan with Linguine......................131
wednesday	Ginger-Cranberry Smoothie with Smoked Ham and Cheese........................106	Roast Chicken Vegetable Soup 114	Swordfish in Spanish Sofrito Sauce 237
thursday	Ham-Baked Egg 107	Rainbow Tomato Plate 115	Mediterranean Steak 136
friday	Italian Omelette 102	Horseradish-Crusted Salmon Salad................116	Veal Picatta 154
saturday	New Orleans Prawn Roll 103	Chinese Chicken Salad...........................117	Spiced Cowboy Steak...........................255

week 2	breakfast	lunch	dinner
sunday	Tomato Frittata 99	Italian Croque Monsieur.....................111	Chicken and Walnuts in Lettuce Puffs..............258
monday	Chicory Filled with Cheese and Roasted Peppers 100	Vietnamese Crab Soup 112	Peasant Country Soup 238
tuesday	Cheddar Scramble 105	Cajun Prawn Salad 113	Beef Teriyaki with Chinese Noodles....................239
wednesday	Ginger-Cranberry Smoothie with Smoked Ham and Cheese 106	Roast Chicken Vegetable Soup 114	Five-Spice Tuna Tataki 150
thursday	Ham-Baked Egg 107	Rainbow Tomato Plate 115	Chicken with Black Bean Salsa and Brown Rice.............................152
friday	Italian Omelette............ 102	Horseradish-Crusted Salmon Salad 116	Veal Piccata 154
saturday	New Orleans Prawn Roll.................. 103	Chinese Chicken Salad............................117	Steak in Port Wine..........................260

which carbs 14-day menu plan (2)

week 1	breakfast	lunch	dinner
sunday	Sausage and Mushroom Egg Pizzetta 101	Hollywood Cobb Salad 125	Thai Peanut-Rub Pork 133
monday	Ham-baked Egg 107	Balsamic and Dill Salmon Salad 124	Pesto Chicken 134
tuesday	Turkey and Cottage Cheese 109	Salad Niçoise 118	Grilled Scallops Parmigiana 138
wednesday	Cheddar Scramble . . .105	Chicken Salad Amandine 119	Seared Sesame Tuna .132
thursday	Chicory Filled with Cheese and Roasted Peppers . . .100	Turkey and Tzatziki Sandwich 120	Garlic Prawn Stir Fry 147
friday	Raspberry Smoothie with Toasted Walnut Oatmeal 108	California Chef's Salad 121	Sole Amandine 149
saturday	Asian Omelette 104	Turkey, Salsa and Citrus Salad 122	Smothered Steak with Caramelised Onions 140

week 2	breakfast	lunch	dinner
sunday	Asian Omelette 104	Turkey and Tzatziki Salad 120	Whisky Pork Chops 142
monday	Ham-baked Egg 107	California Chef's Salad 121	Seared Sesame Tuna..............132
tuesday	Turkey and Cottage Cheese 109	Gammon and Egg Salad 123	Pesto Chicken 134
wednesday	Cheddar Scramble ...105	Balsamic and Dill Salmon Salad 124	Mussels Marinière ...144
thursday	Chicory Filled with Cheese and Roasted Peppers .100	Hollywood Cobb Salad 125	Spicy Crab and Vegetable Stir Fry 145
friday	Asian Omelette 104	Black Bean and Salsa Wraps 126	Thai Peanut-Rub Pork 133
saturday	Raspberry Smoothie with Toasted Walnut Oatmeal 108	Grilled Chilli Chicken 127	Spicy Chicken Legs 156

which carbs
breakfasts

tomato frittata

Frittatas take about 10 minutes to make. They can be made ahead and eaten at room temperature. A frittata needs to be cooked on both sides. Some people flip it in the pan. It's much easier to place it in the oven to finish cooking, under a grill for half a minute, or use this method of covering the frittata with a lid.

tomato frittata

2 whole eggs
6 egg whites
1 medium tomato, cut into 2.5cm (1in) pieces
1 teaspoon dried thyme
50g (2oz) fresh parsley, torn into bite-sized pieces
Salt and freshly ground black pepper
Olive oil spray
6 tablespoons grated semi-skimmed milk mozzarella cheese

Lightly beat whole eggs and egg whites together. Add tomato, thyme, parsley and salt and pepper to taste. Heat a 20–23cm (8–9in) non-stick frying pan over medium heat and spray with olive oil spray. Pour egg mixture into frying pan. Spread to cover pan. Leave to set on the bottom for 1 minute. Sprinkle cheese on top. Turn heat to low, cover with a lid, and leave to cook for 10 minutes or until set. Cut in half and serve on 2 plates.
Makes 2 servings.

bran cereal

225ml (8fl oz) skimmed milk
75g (3oz) high-fibre, no-sugar-added bran cereal

Divide between 2 cereal bowls.
Makes 2 servings.

Per serving: 324 calories, 32.8 grams protein, 36.3 grams carbohydrate, 12.9 grams fat (4.9 saturated), 231 milligrams cholesterol, 575 milligrams sodium, 13.0 grams fibre

helpful hints

● *Dried thyme is used in this recipe. Replace dried herbs after 6 months. If they look grey and old, that's probably how they will taste.*

countdown

● *Start frittata.*
● *While frittata cooks, assemble cereal.*
● *Finish frittata.*

shopping list

DAIRY
　1 small packet semi-skimmed milk mozzarella cheese
FRUIT AND VEG
　1 medium tomato
　1 small bunch parsley
STAPLES
　Dried thyme
　Eggs (8 needed)
　Skimmed milk
　Olive oil spray
　High-fibre, no-sugar-added bran cereal
　Salt
　Black peppercorns

chicory filled with cheese and roasted peppers

This is a quick breakfast that you can put together in minutes. In fact, it's also a good snack. Keep the mixture in the refrigerator and use it as a dip or spread with other vegetables.

chicory filled with cheese and roasted peppers

450g (1lb) low-fat cottage cheese
50g (2oz) low-fat cream cheese
350g (12oz) roasted red peppers, drained and diced
50g (2oz) purple basil, chopped
Salt and freshly ground black pepper to taste
2 large heads chicory

Combine the cottage cheese, cream cheese, roasted red pepper and purple basil by hand in a medium-sized bowl or in a food processor. Season with salt and pepper to taste. Remove any damaged outer leaves from the chicory, break off leaves and divide between 2 plates. Spoon the filling onto the wide end of each leaf and serve.
Makes 2 servings.

bran cereal

225ml (8fl oz) skimmed milk
75g (3oz) high-fibre, no-sugar-added bran cereal

Divide the milk and cereal between 2 bowls.
Makes 2 servings.

Total breakfast one serving: 394 calories, 36g protein, 47g carbohydrate, 11g fat (8g saturated), 44mg cholesterol, 1005mg sodium, 13g fibre

helpful hints

- Buy large heads of chicory if available. The leaves will hold more filling.
- Be sure to drain the roasted red peppers to make a drier filling.
- Ordinary green basil can be substituted for purple basil.

countdown

- Make stuffed chicory
- Assemble cereal.

shopping list

DAIRY
1 pot low-fat cottage cheese (450g/1lb needed)
1 small packet low-fat cream cheese
GROCERY
1 small jar roasted red peppers
FRUIT AND VEG
1 small bunch purple basil
2 large heads of chicory
STAPLES
Skimmed milk
High-fibre, no-sugar-added bran cereal
Salt
Black peppercorns

sausage and mushroom egg pizzetta

Sausage, mushrooms, onion and tomato sauce form the topping for an egg pizza base. This is a fun breakfast that takes about 15 minutes to make. It's great for a weekday or weekend treat, breakfast, lunch or dinner.

sausage and mushroom egg pizzetta

225ml (8fl oz) egg substitute

Freshly ground black pepper

Olive oil spray

125ml (4fl oz) low-fat, no-sugar-added tomato sauce for pasta

2 small low-fat turkey sausages, cut into 2.5cm (1in) slices

6 button mushrooms, sliced

1 tablespoon diced red onion

4 slices reduced-fat mozzarella cheese (75g/3oz)

Preheat the grill. Season the egg substitute with pepper to taste. Set a small (20.5cm/8in) frying pan over a medium-high heat. Spray with olive oil and pour in half the egg substitute. Swirl in the pan to make a thin layer. Allow to cook for 2 minutes, turn over for 1 minute and remove from the heat. Spread the tomato sauce on top. Add the sausage, mushrooms, onion and mozzarella cheese. Place under the grill about 25.5cm (10in) from the heat. Grill for 10 minutes. Carefully slide onto a plate and serve. Repeat for the second serving.

Makes 2 servings.

bran cereal

50g (2oz) high-fibre, no-sugar-added bran cereal

225ml (8fl oz) skimmed milk

Divide between 2 cereal bowls.

Makes 2 servings.

> Total breakfast one serving: 387 calories, 38g protein, 39g carbohydrate, 13g fat (5g saturated), 55mg cholesterol, 1189mg sodium, 15g fibre

helpful hints

- *2 whole eggs can be used instead of egg substitute.*
- *To determine the weight of each sausage or slice of cheese, divide the packet weight by the number of sausages or slices.*

countdown

- *Preheat grill.*
- *Make egg pizza base.*
- *Complete pizza.*

shopping list

DAIRY

1 ball reduced-fat mozzarella cheese (75g/3oz needed)

MEAT

1 packet low-fat turkey sausages (175g/6oz needed)

GROCERY

1 jar low-fat, no-sugar-added tomato sauce for pasta

FRUIT AND VEG

1 packet button mushrooms (6 mushrooms needed)

STAPLES

Red onion

Olive oil spray

Egg substitute

High-fibre, no-sugar-added bran cereal

Skimmed milk

Black peppercorns

italian omelette

A perfect omelette is golden on the top with a delicate creamy centre. The secret is to cook it over medium-high heat for only a couple of minutes while gently scraping the side to make sure all of the egg is cooked.

italian omelette

50g (2oz) ricotta cheese
50ml (2fl oz) bottled low-sugar, low-fat chunky marinara sauce
15g (¹/₂oz) grated Parmesan cheese
350ml (12fl oz) egg substitute
Freshly ground black pepper
2 teaspoons olive oil

Mix ricotta cheese, marinara sauce and Parmesan cheese together and set aside. Mix egg substitute with pepper to taste. Heat oil in a medium-sized non-stick frying pan on medium-high heat. Pour in the egg mixture. Let the eggs set for about 30 seconds. Tip the pan and lightly move the eggs so that they all set. Spread the cheese mixture on half the omelette and fold the omelette in half. Slide out of the pan by tipping the pan and holding a plate vertically against the side of the pan. Turn the pan and plate to invert the omelette on to the plate. Cut in half and serve on 2 plates.
Makes 2 servings.

bran cereal

225ml (8fl oz) skimmed milk
75g (3oz) high-fibre, no-sugar-added bran cereal

Divide between 2 cereal bowls.
Makes 2 servings.

365 calories, 32.6 grams protein, 36.8 grams carbohydrate, 12.4 grams fat (4.5 saturated), 17 milligrams cholesterol, 1076 milligrams sodium, 13.0 grams fibre

new orleans prawn roll

Prawns and hot pepper sauce give this roll-up a hint of New Orleans cooking. The egg is cooked like a crêpe and used as a wrap.

new orleans prawn roll

225g (8oz) cooked prawns, peeled and deveined
2 tablespoons mayonnaise
Several drops hot pepper sauce
Salt and freshly ground black pepper
225ml (8fl oz) egg substitute
Olive oil spray

Coarsely chop the prawns. Add mayonnaise and hot pepper sauce. Add salt and pepper to taste. Mix egg substitute with salt and pepper to taste. Heat a medium-sized non-stick frying pan on medium-high heat. Spray with olive oil spray and pour half the egg substitute into the pan and spread to make a thin layer. Leave to cook for 2 minutes. Turn over for 1 minute. Remove from heat. Spread half the prawn mixture on top. Roll up and place on a plate. Repeat for second serving.
Makes 2 servings.

oatmeal

225ml (8fl oz) oatmeal
450ml (16fl oz) water
225ml (8fl oz) skimmed milk
Artificial sweetener equivalent to 2 teaspoons sugar

To prepare in the microwave, combine oatmeal and water together. Microwave on high for 4 minutes. Stir in milk and sweetener.

Alternatively, combine oatmeal and water in a small saucepan. Bring to the boil. Cook for about 5 minutes over medium heat, stirring occasionally. Stir in milk and sweetener.
Makes 2 servings.

Per serving: 473 calories, 44.3 grams protein, 36.5 grams carbohydrate, 16.0 grams fat (2.6 saturated), 180 milligrams cholesterol, 535 milligrams sodium, 4 grams fibre

helpful hints

● *Cooked, shelled prawns can be found in the fish department or frozen in most supermarkets.*
● *Use the pulse button on a food processor to coarsely chop the prawns.*

countdown

● *Prepare prawn filling.*
● *Make prawn roll.*
● *Assemble cereal.*

shopping list

SEAFOOD
   225g (8oz) cooked, peeled, deveined prawns
STAPLES
   Mayonnaise
   Egg substitute
   Olive oil spray
   Hot pepper sauce
   Skimmed milk
   Oatmeal
   Artificial sweetener
   Salt
   Black peppercorns

asian omelette

Crisp water chestnuts and bean sprouts give an Oriental flavour to this omelette. It's adapted from the popular Chinese dish, Egg Foo Yong.

asian omelette

2 teaspoons olive oil
25g (1oz) fresh bean sprouts
75g (3oz) water chestnuts, drained and sliced
Freshly ground black pepper to taste
450ml (16fl oz) egg substitute
110g (4oz) sliced lean ham, chopped (about 4 slices)

Heat the oil in a non-stick frying pan over a medium-high heat. Add the bean sprouts and water chestnuts and sauté for 1 minute. Season the egg substitute with pepper to taste and pour into the pan, swirling to cover the vegetables. Allow to set for 1 minute. Sprinkle the ham on top, cover and cook 2–3 minutes longer, or until the egg sets to desired consistency. Cut the omelette in half, slide out of the pan and serve. Makes 2 servings.

bran cereal

225ml (8fl oz) skimmed milk
75g (3oz) high-fibre, no-sugar-added bran cereal

Divide the milk and cereal between 2 bowls. Makes 2 servings.

Total breakfast one serving: 369 calories, 42g protein, 44g carbohydrate, 8g fat (1g saturated), 28mg cholesterol, 1146mg sodium, 15g fibre

cheddar scramble

This is a breakfast you can make on the run. The eggs take 1¹/₂ minutes to cook and, best of all, there's no pan to wash.

cheddar scramble

450ml (16fl oz) egg substitute

75g (3oz) sliced reduced-fat Cheddar cheese, (about 4 slices)

Freshly ground black pepper to taste

Combine half of the egg substitute with 2 slices of the cheese in a microwave-safe bowl. Season with pepper to taste. Microwave on high for 1¹/₂ minutes. Stir and then heat for another 30 seconds. Repeat for the second serving. Serve hot.

Makes 2 servings.

bran cereal

225ml (8fl oz) skimmed milk

75g (3oz) high-fibre, no-sugar-added bran cereal

Divide the milk and cereal between 2 bowls.

Makes 2 servings.

Total breakfast one serving: 358 calories, 41g protein, 35g carbohydrate, 10g fat (6g saturated), 32mg cholesterol, 998mg sodium, 13g fibre

helpful hints

- *2 whole eggs and 6 egg whites can be used instead of egg substitute.*
- *To determine the weight of each slice of cheese, divide the packet weight by the number of slices.*

countdown

- *Make eggs.*
- *Assemble cereal.*

shopping list

DAIRY

1 small packet sliced reduced-fat Cheddar cheese (75g/3oz needed)

STAPLES

Egg substitute

Skimmed milk

High-fibre, no-sugar-added bran cereal

Black peppercorns

ginger-cranberry smoothie with smoked ham and cheese

Ginger gives this colourful smoothie an Oriental taste.

helpful hints

- *Frozen or fresh cranberries can be used.*
- *Add a little more water if smoothie is too thick.*
- *Ground ginger is used in this recipe. Replace dried spices after 6 months. They lose their flavour after that time.*

countdown

- *Make smoothie.*
- *Make oatmeal.*
- *Assemble ham and cheese.*

shopping list

DAIRY
1 packet reduced-fat Cheddar cheese
1 small pot non-fat vanilla yoghurt
DELI
1 small packet smoked, lean ham
GROCERY
1 small jar ground ginger
FRUIT AND VEG
1 small bag cranberries or 1 bag frozen cranberries
1 small head lettuce
STAPLES
Skimmed milk
High-fibre, no-sugar-added bran cereal
Artificial sweetener

ginger-cranberry smoothie

50g (2oz) fresh or frozen cranberries
50ml (2fl oz) water
115ml (4fl oz) non-fat vanilla yoghurt
1 teaspoon ground ginger
Artificial sweetener equivalent to 4 teaspoons sugar
450ml (16fl oz) ice cubes

Place cranberries, water, yoghurt, ginger and sweetener in a blender. Blend until smooth. Add the ice cubes and blend until thick. Pour into 2 glasses.
Makes 2 servings.

smoked ham and cheese

Several lettuce leaves
225g (8oz) smoked, lean ham, cut into 1cm (1/2in) cubes
50g (2oz) reduced-fat Cheddar cheese, torn into bite-sized pieces

Place lettuce on 2 plates with ham and cheese sprinkled on top.
Makes 2 servings.

bran cereal

225ml (8fl oz) skimmed milk
75g (3oz) high-fibre, no-sugar-added bran cereal

Divide between 2 cereal bowls.
Makes 2 servings.

Per serving: 394 calories, 38.4 grams protein, 42.6 grams carbohydrate, 13.1 grams fat (6.2 saturated), 76 milligrams cholesterol, 1473 milligrams sodium, 14.2 grams fibre

ham-baked egg

Baked or shirred eggs are easy to make and are a nice change. They take about 12–15 minutes in the oven. I've shortened the time to 2 minutes by 'baking' them in a microwave oven. The secret is to gently prick the egg yolk in 2 places to break the membrane before placing in the microwave.

ham-baked egg

2 teaspoons olive oil
225g (8oz) lean ham torn into bite-sized pieces
2 whole eggs
Salt and freshly ground black pepper

Spoon oil into 2 small ramekins. Divide ham into 2 portions and place in the ramekins. Break 1 egg into each dish. With the tip of a very sharp knife make 2 tiny pricks in each egg yolk, just to break the membrane and let steam escape. Sprinkle with salt and pepper to taste. Place one ramekin in a microwave oven. Cover ramekin with a piece of kitchen paper and microwave on high for 1 minute. Remove and serve. Repeat with second ramekin.
Makes 2 servings.

oatmeal

75g (3oz) oatmeal
450ml (16fl oz) water
225ml (8fl oz) skimmed milk
Artificial sweetener equivalent to 2 teaspoons sugar

To prepare in the microwave, combine oatmeal and water together. Microwave on high for 4 minutes. Stir in milk and sweetener.
Makes 2 servings.
Alternatively, combine oatmeal and water in a small saucepan. Bring to the boil. Cook about 5 minutes over medium heat, stirring occasionally. Stir in milk and sweetener.
Makes 2 servings.

Per serving: 458 calories, 37.2 grams protein, 35.7 grams carbohydrate, 19.1 grams fat (4.9 saturated), 268 milligrams cholesterol, 1110 milligrams sodium, 4 grams fibre

helpful hints

- *Cook the eggs for 1½ minutes (3 minutes total) for a firmer yolk.*
- *Small dessert or glass bowls can be used instead of ramekins. They should measure about 8–10cm (3–4in) wide and 5cm (2in) deep.*

countdown

- *Assemble eggs and ham in ramekins.*
- *Assemble cereal.*
- *Microwave eggs.*

shopping list

DELI
  225g (8oz) lean, smoked ham
STAPLES
  Eggs (2 needed)
  Skimmed milk
  Olive oil
  Oatmeal
  Salt
  Black peppercorns
  Artificial sweetener

raspberry smoothie with toasted walnut oatmeal

When I did some research into smoothies, I was astounded at their high carbohydrate content. But the cool, smooth, frozen drinks are so good that I decided to create one that was quick, easy, delicious – and good for us too. My family proclaimed this one a winner. ● *Use a microwave to make the oatmeal, and this breakfast will take only 10 minutes to make.*

raspberry smoothie

110g (4oz) fresh or frozen
    raspberries
125ml (4fl oz) light raspberry-
    flavoured yoghurt
2 teaspoons vanilla essence
2g (¹/₁₆oz) artificial sweetener
1½ pint glasses full of ice cubes

Place the raspberries, yoghurt, vanilla essence and sweetener in a blender. Blend until smooth. Add the ice cubes and blend until thick. Pour into 2 glasses and serve cold.
Makes 2 servings.

toasted walnut oatmeal

75g (3oz) oatmeal
450ml (16fl oz) water
25g (1oz) walnuts
225ml (8fl oz) skimmed milk
2g (¹/₁₆oz) artificial sweetener
    (optional)

To prepare in the microwave, combine the oatmeal and water in a microwave-safe bowl. Microwave on high for 4 minutes.

Alternatively, to prepare on the hob, combine the oatmeal and water in a small saucepan over a medium-high heat and bring to a boil. Reduce the heat to medium and cook about 5 more minutes, stirring occasionally.

Place the walnuts on a foil-lined tray and toast under the grill for 1 minute, or until lightly toasted. Stir the milk, sweetener and toasted walnuts into the oatmeal. Divide between 2 bowls and serve warm.
Makes 2 servings.

smoked turkey breast

175g (6oz) sliced smoked
    turkey breast, cubed
Several lettuce leaves

Place lettuce on 2 plates with the turkey cubes on top, and serve.
Makes 2 servings.

Total breakfast one serving: 492 calories, 38g protein, 49g carbohydrate, 16g fat (2g saturated), 63mg cholesterol, 149mg sodium, 8g fibre

turkey and cottage cheese

This breakfast is ideal when you're on the go, as it takes only a few minutes to make. ● *The addition of a few pecans to the oatmeal gives it a crunchy texture and nutty flavour.*

turkey and cottage cheese

225g (8oz) low-fat cottage cheese
2 tablespoons dried chives
225g (8oz) sliced roast turkey
   breast

Combine the cottage cheese and chives in a small bowl. Place the turkey slices on 2 plates and spoon the cottage cheese mixture on the slices. Fold the turkey slices in half and serve. *Makes 2 servings.*

pecan oatmeal

75g (3oz) oatmeal
450ml (16fl oz) water
25g (1oz) pecan pieces
225ml (8fl oz) skimmed milk
2g (¹/₁₆oz) artificial sweetener
   (optional)

To prepare in the microwave, combine the oatmeal and water in a microwave-safe bowl. Microwave on high for 4 minutes.

Alternatively, to prepare on the hob, combine the oatmeal and water in a small saucepan over a medium-high heat and bring to a boil. Reduce the heat to medium and cook about 5 more minutes, stirring occasionally.

Place the pecans on a foil-lined tray and toast under the grill for 1 minute, or until golden. Stir the milk, sweetener and toasted pecans into the oatmeal. Divide between 2 bowls and serve. *Makes 2 servings.*

Total breakfast one serving: 473 calories,
   40g protein, 40g carbohydrate, 17g fat (4g saturated),
   52mg cholesterol, 439mg sodium, 5g fibre

helpful hints

● *Other types of fresh herbs such as dill, parsley or basil can be used in place of chives.*
● *Toasting pecans can be tricky, as they burn quickly. Watch them carefully.*

countdown

● *Make turkey.*
● *Make oatmeal.*

shopping list

DAIRY
   1 small pot low-fat cottage
      cheese (225g/8oz needed)
DELI
   225g (8oz) sliced roast turkey
      breast
GROCERY
   1 packet pecan pieces
      (25g/1oz needed)
   1 jar dried chives
STAPLES
   Oatmeal
   Skimmed milk
   Artificial sweetener

which carbs
lunches

italian croque monsieur

Nearly every brasserie in Paris serves a version of croque monsieur (grilled ham and cheese sandwich). Here is an Italian version.

italian croque monsieur

Olive oil spray
4 slices wholemeal bread
110g (4oz) semi-skimmed milk mozzarella cheese, sliced
225g (8oz) lean ham, sliced
1 medium tomato, sliced
25g (1oz) fresh basil, torn into bite-sized pieces (optional)

Pre-heat grill. Line a baking tray with foil and spray with olive oil spray. Place bread on foil and spray bread. Place cheese and then ham on bread. Top with sliced tomato. Grill for 2 minutes or until cheese melts. Remove and sprinkle with basil.
Makes 2 servings.

Per serving: 424 calories, 44.7 grams protein, 26.3 grams carbohydrate, 18.9 grams fat (8.3 saturated), 86 milligrams cholesterol, 1483 milligrams sodium, 6.0 grams fibre

dessert

275g (10oz) watermelon cubes

Divide between 2 small dessert dishes.
Makes 2 servings.

Per serving: 49 calories, 1.0 gram protein, 11.0 grams carbohydrate, 0.6 grams fat (0.1 saturated), 0 milligrams cholesterol, 3 milligrams sodium, 0.8 grams fibre

helpful hint

● *Watermelon cubes can be found in the fruit and veg section of some supermarkets.*

countdown

● *Pre-heat grill.*
● *Make sandwich.*
● *While sandwich toasts, place watermelon in dishes.*

shopping list

DAIRY
  1 small packet semi-skimmed milk mozzarella cheese
DELI
  225g (8oz) lean ham
FRUIT AND VEG
  1 small bunch basil
  1 medium tomato
  1 small container watermelon cubes
STAPLES
  Olive oil spray
  Wholemeal bread

vietnamese crab soup

This soup is filled with the fragrant flavours of South-east Asia. As with most Asian dishes, it takes a little longer to prepare the ingredients, but then it takes less than 5 minutes to cook. Lemongrass, which adds a special lemon flavour to Asian dishes, can be found in some supermarkets. It looks a bit like a spring onion, but the stalks are a pale green colour, hard and dry. Use the white bulbous end for the soup.

helpful hints

- If fresh crab is unavailable, use good-quality pasteurised crab, or prawns.
- A tablespoon lime juice can be substituted for the lemongrass.
- To chop ginger, peel, cut into chunks, and press through a garlic press.. Press over food or bowl to catch the juices as the ginger is pressed.Just the juice is enough to flavour the dish.
- Cubed fresh melon can be found in the fruit and veg section of most supermarkets.

countdown

- Assemble ingredients for soup.
- Place melon cubes in dessert dishes.
- Complete soup.

shopping list

SEAFOOD
  350g (12oz) fresh or pasteurised crabmeat
GROCERY
  1 small bottle sesame oil
FRUIT AND VEG
  1 small bunch lemongrass (2 stalks needed)
  1 lime
  150g (5oz) fresh mange tout
  1 small bag bean sprouts
  1 small bunch spring onions
  1 small container fresh honeydew melon cubes
  1 small piece fresh ginger
STAPLES
  Fat-free, low-sodium chicken stock
  Hot pepper sauce
  Salt
  Black peppercorns

vietnamese crab soup

450ml (16fl oz) fat-free, low-sodium chicken stock

450ml (16fl oz) water

2 stalks lemongrass, tender white base only, sliced

1 tablespoon peeled and coarsely chopped fresh ginger

1 tablespoon lime zest

150g (5oz) fresh mange tout, trimmed

75g (3oz) bean sprouts

350g (12oz) fresh or pasteurised crabmeat, drained

2 tablespoons sesame oil

Several drops hot pepper sauce

Salt and freshly ground black pepper

2 spring onions, sliced

Place chicken stock and water in a large saucepan. Add lemongrass, ginger, lime zest and mange tout. Bring to a simmer on medium heat and cook for 2 minutes. Add bean sprouts and crab. Simmer for 2 more minutes. Remove from heat and add hot pepper sauce, sesame oil and salt and pepper to taste. Ladle into 2 soup bowls and sprinkle spring onions on top.
Makes 2 servings.

Per serving: 343 calories, 37.3 grams protein, 11.8 grams carbohydrate, 15.8 grams fat (2.2 saturated), 133 milligrams cholesterol, 1070 milligrams sodium, 2.6 grams fibre

dessert

275g (10oz) honeydew melon cubes

Divide between 2 small dessert plates.
Makes 2 servings.

Per serving: 57 calories, 1.4 grams protein, 13.4 grams carbohydrate, 0.4 grams fat (0 saturated), 0 milligrams cholesterol, 14 milligrams sodium, 0.5 grams fibre

rosemary-roasted pork   **p83**

chicory filled with cheese and roasted peppers   p100

cajun prawn salad

The hot spices of Louisiana Cajun country flavour this quick prawn salad.

cajun prawn salad

2 tablespoons no-sugar-added oil
    and vinegar dressing
2 garlic cloves, crushed
1/2 teaspoon cayenne
1 teaspoon dried oregano
1 teaspoon dried thyme
350g (12oz) cooked prawns,
    peeled, deveined and cut in half
1 small head cos lettuce heart
1 medium red pepper, cut into
    small cubes

In a small bowl, mix dressing with garlic, cayenne, oregano and thyme. Add prawns and toss well. Tear lettuce into bite-sized pieces and place on 2 plates. Mix red pepper with prawns and spoon prawns and dressing over lettuce. *Makes 2 servings.*

Per serving: 301 calories, 37.2 grams protein, 10.6 grams carbohydrate, 11.7 grams fat (1.9 saturated), 260 milligrams cholesterol, 342 milligrams sodium, 0.9 grams fibre

dessert

2 oranges

Divide between 2 small plates. *Makes 2 servings.*

Per serving: 62 calories, 1.2 grams protein, 15.4 grams carbohydrate, 0.2 grams fat (0 saturated), 0 milligrams cholesterol, 0 milligrams sodium, 3.1 grams fibre

helpful hints

● *Cooked, shelled prawns can be found in the fish department or frozen in the frozen section of most supermarkets.*
● *Prepared Cajun spice mix can be used instead of the spice mixture in the recipe. Make sure no sugar or salt is added to the mixture.*
● *Dried oregano, thyme and cayenne pepper are used in this recipe. Replace dried herbs after 6 months. If they look grey and old, that's probably how they will taste.*

countdown

● *Make dressing.*
● *Complete salad.*

shopping list

SEAFOOD
    350g (12oz) cooked, peeled
        and deveined prawns
FRUIT AND VEG
    1 small head cos lettuce heart
    1 medium red pepper
    2 oranges
STAPLES
    Dried thyme
    Dried oregano
    Cayenne pepper
    No-sugar-added oil and
        vinegar dressing
    Garlic

roast chicken vegetable soup

A cheery bowl of soup is a treat any time of year. This soup uses roasted, ready-to-eat chicken and can be ready in less than 15 minutes. The soup tastes great the second day. Make extra if you have time and save for a second day or freeze.

helpful hints

- *Any type of mushroom can be used.*
- *Buy good-quality Parmesan cheese and grate it yourself or chop it in the food processor. Freeze the extra: you can spoon out what you need and leave the rest frozen.*
- *Fresh pineapple cubes can be found in the fruit and veg section of most supermarkets.*

countdown

- *Start soup.*
- *While soup cooks, assemble pineapple dessert.*
- *Complete soup.*

shopping list

DELI
    225g (8oz) roasted, ready-to-eat chicken pieces
FRUIT AND VEG
    225g (8oz) mushrooms
    1 small bunch thyme or dried thyme
    1 small container fresh pineapple cubes
STAPLES
    Yellow onion
    Celery
    Fat-free, low-sodium chicken stock
    Parmesan cheese
    Olive oil
    Salt
    Black peppercorns

roast chicken vegetable soup

2 teaspoons olive oil
110g (4oz) sliced yellow onion
1 celery stalk, sliced
225g (8oz) mushrooms, sliced
450ml (16fl oz) fat-free, low-sodium chicken stock
225ml (8fl oz) water
2 large sprigs fresh thyme or 1 teaspoon dried thyme
225g (8oz) roasted, ready-to-eat chicken pieces
Salt and freshly ground black pepper
2 tablespoons grated Parmesan cheese

Heat oil in a large saucepan over medium-high heat and add onion and celery. Sauté for 3 minutes. Add mushrooms, stock, water and thyme. Reduce heat to medium and simmer for 7 minutes. Add chicken and cook for 2 minutes or until chicken is warmed through. Remove thyme sprigs and add salt and pepper to taste. Spoon into 2 soup bowls and sprinkle Parmesan on top.
Makes 2 servings.

Per serving: 334 calories, 44.8 grams protein, 8.3 grams carbohydrate, 13.5 grams fat (3.6 saturated), 103 milligrams cholesterol, 858 milligrams sodium, 0.5 grams fibre

dessert

275g (10oz) pineapple cubes

Divide between 2 dessert dishes.
Makes 2 servings.

Per serving: 77 calories, 0.6 grams protein, 19.2 grams carbohydrate, 0.7 grams fat (0 saturated), 0 milligrams cholesterol, 1 milligram sodium, 2.4 grams fibre

rainbow tomato plate

This colourful salad plate accented with red and yellow tomatoes takes only 5 minutes to assemble.

rainbow tomato plate

2 small red tomatoes, sliced

2 small yellow tomatoes, sliced

1 medium cucumber, peeled and
   sliced

25g (1oz) pinenuts

175g (6oz) smoked chicken
   breast, cut into cubes

2 tablespoons no-sugar-added oil
   and vinegar dressing

Salt and freshly ground black
   pepper

Arrange the sliced tomatoes and cucumber in circles on 2 plates, alternating red tomato slices, yellow tomato slices and cucumber slices. The slices should cover the plate. Sprinkle chicken cubes and pinenuts over tomatoes. Drizzle dressing over the top. Sprinkle with salt and pepper to taste.

Makes 2 servings.

Per serving: 354 calories, 32.1 grams protein, 15.1 grams carbohydrate, 13.0 grams fat (2.2 saturated), 72 milligrams cholesterol, 161 milligrams sodium, 0.9 grams fibre

dessert

225ml (8fl oz) non-fat fruit yoghurt

Divide yoghurt between 2 small dessert bowls.

Makes 2 servings.

Per serving: 70 calories, 5.5 grams protein, 11.5 grams carbohydrate, 0 grams fat (0 saturated), 3 milligrams cholesterol, 95 milligrams sodium, 0 grams fibre

helpful hints

- *Any type of tomatoes can be used.*
- *Any flavour non-fat yoghurt can be used for dessert.*
- *Extra pinenuts can be stored in the freezer.*

countdown

- *Make salad plate.*
- *Serve yoghurt.*

shopping list

DAIRY

   1 pot non-fat fruit yoghurt

DELI

   175g (6oz) smoked chicken
      breast

GROCERY

   1 small packet pinenuts

FRUIT AND VEG

   2 small red tomatoes

   2 small yellow tomatoes

   1 medium cucumber

STAPLES

   No-sugar-added oil and
      vinegar dressing

   Salt

   Black peppercorns

horseradish-crusted salmon salad

A spicy, creamy crust covers the rich salmon fillet for this quick lunch. The salmon tastes great served either hot or at room temperature.

horseradish-crusted salmon salad

Olive oil spray
225g (8oz) salmon fillet
Salt and freshly ground black pepper
2 tablespoons prepared horseradish
2 tablespoons mayonnaise
150g (5oz) washed, ready-to-eat cos lettuce leaves
1 medium cucumber, peeled and sliced

Pre-heat grill. Line a baking tray with foil and spray with olive oil spray. Place salmon on the tray. Sprinkle with salt and pepper to taste. Grill for 3 minutes. Mix horseradish and mayonnaise together. Remove salmon and turn over. Spread with horseradish mixture. Return to grill for 3 minutes. Place lettuce and cucumber on 2 plates. Remove salmon and divide in half. Place over salad.
Makes 2 servings.

Per serving: 340 calories, 30.4 grams protein, 8.7 grams carbohydrate, 19.3 grams fat (3.4 saturated), 85 milligrams cholesterol, 181 milligrams sodium, 1.5 grams fibre

dessert

2 medium apples

Serve 1 apple per person.
Makes 2 servings.

Per serving: 81 calories, 0.3 grams protein, 21.1 grams carbohydrate, 0.5 grams fat (0.1 saturated), 0 milligrams cholesterol, 0 milligrams sodium, 3.7 grams fibre

chinese chicken salad

Adding Chinese five-spice powder and soy sauce to a bottled oil and vinegar dressing gives this salad an aromatic Chinese flavour.

chinese chicken salad

1 tablespoon low-sodium soy sauce

1/2 teaspoon five-spice powder

2 tablespoons no-sugar-added oil and vinegar dressing

75g (3oz) bean sprouts

225g (8oz) roasted, ready-to-eat chicken pieces

Salt and freshly ground black pepper

175g (6oz) sliced Chinese cabbage

4 clementines, peeled and segmented

In a medium-sized bowl, mix soy sauce, five-spice powder and dressing together. Add the bean sprouts and chicken and toss well. Add salt and pepper to taste. Place cabbage on 2 plates and spoon chicken mixture on top. Sprinkle clementine segments on top.

Makes 2 servings.

Per serving: 388 calories, 40.6 grams protein, 28.9 grams carbohydrate, 14.5 grams fat (2.5 saturated), 96 milligrams cholesterol, 485 milligrams sodium, 2.4 grams fibre

helpful hints

- *Chinese cabbage is also called Chinese leaves.*
- *Any type of lettuce can be used.*

countdown

- *Mix dressing ingredients together.*
- *Complete salad.*
- *Assemble dessert.*

shopping list

MEAT

225g (8oz) roasted, ready-to-eat chicken pieces

GROCERY

1 small jar five-spice powder

FRUIT AND VEG

1 small Chinese cabbage (Chinese leaves)

1 small packet fresh bean sprouts

4 clementines

STAPLES

Low-sodium soy sauce

No-sugar-added oil and vinegar dressing

Salt

Black peppercorns

salad niçoise

This quick salad from the French Riviera is filled with olives, tomatoes, asparagus and tuna. These ingredients were chosen to give a variety of textures, colours and flavours: crisp, pale green lettuce; ripe red tomatoes; soft, pink tuna; and dark green asparagus. Use this recipe as a base and create your own version of this classic, using other ingredients or leftovers.

helpful hint

- *Use the dressing recipe provided here or buy a no-sugar-added oil and vinegar dressing and add diced red onion.*

countdown

- *Make dressing.*
- *Blanch asparagus.*
- *Assemble salad.*

shopping list

GROCERY

350g (12oz) tinned low-sodium, solid white tuna, packed in water

1 jar or tin pitted black olives

FRUIT AND VEG

225g (8oz) fresh asparagus

1 bag washed, ready-to-eat lamb's lettuce or French-style salad leaves

2 medium tomatoes

2 medium oranges

STAPLES

Red onion

Dijon mustard

Red wine vinegar

Olive oil

Salt

Black peppercorns

salad niçoise

50ml (2fl oz) red wine vinegar
2 tablespoons Dijon mustard
50g (2oz) red onion, diced
2 tablespoons water
2 tablespoons olive oil
Salt and freshly ground black pepper to taste
350g (12oz) low-sodium, solid white tuna, drained and rinsed
225g (8oz) fresh asparagus
150g (5oz) washed, ready-to-eat lamb's lettuce or French-style salad leaves
2 medium tomatoes, cut into wedges
8 pitted black olives, quartered

To prepare the vinaigrette dressing, whisk the vinegar and mustard together in a large bowl with the onion and water. Whisk in the oil to a smooth consistency. Season with salt and pepper to taste. Flake the tuna into the vinaigrette.

Cut or snap off the 2.5cm (1in) fibrous stem on the asparagus and discard. Slice the remaining asparagus into 5cm (2in) pieces. Bring a medium-sized saucepan of water to a boil. Add the asparagus. As soon as the water comes back to a boil, drain the asparagus and refresh in cold water. (If using thick asparagus boil for 5 minutes.) To microwave the asparagus instead, place asparagus in a microwave-safe bowl and microwave on high for 4 minutes. Add the asparagus to the tuna mixture and toss gently. Divide the lettuce between 2 plates. Spoon the tuna-asparagus mixture over the lettuce. Arrange the tomato wedges around the plate, sprinkle the olives over the top and serve. *Makes 2 servings.*

One serving: 424 calories, 51g protein, 14g carbohydrate, 20g fat (2g saturated), 75mg cholesterol, 1283mg sodium, 3g fibre

dessert

2 medium oranges

Divide the oranges between 2 plates and serve. *Makes 2 servings.*

One serving: 62 calories, 1g protein, 15g carbohydrate, 0g fat (0g saturated), 0mg cholesterol, 0mg sodium, 3g fibre

chicken salad amandine

Almonds and apples add a crunchy texture and varied flavours to this chicken salad. Use leftover roasted chicken or shop-bought roasted chicken for a fast meal.

chicken salad amandine

2 tablespoons flaked almonds

2 tablespoons mayonnaise made with olive or soya bean oil

50ml (2fl oz) non-fat, plain yoghurt

4 teaspoons dried tarragon

Salt and freshly ground black pepper to taste

225g (8oz) roast chicken breast, skin removed and cut into 2.5cm (1in) pieces

2 celery stalks, sliced

1 Golden Delicious apple, cored and cut into 1cm (½in) cubes

1 small head radicchio

Place almonds on a foil-lined tray and toast under the grill for 1 minute. Alternatively, toast in a non-stick frying pan over a medium heat for 1 minute, or until golden. Combine the mayonnaise, yoghurt and tarragon in a medium-size bowl. Season with salt and pepper to taste. Add the chicken, celery, toasted almonds and apple. Toss well and adjust seasonings if necessary. Carefully remove the leaves from the radicchio, making them into small cups. Spoon the chicken salad into the radicchio leaves. Serve on 2 plates.

Makes 2 servings.

One serving: 457 calories, 43g protein, 24g carbohydrate, 23g fat (3g saturated), 101mg cholesterol, 282mg sodium, 5g fibre

helpful hints

- *Make sure the tarragon is less than 6 months old. It should be a green colour, not brown or grey.*
- *Any type of lettuce can be used.*
- *Toasting almonds intensifies their flavour, but can be tricky. Watch them carefully, as they burn easily. This step can be omitted.*

countdown

- *Toast almonds.*
- *Make salad.*

shopping list

DAIRY
    1 pot non-fat, plain yoghurt
DELI
    225g (8oz) roast chicken breast
GROCERY
    1 small packet flaked almonds (25g/1oz needed)
FRUIT AND VEG
    1 Golden Delicious apple
    1 small head radicchio
STAPLES
    Celery
    Mayonnaise made with olive or soya bean oil
    Dried tarragon
    Salt
    Black peppercorns

helpful hint

- Buy ready-to-eat shredded lettuce.

countdown

- Make tzatziki.
- Make sandwich.

shopping list

DAIRY

1 pot low-fat plain yoghurt

DELI

225g (8oz) sliced roast turkey breast

GROCERY

1 small packet pistachio nuts (35g/1½oz needed)

FRUIT AND VEG

Half a cucumber

1 bunch fresh mint

1 bag washed, ready-to-eat, shredded lettuce

STAPLES

Garlic

Red onion

Wholemeal bread

Salt

Black peppercorns

turkey and tzatziki sandwich

The refreshing flavour of mint and cucumber mingle with roasted turkey in this grilled Middle Eastern sandwich. Tzatziki is a yoghurt sauce that can also be used as a vegetable dip. It takes only seconds to make in a food processor.

turkey and tzatziki sandwich

Half a cucumber, peeled and seeded

125ml (4fl oz) low-fat, plain yoghurt

2 medium-sized garlic cloves, crushed

2 tablespoons chopped fresh mint

50g (2oz) red onion, chopped

Salt and freshly ground black pepper to taste

2 slices wholemeal bread, toasted

225g (8oz) sliced roast turkey breast, skinned and cut into 2.5cm (1in) pieces

75g (3oz) washed, ready-to-eat, shredded lettuce

Chop the cucumber in the bowl of a food processor and drain. Stir the yoghurt, garlic, mint and onion into the food processor bowl with the drained cucumber. Season with salt and pepper to taste.

Place a slice of toasted bread on each plate. Top with roast turkey and shredded lettuce. Spoon a little tzatziki over the lettuce. Serve any extra lettuce and sauce on the side.

Makes 2 servings.

One serving: 302 calories, 40g protein, 23g carbohydrate, 6g fat (1g saturated), 81mg cholesterol, 241mg sodium, 6g fibre

pistachios

35g (1½oz) shelled pistachio nuts

Divide the pistachios between 2 plates and serve.

Makes 2 servings.

One serving: 131 calories, 5g protein, 6g carbohydrate, 11g fat (1g saturated), 0mg cholesterol, 2mg sodium, 0g fibre

california chef's salad

Julienned slices of ham, turkey, roast beef and cheese alongside an array of fresh vegetables are the basis for this American favourite. The addition of alfalfa sprouts gives this dish a modern 'California' touch. • Traditionally, the ingredients in a Chef's Salad are cut in julienne strips (large match sticks). However, if you are pressed for time, you can slice them in a food processor fitted with a thick slicing blade. • You can use whatever lean cold meats and vegetables you have on hand, referring to the proportions given in the recipe as a guideline.

california chef's salad

50ml (2fl oz) balsamic vinegar

1 tablespoon Dijon mustard

2 tablespoons water

2 tablespoons rapeseed oil

Salt and freshly ground black pepper to taste

8 large cos lettuce leaves, washed, dried and sliced

Half a cucumber, peeled and julienned

1 medium-sized red pepper, julienned

35g (1¹/₂oz) reduced-fat Swiss or Gruyère cheese, julienned

50g (2oz) sliced smoked deli chicken breast, julienned

50g (2oz) sliced lean deli roast beef, julienned

50g (2oz) sliced lean deli ham, julienned

1 large handful alfalfa sprouts

Mix the vinegar and mustard together in a small bowl until smooth. Add the water and oil, blending well. Season with salt and pepper to taste. Divide the lettuce leaves between 2 plates. Place the remaining ingredients on the leaves in pie-shaped segments, like the spokes of a wheel. Spoon the dressing over the top and serve.

Makes 2 servings.

One serving: 400 calories, 34g protein, 19g carbohydrate, 22g fat (5g saturated), 71mg cholesterol, 519mg sodium, 2g fibre

helpful hints

- Ask the deli to cut the meat in 1cm (½in) slices to make it quick to cut the slices into 1cm (½in) julienne strips.
- If reduced-fat Swiss or Gruyère cheese is not available, use another reduced-fat hard cheese.
- Use any type of sprouts.
- If making salad in advance, add dressing just before serving.
- Any type of no-sugar-added dressing can be used instead of the dressing recipe given.

countdown

- Make dressing.
- Prepare ingredients.
- Assemble salad.

shopping list

DAIRY

    35g (1¹/₂oz) reduced-fat Swiss or Gruyère cheese

DELI

    50g (2oz) sliced smoked chicken breast
    50g (2oz) sliced lean roast beef
    50g (2oz) sliced lean deli ham

FRUIT AND VEG

    1 head cos lettuce
    Half a cucumber
    1 medium-sized red pepper
    1 container alfalfa sprouts

STAPLES

    Rapeseed oil
    Dijon mustard
    Balsamic vinegar
    Salt
    Black pepper

turkey, salsa and citrus salad

helpful hint

- *Any type of lettuce can be used.*

countdown

- *Prepare ingredients.*
- *Assemble salad.*

shopping list

MEAT

225g (8oz) sliced lean smoked turkey breast

GROCERY

1 jar no-sugar-added tomato salsa (225g/8oz needed)

FRUIT AND VEG

1 ripe small avocado

2 small oranges

1 container alfalfa sprouts

1 small head curly endive

2 medium plums

STAPLES

Salt

Black peppercorns

The nutty flavour and creamy texture of ripe avocado blends well with sweet orange and smoky turkey in this quick salad – only 5 minutes from start to finish. • Ask the greengrocer for a ripe avocado if you don't find one displayed. Sometimes they don't display ones that will ripen within a day. A quick way to help avocados ripen is to remove the stem, place the avocado in a paper bag and leave in a warm spot. • Curly endive has a loose head with lacy, green-rimmed leaves that curl at the pointed tips.

turkey, salsa and citrus salad

225g (8oz) sliced lean smoked turkey breast, cut into 2.5cm (1in) cubes

1 ripe small avocado, pitted and cut into 2.5cm (1in) cubes

225g (8oz) no-sugar-added tomato salsa

2 small oranges, peeled and cut into 2.5cm (1in) cubes

1 large handful alfalfa sprouts

Salt and freshly ground black pepper to taste

Several curly endive leaves

Combine the turkey, avocado and salsa in a medium-sized bowl, tossing well. Gently stir in the orange cubes and sprouts. Season with salt and pepper to taste. Place the curly endive on 2 plates, spoon the turkey-avocado mixture on top and serve.

Makes 2 servings.

One serving: 464 calories, 40g protein, 33g carbohydrate, 19g fat (3g saturated), 80mg cholesterol, 850mg sodium, 12g fibre

dessert

2 medium plums, halved and stoned

Slice the plums. Divide between 2 plates and serve.

Makes 2 servings.

One serving: 36 calories, 1g protein, 9g carbohydrate, 0g fat (0g saturated), 0mg cholesterol, 0mg sodium, 0.5g fibre

gammon and egg salad

Egg salad is available on lunch menus, or it can be made from scratch at home. Wherever you eat it, use this recipe as a portion guideline. It is made with 2 whole eggs and 6 egg whites to produce a light, tasty result.

gammon and egg salad

8 eggs (only 2 yolks are used)
225g (8oz) sliced lean gammon
2 tablespoons mayonnaise made with olive or soya bean oil
2 tablespoons Dijon mustard
2 tablespoons warm water
2 tablespoons diced red onion
10g (½oz) fresh flat leaf parsley, chopped
2 celery stalks, diced
Salt and freshly ground black pepper to taste
Several cos leaves, torn into bite-sized pieces
2 medium tomatoes, quartered

Preheat the grill. Place the eggs in a medium saucepan and cover with cold water. Set over a medium-high heat and bring to a boil. Reduce the heat to low and gently simmer for 12 minutes. Drain the hot water and fill the pan with cold water. When the eggs are cool to the touch, peel, cut in half and discard 6 of the yolks. Mash the remaining 2 whole eggs and 6 egg whites with a fork.

Meanwhile, place the gammon in one layer on a foil-lined tray and toast under the grill until brown. Combine the mayonnaise, mustard, water, onion and parsley in a bowl. Stir in the eggs and celery, mixing well. Season with salt and pepper to taste. Place the lettuce and tomatoes on 2 plates. Spoon the egg salad on top of the lettuce. Cut the browned gammon into bite-sized pieces and sprinkle over the egg salad. Serve.
Makes 2 servings.

> One serving: 411 calories, 41g protein, 17g carbohydrate, 21g fat (4g saturated), 270mg cholesterol, 1743mg sodium, 1g fibre

dessert

4 good handfuls fresh strawberries

Divide the strawberries between 2 dessert bowls and serve.
Makes 2 servings.

> One serving: 45 calories, 1g protein, 11g carbohydrate, 1g fat (0g saturated), 0mg cholesterol, 2mg sodium, 3g fibre

helpful hints

● *You can make the egg salad in a food processor or with a hand-held blender. Be careful to pulse the blades and watch that it does not become too finely chopped or mushy.*

countdown

● *Preheat grill.*
● *Make hard-boiled eggs.*
● *Make egg salad.*

shopping list

DELI
  225g (8oz) sliced lean gammon
FRUIT AND VEG
  1 bunch flat leaf parsley
  1 head cos lettuce
  2 medium tomatoes
  1 punnet fresh strawberries
STAPLES
  Celery
  Eggs
  Mayonnaise made with olive or soya bean oil
  Dijon mustard
  Red onion
  Salt
  Black peppercorns

helpful hints

- This can be made with any type of fresh or leftover fish.
- Make sure the jar of dried dill is less than 6 months old. For optimum flavour, the dill should be a green colour, not brown or grey.

countdown

- Sauté salmon.
- Make salad.

shopping list

FISH

225g (8oz) salmon fillet

FRUIT AND VEG

Half a cucumber

1 small bunch fresh dill or 1 jar dried

2 medium-sized green peppers

1 punnet fresh raspberries

STAPLES

Olive oil spray

Mayonnaise made with olive or soya bean oil

Balsamic vinegar

Salt

Black peppercorns

balsamic and dill salmon salad

Fresh salmon mixed with cucumber and dill makes a richly-flavoured, yet light, salmon salad. If you have time, double the recipe and save half for another lunch.

balsamic and dill salmon salad

2 tablespoons mayonnaise made with olive or soya bean oil

4 teaspoons balsamic vinegar

10g (½oz) fresh dill or 2 teaspoons dried

Half a cucumber, deseeded and diced

Olive oil spray

225g (8oz) salmon fillet

Salt and freshly ground black pepper to taste

2 medium-sized green peppers, halved and deseeded

Combine the mayonnaise, balsamic vinegar, dill and cucumber in a small bowl. Set a non-stick frying pan over a medium-high heat and spray with olive oil. Add the salmon and sauté for 3 minutes. Turn and sauté for 2 more minutes. Flake the salmon into the mayonnaise mixture with a fork. Season with salt and pepper to taste and mix gently. Spoon the mixture into the pepper halves and serve.

Makes 2 servings.

One serving: 364 calories, 31g protein, 13g carbohydrate, 20g fat (4g saturated), 85mg cholesterol, 159mg sodium, 1g fibre

dessert

350g (12oz) fresh raspberries

Divide the raspberries between 2 dessert bowls and serve.

Makes 2 servings.

One serving: 61 calories, 1g protein, 14g carbohydrate, 1g fat (0g saturated), 0mg cholesterol, 0mg sodium, 6g fibre

hollywood cobb salad

Roasted chicken breast, avocado and lettuce were key ingredients in Robert Cobb's first Cobb salad, which he served at the Brown Derby restaurant at Hollywood and Vine in the 1930s. It was so popular among the Hollywood moguls that it has become a favourite on restaurant menus throughout the States.

hollywood cobb salad

175g (6oz) finely sliced iceberg lettuce

75g (3oz) finely sliced chicory or curly endive

2 medium tomatoes, cut into large dice

225g (8oz) sliced skinless deli chicken breast, cut into 2.5cm (1in) cubes

half a small ripe avocado, stoned, peeled and cubed

2 tablespoons dried chives

2 tablespoons no-sugar-added oil and vinegar dressing

Arrange the iceberg and curly endive lettuce in 2 shallow bowls or on 2 plates. Arrange the tomatoes, chicken and avocado in rows over the lettuce. Sprinkle with the chives, drizzle with dressing and serve.
Makes 2 servings

One serving: 378 calories, 40g protein, 11g carbohydrate, 21g fat (4g saturated), 96mg cholesterol, 183mg sodium, 3g fibre

dessert

2 medium peaches

Divide the peaches between 2 plates and serve.
Makes 2 servings.

One serving: 37 calories, 1g protein, 10g carbohydrate, 0g fat (0g saturated), 0mg cholesterol, 0mg sodium, 1g fibre

helpful hints

● Ask the deli to cut the chicken breast into 2.5cm (1in) thick slices to make it easier to cut into cubes.
● A hard-boiled egg can be substituted for the avocado.
● To speed the ripening of an avocado, remove the stem and store it in a paper bag in a warm spot.

countdown

● Make dressing.
● Prepare ingredients.
● Assemble salad.

shopping list

DELI
   225g (8oz) sliced skinless deli chicken breast
GROCERY
   1 jar dried chives
FRUIT AND VEG
   1 head iceberg lettuce
   1 small head chicory or curly endive
   2 medium tomatoes
   1 small avocado
   2 medium peaches
STAPLES
   No-sugar-added oil and vinegar dressing

black bean and salsa wraps

helpful hints

● Look for cos lettuce with large leaves.

● Black bean pâté is usually located with the dips and nachos in the snack section of the supermarket.

● If black bean pâté is unavailable use reduced-fat refried beans instead.

countdown

● Prepare ingredients.
● Assemble wraps.

shopping list

DAIRY

1 pot light fruit-flavoured yoghurt

1 packet grated, reduced-fat Cheddar cheese (50g/2oz needed)

DELI

225g (8oz) sliced turkey breast

GROCERY

1 jar no-sugar-added black bean pâté

1 jar no-sugar-added tomato salsa (225g (8oz) needed)

FRUIT AND VEG

1 head cos lettuce

With the help of prepared black bean pâté and deli turkey breast, you can assemble this lunch in 5 minutes. It can be made the night before and stored in the refrigerator until needed for lunch. You can use these wraps as hors d'oeuvres or eat them on a picnic.

black bean and salsa wraps

12 large cos leaves, washed and patted dry

12 x 30.5 x 10cm (11 x 4in) rectangles foil, parchment paper or greaseproof paper

50g (2oz) prepared no-sugar-added black bean pâté

50g (2oz) grated reduced-fat Cheddar cheese

225g (8oz) sliced turkey breast

225g (8oz) no-sugar-added tomato salsa

Remove 1 inch of the thick stem from each lettuce leaf and crush the remaining stem so that the leaf lies flat. Place the rectangles of foil on the work surface. Place one leaf on each square. Spread the pâté on each leaf and sprinkle with cheese. Top with a layer of turkey. Roll the lettuce up lengthwise like a cigar. Wrap the foil tightly around the lettuce to hold it in place. Cut in half crosswise and serve on 2 plates with the salsa on the side.

Makes 2 servings.

One serving: 349 calories, 15g protein, 17g carbohydrate, 5g fat (3g saturated), 10mg cholesterol, 1070mg sodium, 5g fibre

dessert

225g (8oz) light fruit-flavoured yoghurt

Divide the yoghurt between 2 dessert bowls and serve.

Makes 2 servings.

One serving: 50 calories, 32g protein, 0g carbohydrate, 4g fat (1g saturated), 80mg cholesterol, 72mg sodium, 0g fibre

grilled chilli chicken

This chicken dish is full of hot, spicy Southwestern flavours, and it tastes delicious served over a cool bed of lettuce with the Green Onion Dressing.

grilled chilli chicken

110g (4oz) red onion, chopped

2 medium-sized garlic cloves, crushed

1 tablespoon chilli powder

1 teaspoon ground cumin

Pinch salt

Pinch freshly ground black pepper

225g (8oz) boneless, skinless chicken breasts

50ml (2fl oz) freshly squeezed lemon juice (2 lemons)

2 tablespoons Dijon mustard

4 teaspoons olive oil

1 tablespoon water

4 spring onions, sliced

Half a small head cos lettuce, torn into bite-sized pieces

2 medium tomatoes, cut into wedges

Preheat the grill. Combine the onion, garlic, chilli powder, cumin, salt and pepper in a small bowl. Remove any visible fat from the chicken and poke several holes in the meat with a knife or fork. Place in a bowl and spread the marinade evenly over the chicken. Let it marinate for 15 minutes, turning once. Cover a baking tray with foil. Place the chicken on the tray and grill it 10–12.5cm (4–5in) from the heat for 5 minutes. Turn and grill for another 5 minutes. Remove from the grill and let cool. When cool, slice into strips. Whisk the lemon juice and mustard together in a small bowl. Whisk in the oil and then the water. Stir in the spring onions. Place the lettuce on 2 plates. Top with the tomatoes and chicken strips. Drizzle the dressing over the salad or serve on the side.

Makes 2 servings.

> One serving: 367 calories, 41g protein, 18g carbohydrate, 16g fat (3g saturated), 96mg cholesterol, 603mg sodium, 1g fibre

helpful hints

● *Chop onion, garlic and spices together in a food processor to make a quick marinade.*

● *If pressed for time, use a bottled, no-sugar-added dressing and add spring onions to it.*

countdown

● *Preheat grill.*

● *While chicken marinates, prepare greens and make dressing.*

shopping list

MEAT

　225g (8oz) boneless, skinless chicken breasts

FRUIT AND VEG

　1 small head cos lettuce

　2 medium tomatoes

　2 medium lemons

　1 small bunch spring onions (4 needed)

STAPLES

　Red onion

　Garlic

　Olive oil

　Ground cumin

　Chilli powder

　Dijon mustard

　Salt

　Black peppercorns

which carbs
dinners

turkey and tzatsiki sandwich p120

black bean and salsa wraps   **p126**

crispy cod with ratatouille

For this quick meal, freshly made ratatouille, a tasty blend of Provençal vegetables, is combined with juicy fish fillets. Coating the fish fillet with polenta gives it a crispy crust without having to deep-fry it.

I am often asked how to cook fish so that it's juicy and not dried out. The general rule is to cook fish for 10 minutes for each 2.5cm (1in) of thickness. If the fish is thicker, cook it a little longer, or if thinner, cook it a shorter time.

crispy cod

350g (12oz) cod fillet
2 tablespoons polenta
Salt and freshly ground black
    pepper
2 teaspoons olive oil

Wash fish fillet and pat dry with kitchen paper. Season polenta with salt and pepper to taste. Dip fish into polenta, making sure both sides are well coated. Heat olive oil in a medium-sized non-stick frying pan on medium-high heat. Add fish and sauté for 5 minutes. Turn and sauté another 5 minutes for a 2.5cm (1in) thick fillet. Reduce cooking time to 8 total minutes for 1cm ($^1/_2$in) fillet. Divide in half and serve.
Makes 2 servings.

> Per serving: 203 calories, 29.3 grams protein, 5.6 grams carbohydrate, 6.0 grams fat (1.0 saturated), 116 milligrams cholesterol, 136 milligrams sodium, 0 grams fibre

ratatouille

175g (6oz) aubergine, washed and
    sliced
175g (6oz) courgettes, washed
    and sliced
110g (4oz) sliced red onion
2 medium garlic cloves, crushed
450ml (16fl oz) low-sodium, low-
    sugar tomato or pasta sauce
115ml (4fl oz) water
2 teaspoons olive oil
Salt and freshly ground black
    pepper

Add aubergine, courgettes, onion, garlic, tomato sauce and water to a medium-sized saucepan. Bring to a simmer over medium-high heat. Lower heat and cover. Simmer for 15 minutes. Vegetables should be cooked through but a little firm. Stir in olive oil and add salt and pepper to taste.
Makes 2 servings.

> Per serving: 223 calories, 5.9 grams protein, 18.9 grams carbohydrate, 4.7 grams fat (0.6 saturated), 0 milligrams cholesterol, 44 milligrams sodium, 3.5 grams fibre

helpful hints

- *You can use haddock or bass in place of cod.*
- *For the pumpkin pudding, use the mixture of spices given or use a mixed spice mixture, making sure no sugar has been added.*

countdown

- *Start ratatouille.*
- *Make pumpkin pudding.*
- *Prepare fish.*

crispy cod with ratatouille continued

shopping list

DAIRY

  1 pot non-fat vanilla yoghurt

FISH

  350g (12oz) cod fillets

GROCERY

  1 small packet polenta

  1 small tin 100% pure pumpkin

  1 small packet pecan pieces

FRUIT AND VEG

  175g (6oz) aubergine

  175g (6oz) courgettes

STAPLES

  Red onion

  Garlic

  Olive oil

  Low-sodium, low-sugar
    tomato or pasta sauce
    (450ml/16fl oz needed)

  Artificial sweetener

  Ground cinnamon

  Grated nutmeg

  Salt

  Black peppercorns

pumpkin pudding

175ml (6fl oz) tinned 100% pure
  pumpkin

175ml (6fl oz) non-fat vanilla
  yoghurt

⅛ teaspoon ground cinnamon

⅛ teaspoon grated nutmeg

Artificial sweetener equivalent to
  2 teaspoons sugar

2 tablespoons pecan pieces

Mix together pumpkin, cinnamon, nutmeg and sweetener. Fold into yoghurt. Toast pecan pieces in the oven or under a grill until golden, about 2 minutes. Divide pumpkin mixture between 2 small dessert bowls or ramekins and sprinkle pecans on top.

Makes 2 servings.

Per serving: 162 calories, 6.2 grams protein, 18.4 grams carbohydrate, 8.4 grams fat (0.9 saturated), 2 milligrams cholesterol, 73 milligrams sodium, 3.7 grams fibre

aubergine parmesan with linguine

Aubergine parmesan, my husband's favourite dish, is a Neapolitan dish made with slices of fried aubergine baked in a rich tomato sauce and Parmesan cheese. I've created this quick version by microwaving the slices instead. It also makes the dish much lighter, as fried aubergine soaks up a lot of oil during the cooking.

aubergine parmesan with linguine

Olive oil spray
225g (8oz) aubergine, cut into 0.5cm (¼in) slices
Salt and freshly ground black pepper
350ml (12fl oz) low-sodium, no-sugar-added, tomato sauce
175g (6oz) lean minced beef
40g (1½oz) rocket leaves
110g (4oz) low-fat ricotta cheese
3 tablespoons water
3 tablespoons grated Parmesan cheese
50g (2oz) wholemeal linguine
2 teaspoons olive oil

Pre-heat the grill. Bring a large saucepan filled with 3–4 litres (5–7 pints) of water to the boil. Arrange aubergine slices on a 23–25cm (9–10in) microwave-safe pie dish. Spray with olive oil spray and sprinkle with salt and pepper to taste. Cover with clingfilm or a plate. Microwave on high for 3 minutes. Carefully remove cover. Remove aubergine to a plate and set aside.

Mix tomato sauce and minced beef together in a microwave-safe bowl. Microwave on high for 3 minutes. Spoon a layer of meat sauce into the bottom of the pie dish. Place rocket leaves over sauce. Place a layer of aubergine slices over the sauce and sprinkle with a little salt and pepper to taste. Repeat with the sauce, aubergine and salt and pepper. Mix ricotta cheese with water to form a sauce consistency. Add more water if necessary. Spoon ricotta cheese over top of aubergine dish. Sprinkle with Parmesan cheese. Grill for 5 minutes until sauce is bubbly and cheese melted. Place linguine in boiling water for 9 minutes. Drain and toss with olive oil and add salt and pepper to taste.

Place linguine on 2 dinner plates and serve aubergine parmesan on top.
Makes 2 servings.

Per serving: 597 calories, 53.3 grams protein, 50.1 grams carbohydrate, 19.1 grams fat (10.1 saturated), 122 milligrams cholesterol, 446 milligrams sodium, 9.1 grams fibre

helpful hints

● *Buy good-quality Parmesan cheese and grate it yourself. Freeze the extra: you can spoon out what you need and leave the rest frozen.*
● *This dish can be prepared and assembled in advance and refrigerated several hours or overnight. Bring to room temperature and grill as needed.*

countdown

● *Pre-heat grill.*
● *Boil water for pasta.*
● *Microwave aubergine.*
● *Mix ricotta.*
● *Assemble aubergine parmesan and place under grill.*
● *Boil linguine.*

shopping list

DAIRY
1 small pot low-fat ricotta cheese
MEAT
175g (6oz) lean minced beef
GROCERY
1 small packet wholemeal linguine (50g/2oz needed)
FRUIT AND VEG
225g (8oz) aubergine
1 small bunch rocket
STAPLES
Parmesan cheese
Olive oil
Low-sodium, no-sugar-added tomato sauce (350ml/12fl oz needed)
Salt
Black peppercorns

seared sesame tuna

Seared tuna with black and white sesame seeds is served in many restaurants, but you can make it at home in minutes. ● *Flavour can vary considerably among the species of tuna. The yellowfin tuna is more delicately flavoured and particularly worth looking for.* ● *Black sesame seeds are available in some supermarkets and many health food shops. You can use either all white sesame seeds, all black or a combination of both.* ● *A side dish of bok choy and shiitake noodles completes this Oriental-style meal.*

helpful hints

● *To chop fresh ginger quickly, cut it into small cubes and press through a garlic press with large holes. If using a press with small holes, just catch the juice that you squeeze out; it will give enough flavour for this recipe.*

● *To save clean-up time, cook the tuna first, then remove and stir-fry the bok choy and pasta in the same wok.*

● *To avoid having to look back at the recipe as you stir-fry, line up the ingredients on a board or plate in order so you know which ingredient to add next.*

● *For crisp, not steamed, stir-fried vegetables, start with a very hot wok or frying pan. Let the vegetables sit a minute before tossing to allow the wok to regain its heat.*

seared sesame tuna

275g (10oz) fresh tuna steak
3 tablespoons sesame seeds
4 teaspoons olive oil
Salt and freshly ground black
     pepper to taste

Rinse the tuna and pat dry with kitchen paper. Spoon the sesame seeds over both sides of the tuna, pressing the seeds into the fish with the back of a spoon. Heat the oil in a wok or non-stick frying pan over a high heat. When the oil begins to smoke, add the tuna. Brown for 1 minute, then turn. Brown for another minute, then lower the heat to medium-high. Cook for another 3–4 minutes. Season with salt and pepper to taste. The tuna should be seared outside and just barely warm inside. Immediately remove from the pan to slow the cooking process. Cut the tuna in half, divide between 2 plates and serve.
Makes 2 servings.

One serving: 353 calories, 36g protein,
1g carbohydrate, 23g fat (4g saturated),
53mg cholesterol, 60mg sodium, 0g fibre

thai peanut-rub pork

This blend of spices and peanuts rubbed into the pork forms a well-seasoned crust. Rubs are a quick way to add flavour to meats and a great alternative to marinades, since you don't have to wait for the meat to absorb the marinade flavours. These Thai spices are fun, easy to use, and provide a different way to spice up pork tenderloin.

thai peanut-rub pork

Olive oil spray

20 dry-roasted, unsalted peanuts (2 tablespoons when ground)

10g (1/2oz) fresh coriander leaves

1 1/2 teaspoons garlic powder

1 tablespoon ground coriander

2g (1/16oz) artificial sweetener

Pinch of cayenne pepper

275g (10oz) pork tenderloin

Preheat the grill. Line a baking tray with foil, and spray with olive oil. Chop the peanuts and coriander leaves in a food processor. Add the garlic powder, ground coriander, artificial sweetener and cayenne, pulsing to incorporate. Alternatively, chop and mix by hand. Remove any visible fat from the pork. Rub the mixture on both sides of the pork, pressing the mixture onto the meat and making sure all the sides are coated. Place on baking tray and grill 20.5cm (8in) from the heat for 7 minutes, then turn and grill for another 8 minutes. The pork is done when a meat thermometer registers 70°C (160°F). Remove the pork to a plate and cover with foil to keep warm. Slice before serving.
Makes 2 servings.

> One serving: 333 calories, 45g protein, 6g carbohydrate, 15g fat (4g saturated), 133mg cholesterol, 137mg sodium, 1g fibre

stir-fry broccoli noodles

50g (2oz) wholemeal tagliatelle

110g (4oz) broccoli florets

2 tablespoons oyster sauce

2 tablespoons rice vinegar

Olive oil spray

4 medium-sized garlic cloves, crushed

10g (1/2oz) chopped fresh coriander leaves

Bring a large saucepan of water to the boil, add the noodles and boil for 8 minutes. Add the broccoli and boil for 2 minutes. Drain and set aside. Combine the oyster sauce and vinegar, then set aside. Spray a wok or frying pan with olive oil and place over a high heat. Add the tagliatelle, broccoli and garlic. Stir-fry for 2 minutes, then push the ingredients to the sides of the pan. Add the oyster sauce mixture and toss well. Serve sprinkled with chopped coriander leaves.
Makes 2 servings.

> One serving: 208 calories, 10g protein, 37g carbohydrate, 3g fat (1g saturated), 0mg cholesterol, 491mg sodium, 6g fibre

helpful hints

- *If rice vinegar is unavailable, use 1 tablespoon water mixed with distilled white vinegar.*
- *Chop the coriander leaves for both recipes at one time and divide accordingly.*
- *To avoid having to look back at the recipe as you stir-fry, line up the ingredients on a board or plate in order so you know which ingredient to add next.*
- *For crisp, not steamed, stir-fried vegetables, start with a very hot wok. Let the vegetables sit for a minute before tossing to allow the wok to regain its heat.*

countdown

- *Preheat grill.*
- *Make pork dish.*
- *While pork cooks, make broccoli noodles.*

shopping list

MEAT
275g (10oz) pork tenderloin
GROCERY
1 small packet dry roasted, unsalted peanuts (20 needed)
1 small packet wholemeal tagliatelle (50g/2oz needed)
1 small bottle oyster sauce
1 small bottle rice vinegar
FRUIT AND VEG
1 small bunch fresh coriander
1 packet broccoli florets (110g/4oz needed)
STAPLES
Garlic
Olive oil spray
Garlic powder
Ground coriander
Artificial sweetener
Cayenne pepper

pesto chicken

Pesto is a flavourful Italian sauce filled with garlic, basil, pine nuts, parsley and olive oil. It's most widely used as a luscious dressing for pasta. Typically, pesto is not cooked. In this recipe, the sauce is added to the cooked chicken for a minute just before serving. The sauce is warmed by the chicken, while still preserving the fresh basil and parsley flavours.
● Steaming or boiling artichokes takes about 45 minutes. To cut the time in half, cut the artichokes in half and cook them in about 5cm (2in) of water for 20 minutes. The artichokes can also be cooked in a microwave, as described in this recipe. ● Artichokes may be served hot or cold. To eat, pull off the outer petals one at a time. Dip the base of each petal into the sauce; pull the petal through your teeth to remove the soft, pulpy portion of petal, then discard. For this recipe, the fuzzy section near the base, called the choke, will be removed. The bottom, or heart, of the artichoke is entirely edible. Many think it's the best part. Cut it into small pieces and dip in the sauce.

helpful hints

- Pesto can be found in jars on the supermarket shelves, usually next to the pasta.
- Artichokes are not available all year round. Asparagus or broccoli can be steamed or microwaved and served with this dressing instead.
- Fresh figs are not available all year round. Plums, apricots or pears can be substituted.

countdown

- Start artichokes.
- Make pasta.
- Make chicken.

shopping list

MEAT

350g (12oz) boneless, skinless chicken breast

1 small jar pesto
(50g/2oz needed)

1 packet wholemeal tagliatelle
(50g/2oz needed)

2 medium artichokes

4 medium figs

STAPLES

No-sugar-added oil and vinegar dressing

Salt

Black peppercorns

pesto chicken

50g (2oz) wholemeal tagliatelle
Salt and freshly ground black pepper to taste
350g (12oz) boneless, skinless chicken breast
50g (2oz) shop-bought pesto

Bring a large saucepan of water to a boil. Add the pasta and boil for 8 minutes, or according to the packet's instructions. Do not overcook. Drain, leaving about 3 tablespoons of pasta water on the pasta. Divide between 2 dinner plates and season with salt and pepper to taste.

Remove all visible fat from the chicken and pound the breast flat with the palm of your hand or a heavy pan to about 1cm (½in) thick. Set a non-stick frying pan over a medium-high heat and add the chicken. Brown for 2 minutes on each side, seasoning the cooked sides with salt and pepper. Lower the heat to medium and sauté for another minute. Spoon the pesto over the chicken. Remove the pan from the heat. Cover and let sit for 1 minute. Divide the chicken and spoon over the pasta to serve. Makes 2 servings.

One serving: 427 calories, 57g protein, 6g carbohydrate, 20g fat (5g saturated), 154mg cholesterol, 416mg sodium, 2g fibre

steamed artichokes

2 medium artichokes

2 tablespoons no-sugar-added oil and vinegar dressing

Cut the stem off the artichokes as close to the base as possible. Cut off the top quarter and prickly points of visible leaves. Slice the artichokes in half from top to stem. Scrape out the fuzzy chokes with a spoon. Remove the small inner leaves (they're usually purple) and discard. Fill a large non-stick frying pan with 2.5cm (1in) of water, place the artichokes cut-side down and bring to the boil. Cover and boil for 20 minutes. Check after the first 10 minutes and add more water if needed.

Alternatively, to cook artichokes in the microwave, set the artichokes in a deep, microwave-safe bowl. Add 125ml (4fl oz) water, cover the bowl with cling film and microwave for 7–8 minutes on high, giving the bowl a quarter turn halfway through the cooking time. Allow to stand for 5 minutes.

The artichokes are done when a petal pulls off easily. Remove the cooked artichokes from the pan and place on 2 plates. Place the dressing in 2 small bowls on the side and use as dipping sauce for the artichoke leaves and hearts. *Makes 2 servings.*

One serving: 181 calories, 6g protein, 25g carbohydrate, 9g fat (1g saturated), 0mg cholesterol, 233mg sodium, 0g fibre

dessert

4 medium figs

Divide the figs between 2 plates and serve. *Makes 2 servings.*

One serving: 74 calories, 1g protein, 19g carbohydrate, 0.5g fat (0g saturated), 0mg cholesterol, 0mg sodium, 3g fibre

mediterranean steak

Sautéed steak flavoured with the bountiful produce of the Mediterranean provides a quick, 15-minute dinner.

Pre-cooked, packaged couscous takes only 5 minutes to make. It's made from semolina flour and is in fact a form of pasta rather than a grain as many people think. You just boil water, remove from heat, add the couscous, cover, and leave to stand. For this dinner, I've added fresh mint and chopped tomatoes to add a fresh flavour that goes well with the steak.

mediterranean steak

350g (12oz) steak (sirloin or fillet)
½ teaspoon cayenne pepper
Olive oil spray
3 tablespoons sliced pimiento-stuffed green olives
2 tablespoons capers
Salt and freshly ground black pepper

Remove fat from steak and sprinkle both sides with cayenne. Heat a small, non-stick frying pan over medium-high heat. Spray with olive oil spray. Brown steak for 2 minutes per side. Sprinkle olives and capers into frying pan and over steak. Lower heat to medium and cook 2 minutes for medium-rare. Cook 2 minutes longer for thick steak. Add salt and pepper to taste.

To serve, place couscous on 2 dinner plates, carve steak and place on top. Spoon any pan juices over steak.
Makes 2 servings.

> Per serving: 356 calories, 55.8 grams protein, 0.3 grams carbohydrate, 16.4 grams fat (7.1 saturated), 140 milligrams cholesterol, 548 milligrams sodium, 0 grams fibre

minted couscous

115ml (4fl oz) water
50g (2oz) couscous
1 small tomato, diced
½ cucumber, cut into cubes
15g (½ oz) chopped fresh mint
Salt and freshly ground black pepper

Bring water to the boil. Remove from heat and add couscous, tomatoes and cucumber. Cover with a lid and leave to stand for 5 minutes. When ready, fluff with a fork. Add mint and salt and pepper to taste.
Makes 2 servings.

> Per serving: 144 calories, 5.9 grams protein, 30.0 grams carbohydrate, 0.9 grams fat (0 saturated), 0 milligrams cholesterol, 11 milligrams sodium, 1.9 grams fibre

spiced peaches

2 medium peaches, stoned and
   sliced
1 teaspoon ground cinnamon
1 teaspoon allspice
Artificial sweetener equivalent to
   1 teaspoon sugar
2 sprigs fresh mint

Arrange peach slices in a circle on 2 small
dessert plates. Mix cinnamon, allspice and
sweetener together. Sprinkle mixture over
peach slices. Place both dishes in a microwave
oven on high for 1 minute. Remove, garnish
with mint leaves, and serve.
Makes 2 servings.

Per serving: 39 calories, 0.6 grams protein, 10.7 grams
carbohydrate, 0.1 gram fat (0 saturated), 0 milligrams
cholesterol, 0 milligrams sodium, 0.5 grams fibre

shopping list

FRUIT AND VEG
   1 small bunch fresh mint
   1 small tomato
   2 medium peaches
   ½ cucumber
MEAT
   350g (12oz) steak (sirloin
      or fillet)
GROCERY
   1 small packet couscous
   1 small jar/can pimiento-
      stuffed green olives
   1 small jar capers
   1 small jar allspice
STAPLES
   Olive oil spray
   Cayenne pepper
   Ground cinnamon
   Artificial sweetener
   Salt
   Black peppercorns

grilled scallops parmigiana

Sweet, juicy scallops are easy to cook. The secret to this meal is buying fresh, good quality scallops. ● These baked Parmesan scallops take only 15 minutes to make, and the courgettes can be cooked while the scallops bake, so the entire meal can be prepared in 15 to 20 minutes. ● Scallops are readily available. You can use any type for this recipe. If you buy small scallops, then bake them for only 10 minutes.

helpful hints

● *Buy good quality Parmesan cheese and grate it yourself. Freeze extra for quick use later – simply spoon out what you need and leave the rest frozen.*

● *Any type of berries can be used.*

● *To save cleaning an extra pan, use the same one to cook the spinach and courgettes.*

● *The spinach and courgettes can be cooked in a microwave oven. Place in separate microwave-safe bowls and microwave the spinach on high for 2–3 minutes and the courgettes on high for 3–4 minutes. Toss the courgettes with olive oil and lemon juice; season with salt and pepper to taste.*

countdown

● *Preheat oven to 180°C/350°F/gas mark 4.*
● *Start scallops.*
● *Make spinach.*
● *Make courgettes.*
● *Complete scallops.*

grilled scallops parmigiana

350g (12oz) large scallops, rinsed
50ml (2fl oz) white wine
2 teaspoons olive oil
2 large handfuls washed, ready-to-eat fresh spinach
10g (½oz) freshly grated Parmesan cheese
Salt and freshly ground black pepper to taste

Preheat the oven to 180°C/350°F/gas mark 4. Place the scallops in a small baking dish just large enough to hold the scallops in one layer. Add the wine, tossing to coat the scallops. Bake for 15 minutes. While the scallops are baking, heat the oil in a medium-sized non-stick frying pan over a medium-high heat. Add the spinach, and sauté 2–3 minutes, or until wilted. Spoon onto 2 dinner plates. Remove the scallops from the oven and turn on the grill. When the grill is hot, sprinkle Parmesan cheese over the scallops and place under the grill for 1 minute, or until golden. Watch them carefully, as they will brown very quickly. Season with salt and pepper to taste. Spoon over the spinach and serve. *Makes 2 servings.*

One serving: 286 calories, 37g protein, 9g carbohydrate, 10g fat (3g saturated), 63mg cholesterol, 573mg sodium, 4g fibre

lemon-pepper courgettes

2 teaspoons olive oil
225g (8oz) courgettes, sliced
2 tablespoons freshly squeezed lemon juice (1 lemon)
¼ teaspoon freshly ground black pepper
Salt to taste

In the frying pan used for the spinach, heat the oil over a medium-high heat. Add the courgettes and sauté for 5 minutes. Toss with the lemon juice and pepper. Season with salt to taste. Serve with the scallops. *Makes 2 servings.*

One serving: 62 calories, 2g protein, 5g carbohydrate, 5g fat (1g saturated), 0mg cholesterol, 4mg sodium, 1g fibre

kiwi-berry jumble

2 kiwis, peeled and cubed
175g (6oz) fresh raspberries

Combine the kiwi cubes and the raspberries.
Spoon into 2 dessert bowls and serve.
Makes 2 servings.

> One serving: 77 calories, 1g protein,
> 18g carbohydrate, 1g fat (0g saturated),
> 0mg cholesterol, 4mg sodium, 3g fibre

shopping list

SEAFOOD
  350g (12oz) large scallops
GROCERY
  1 small bottle dry white wine
FRUIT AND VEG
  1 bag washed, ready-to-eat
    fresh spinach
  225g (8oz) courgettes
  2 lemons
  2 kiwis
  1 punnet fresh raspberries
STAPLES
  Olive oil
  Parmesan cheese
  Salt
  Black peppercorns

smothered steak with caramelised onions

helpful hints

- Beef fillet, sirloin, rump, skirt or flank steak can also be used.
- Fresh pineapple cubes are available in the fruit and veg sections of some supermarkets.
- Any type of lettuce can be used.
- If pressed for time, omit the Pineapple Kebabs and serve 110g (4oz) of pineapple cubes per person.

countdown

- Preheat grill.
- Make steak.
- Make salad.
- Assemble pineapple.

Caramelised onions, mushrooms and garlic are perfect toppings for steak. There's no reason to shy away from enjoying a steak if you pick a lean cut. ● *Here it is served with succulent artichoke hearts and followed by a simple pineapple dessert.*

smothered steak with caramelised onions

275g (10oz) top loin steak, visible fat removed
Olive oil spray
225g (8oz) red onion, sliced
125ml (4fl oz) fat-free, low-salt chicken stock
4 medium-sized garlic cloves, crushed
225g (8oz) portobello mushrooms, sliced
Salt and freshly ground black pepper to taste

Line a baking tray with foil and place under the grill. Spray the steak with oil on both sides and set aside. Heat a small non-stick frying pan over a medium-high heat and add the onion. Sauté for 1 minute. Add the chicken stock, cover with a lid and cook over a high heat for 3 minutes. Uncover and cook for another minute, or until all of the liquid has evaporated. Add the garlic and mushrooms and sauté for 2 minutes. Season with salt and pepper to taste. Remove the hot baking tray from the grill and place the steak on tray. Grill for 4 minutes for a 2.5cm (1in) thick steak, another 4 minutes for thicker steak and 2 minutes for a thinner one. Turn the steak and season the cooked side. Transfer the steak to 2 plates, smother with the onion and mushrooms and serve.
Makes 2 servings.

One serving: 365 calories, 53g protein, 10g carbohydrate, 14g fat (6g saturated), 127mg cholesterol, 237mg sodium, 0g fibre

salad of artichoke hearts

Several red lettuce leaves, washed
and torn into bite-sized pieces
75g (3oz) artichoke hearts,
drained and sliced thinly
2 tablespoons no-sugar-added oil
and vinegar dressing

Place lettuce on 2 plates and top with the
artichoke hearts. Drizzle with salad dressing and
serve.
Makes 2 servings.

One serving: 90 calories, 1g protein,
3g carbohydrate, 9g fat (1g saturated),
0mg cholesterol, 234mg sodium, 1g fibre

pineapple kebabs

1 tablespoon ground cinnamon
2g (¹/₁₆ oz) artificial sweetener
275g (10oz) pineapple cubes
2 skewers

Line a baking tray with foil. Mix the cinnamon
and sweetener together in a medium-sized
bowl. Toss the pineapple cubes in the mixture,
making sure all sides are coated. Thread the
cubes onto 2 skewers and place on the baking
tray. Grill 6 to 7 inches from the heat for 5
minutes. Turn the skewers over and grill for an
additional 3 minutes. Serve warm.
Makes 2 servings.

One serving: 86 calories, 1g protein,
23g carbohydrate, 1g fat (0g saturated),
0mg cholesterol, 3mg sodium, 2g fibre

shopping list

MEAT
  275g (10oz) top loin steak
GROCERY
  1 tin or jar artichoke hearts
FRUIT AND VEG
  225g (8oz) portobello
    mushrooms
  1 small head red lettuce
    leaves
  1 container fresh pineapple
    cubes
STAPLES:
  Garlic
  Red onion
  Olive oil spray
  No-sugar-added oil and
    vinegar dressing
  Fat-free, low-salt chicken
    stock
  Ground cinnamon
  Artificial sweetener
  Salt
  Black peppercorns

whisky pork chops

Whisky lends an intriguing flavour to this simple French pork dish. This is a hearty meal and takes about 30–40 minutes to make from start to finish. ● *Enjoy it with full-flavoured rosemary lentils and beetroot salad, followed by a refreshing cinnamon grapefruit.*

whisky pork chops

2 teaspoons olive oil

2 x 150g (5oz) boneless, centre
    loin pork chops, visible fat
    removed

125ml (4fl oz) whisky

125ml (4fl oz) fat-free, low-sodium
    chicken stock

2 tablespoons Dijon mustard

Salt and freshly ground black
    pepper to taste

Heat the oil in a medium-sized non-stick frying pan over a medium-high heat. Add the pork chops and brown for 2 minutes on both sides. Pour off excess fat. Add the whisky and flambé: if cooking over gas, warm the whisky in the pan for a few seconds and then tip the pan to let the flame ignite the liquid. Immediately remove from the heat and let the flame burn down. If you cook with electric heat, then throw a lighted match into the warmed whisky. Be sure to remove the match before serving.

Stir in the stock, cover and lower the heat. Cook over a low heat for 3 minutes, or until the chops are cooked through and a meat thermometer registers 70°C/160°F. Remove the chops to a plate and cover with foil to keep warm. Add the mustard and blend in with the sauce. Cook for 1–2 minutes to reduce and slightly thicken. Season with salt and pepper to taste. Remove the chops to 2 plates, spoon the sauce over them and serve.

Makes 2 servings.

One serving: 448 calories, 42g protein,
1g carbohydrate, 12g fat (3g saturated),
133mg cholesterol, 596mg sodium, 0g fibre

helpful hints

● *Lentils don't need to be soaked and will cook in about 20 minutes. Start them first so that they will be ready by the time the pork is finished.*

● *For safety's sake, when flambéing, keep the pan lid nearby to snuff out the flame if necessary.*

● *Use cooked beetroots from the fruit and veg section of the supermarket.*

● *You can buy whisky in miniature bottles at many supermarkets and most off-licences.*

countdown

● *Start lentils.*

● *Preheat grill.*

● *Make pork chops.*

● *Assemble salad.*

● *Make cinnamon grapefruit.*

rosemary lentils

225ml (8fl oz) fat-free, low-sodium chicken stock

225ml (8fl oz) water

110g (4oz) red lentils

110g (4oz) yellow onion, diced

2 teaspoons fresh rosemary or 1 teaspoon dried

2 medium-sized garlic cloves, crushed

Salt and freshly ground black pepper to taste

10g (1/2oz) chopped fresh parsley

Bring the stock and water to a rolling boil in a medium-sized pot. Add the lentils, onion, rosemary and garlic slowly, so that the water does not stop boiling. Reduce the heat to medium, cover with a lid and simmer for 20 minutes. Remove the lid and continue to cook over a high heat, until any remaining liquid has been absorbed. Season, sprinkle with fresh parsley and serve with the pork.

Makes 2 servings.

One serving: 85 calories, 7g protein, 15g carbohydrate, 0.5g fat (0g saturated), 0mg cholesterol, 285mg sodium, 2g fibre

beetroot salad

450g (1lb) cooked beetroots, sliced

2 tablespoons distilled white vinegar

2g (1/16oz) artificial sweetener

Place the sliced beetroot on 2 salad plates. Combine the vinegar and sweetener, spoon over the beetroot and serve.

Makes 2 servings.

One serving: 58 calories, 2g protein, 15g carbohydrate, 0g fat (0g saturated), 0mg cholesterol, 285mg sodium, 0g fibre

cinnamon grapefruit

1 grapefruit

1/2 teaspoon cinnamon

2g (1/16oz) artificial sweetener

Preheat the grill. Line a baking tray with foil or use a small oven-to-table dish. Peel the grapefruit over a bowl to catch the juice. With a serrated knife, cut the grapefruit into 1cm (1/2in) slices (as you would slice a tomato). Place in a single layer in the dish. Sprinkle with the cinnamon and grill for 3 minutes. Mix the sweetener into the grapefruit juice and spoon over the grilled grapefruit before serving.

Makes 2 servings.

One serving: 40 calories, 1g protein, 11g carbohydrate, 0g fat (0g saturated), 0mg cholesterol, 0mg sodium, 1g fibre

shopping list

MEAT

2 x 150g (5oz) boneless, centre loin pork chops

GROCERY

1 small bottle whisky

FRUIT AND VEG

1 packet cooked beetroots

1 small packet red lentils

1 small bunch fresh parsley

1 small bunch fresh rosemary or 1 jar dried

1 grapefruit

STAPLES

Yellow onion

Garlic

Olive oil

Distilled white vinegar

Fat free, low-sodium chicken stock

Dijon mustard

Ground cinnamon

Artificial sweetener

Salt

Black peppercorns

mussels marinière

Imagine eating on the quay in Deauville, France, watching the fishing boats come in, breathing the fresh sea air and drinking a glass of chilled white wine. What a treat! Moules à la Marinière, or Mussels in White Wine, is a French dish normally enjoyed in these quaint surroundings. If you can't go to France, prepare this dish for an experience almost as satisfying! It takes less than 15 minutes to prepare, never mind the fabulous taste. ● Store mussels in the refrigerator. When ready for use, carefully scrub them with a vegetable brush under cold water. Scrape off the beard or thin hairs along the shell. Their shells should be tightly closed or snap shut when tapped. Discard any that do not close. ● Serve the mussels in large soup bowls with the reduced stock.

helpful hint

● The onion, celery and carrots can be sautéed ahead of time. Cook the mussels in wine just before serving.

countdown

● Prepare ingredients.
● Cook vegetables.
● Add mussels.

shopping list

SEAFOOD
900g (2lb) mussels
GROCERY
1 small bottle dry white wine
FRUIT AND VEG
1 small bunch fresh parsley
1 bag washed, ready-to-eat young salad leaves
STAPLES
Celery
Yellow onion
Carrots
Olive oil
No-sugar-added oil and vinegar dressing
Multi-grain bread
Black peppercorns

mussels marinière

2 teaspoons olive oil
110g (4oz) sliced yellow onion
2 celery stalks, sliced
2 medium carrots, sliced
125ml (4fl oz) dry white wine
Freshly ground black pepper to taste
900g (2lb) mussels
10g (½oz) fresh parsley, chopped
2 slices multi-grain bread

Heat the oil in a large saucepan over a medium-high heat. Sauté the onion, celery and carrots until they start to cook but not colour, about 5 minutes. Add the wine and freshly ground pepper to taste. Add the mussels and cover tightly with a lid. Bring to a boil and let boil for about 3 more minutes. The wine will boil up over the mussels causing them to open. As soon as they open, remove the pan from the heat. Do not over cook.

Lift the mussels out of the pan with a slotted spoon and divide between 2 large soup bowls. Discard any closed mussels – do not try to force them open. Sprinkle with parsley and serve. Meanwhile, bring the liquid to the boil and reduce rapidly by half. Ladle out the reduced stock to serve, leaving 0.5cm (¼in) of the stock in the pan – it may have some sand from the mussels in it. Serve with bread to dip in the stock. Makes 2 servings.

One serving: 374 calories, 33g protein, 31g carbohydrate, 11g fat (1g saturated), 64mg cholesterol, 861mg sodium, 5g fibre

young salad leaves

2 large handfuls washed, ready-to-eat young salad leaves
2 tablespoons no-sugar-added oil and vinegar dressing

Toss the salad leaves with the dressing. Makes 2 servings.

8g fat (1g saturated), 0mg cholesterol, 81mg sodium, 0g fibre

Crispy Cod with Ratatouille **p129**

Mediterranean Steak with couscous **p136**

spicy crab and vegetable stir-fry

Oriental spices give this crab a zesty tang. In Vietnam this dish is normally made with whole crab claws in the shell. I have simplified the shopping and cooking by using tinned or frozen crab. ● This entire meal is made in a wok. A non-stick frying pan can also be used and you will still achieve a good result. ● Lemon grass has long, thin, green-grey leaves with a spring onion-like base. Slice the end off the bulb and cut slices up to the woody part of the stem. Grated lemon rind can be substituted. ● Follow with an indulgent-tasting parfait for dessert.

spicy crab and vegetable stir-fry

375g (13oz) crabmeat, drained
50g (2oz) tomato purée
½ teaspoon hot pepper sauce
125ml (4fl oz) water
2g (¹/₁₆oz) artificial sweetener
4 teaspoons rapeseed oil
50g (2oz) chopped shallots
2 medium-sized garlic cloves, crushed
2 tablespoons chopped fresh ginger or 2 teaspoons ground ginger
4 stalks lemon grass, sliced, or grated rind from 2 lemons
225g (8oz) fresh bean sprouts
225g (8oz) mange tout, trimmed
2 tablespoons unsalted, roasted peanuts, chopped

Flake the crabmeat with a fork into a medium-sized bowl, looking carefully for any shell or cartilage that might remain. Combine the tomato purée, hot pepper sauce, water and artificial sweetener in a small bowl and set aside. Make sure all ingredients are prepared and ready for stir-frying. Heat the oil in a wok or frying pan over a high heat until smoking. Add the shallots, garlic, ginger and lemon grass and stir-fry for 2 minutes. Add the bean sprouts and mange tout. Stir-fry for another 2 minutes. Add the crab and stir-fry for 3 more minutes.

Push the ingredients to the sides of pan leaving a well in the centre. Add the sauce and toss with the ingredients for an additional minute. Remove to 2 plates, sprinkle with peanuts and serve.
Makes 2 servings.

One serving: 493 calories, 52g protein, 25g carbohydrate, 23g fat (3g saturated), 144mg cholesterol, 694mg sodium, 4g fibre

helpful hints

● Use a food processor to chop the shallots and peanuts.

● To chop fresh ginger quickly, cut it into small cubes and press through a garlic press with large holes. If using a press with small holes, just catch the juice that is squeezed out; it will give enough flavour for the recipe.

● If using ground ginger instead of fresh, add it to the sauce.

● To avoid having to look back at the recipe as you stir-fry, line up the ingredients on a board or plate in order so you know which ingredient to add next.

● For crisp, not steamed, stir-fried vegetables, start with a very hot wok or frying pan. Let the vegetables sit a minute before tossing to allow the wok to regain its heat.

● Any type of berries can be used.

● Any flavour of light yoghurt can be used.

● Be careful toasting the pecans, as they burn easily.

spicy crab and vegetable stir-fry continued

countdown

- *Prepare all ingredients*
- *Stir-fry crab dish.*
- *Prepare parfait.*

shopping list

DAIRY

  1 pot light white chocolate–strawberry flavoured yoghurt

GROCERY

  375g (13oz) tinned or frozen sweet crabmeat

  1 tube tomato purée

  1 small packet roasted peanuts (25g/1oz needed)

  1 small packet pecans (10g/¹/₂oz needed)

FRUIT AND VEG

  2 large shallots

  1 small piece fresh ginger or 1 jar ground

  1 small bunch lemon grass (4 stalks needed)

  225g (8oz) fresh bean sprouts

  225g (8oz) mange tout

  1 punnet fresh raspberries

STAPLES

  Garlic

  Rapeseed oil

  Hot pepper sauce

  Artificial sweetener

raspberry parfait

110g (4oz) fresh raspberries

2g (¹/₁₆oz) artificial sweetener (optional)

225ml (8fl oz) light, white chocolate–strawberry yoghurt

6 pecan pieces, toasted (1 tablespoon)

Purée the raspberries in a food processor and blend in the artificial sweetener. Scoop half the yoghurt into 2 bowls or parfait glasses. Pour in half the sauce and top with the remaining yoghurt. Pour the remaining sauce over the yoghurt and top with the toasted pecans.

    Refrigerate until ready to serve.

Makes 2 servings.

> One serving: 110 calories, 5g protein, 15g carbohydrate, 4g fat (0.5g saturated), 3mg cholesterol, 58mg sodium, 2g fibre

garlic prawn stir-fry

Garlic, cashew nuts and sesame oil flavour this quick prawn dinner. ● *The cooking time for this dinner is about 8 minutes.* ● *Use the helpful hint suggestions for quick preparation of the ingredients to make this a complete 15-minute meal.*

garlic prawn stir-fry

2 tablespoons low-sodium soy
  sauce
2 tablespoons rice vinegar
2 tablespoons chopped fresh
  ginger
6 medium-sized garlic cloves,
  crushed
Several drops hot pepper sauce
4 teaspoons sesame oil
2 slices yellow onion
½ medium-sized red pepper,
  sliced
350g (12oz) medium prawns,
  peeled and deveined
225g (8oz) mange tout, trimmed
2 tablespoons cashews

Combine the soy sauce, rice vinegar, ginger, garlic and hot sauce in a small bowl. Make sure all ingredients are prepared and ready for cooking.

Heat the sesame oil in a wok or frying pan over a high heat. When the oil is smoking, add the onion and red pepper. Stir-fry for 3 minutes. Add the prawns and mange tout and stir-fry for 2 minutes. Add the cashews and sauce and continue to stir-fry, tossing continuously for 2 minutes. Add salt to taste. Divide between 2 plates and serve.

Makes 2 servings.

One serving: 411 calories, 41g protein, 21g carbohydrate, 18g fat (3g saturated), 260mg cholesterol, 944mg sodium, 2g fibre

helpful hints

● *Buy peeled prawns – it is well worth the time otherwise spent shelling them yourself.*

● *Washed and sliced cabbage can be used instead of the Chinese cabbage, but should be microwaved for 1 minute first.*

● *To chop fresh ginger quickly, cut it into small cubes and press through a garlic press with large holes. If using a press with small holes, just catch the juice that is squeezed out; it will give enough flavour for the recipe.*

● *If rice vinegar is not available, use 1 tablespoon water mixed with 1 tablespoon distilled white wine vinegar.*

● *To avoid having to look back at the recipe as you stir-fry, line up the ingredients on a board or plate in order so you know which ingredient to add next.*

● *For crisp, not steamed, stir-fried vegetables, start with a very hot wok or frying pan. Let the vegetables sit a minute before tossing to allow the wok to regain its heat.*

garlic prawn stir-fry continued

chinese cabbage and bean sprouts

countdown

- *Prepare ingredients.*
- *Make cabbage and bean sprouts.*
- *Make prawn stir-fry.*

shopping list

SEAFOOD

  350g (12oz) medium prawns

GROCERY

  1 small packet cashew nuts (25g/1oz needed)

  1 small bottle sesame oil

  1 small bottle low-carbohydrate miso dressing

  1 small bottle rice vinegar

FRUIT AND VEG

  1 medium-sized red pepper

  1 small piece fresh ginger

  225g (8oz) mange tout

  1 small head Chinese cabbage (Chinese leaves)

  1 small packet fresh bean sprouts

STAPLES

  Yellow onion

  Garlic

  Hot pepper sauce

  Low-sodium soy sauce

50g (2oz) thinly sliced Chinese cabbage (Chinese leaves)

60g (2½oz) fresh bean sprouts

2 tablespoons low-carbohydrate miso dressing

Place the cabbage and bean sprouts in a small bowl and toss with dressing. Serve with the stir-fry.

Makes 2 servings.

One serving: 73 calories, 5g protein, 8g carbohydrate, 3g fat (0.5g saturated), 0mg cholesterol, 321mg sodium, 1g fibre

sole amandine

Sole Amandine, a French classic, appears on menus at French restaurants, from the most elegant to simple brasseries. Dressed up or down, lemon juice and almonds are all the fillet of sole needs to give it a wonderful flavour. ● *This quick dinner takes only 10 minutes to make. It's a perfect mid-week meal when you're on the run.*

sole amandine

350g (12oz) sole fillet
4 teaspoons olive oil
Salt and freshly ground black
  pepper to taste
2 tablespoons flaked almonds
2 tablespoons freshly squeezed
  lemon juice (1 lemon)
2 tablespoons freshly chopped
  parsley (optional)

Rinse the sole and pat dry with kitchen paper. Heat the oil in a medium-sized non-stick frying pan over a medium-high heat. Sauté the fish for 2 minutes on each side. Remove to 2 plates, season with salt and pepper to taste and cover with foil to keep warm. Add the almonds to the same frying pan and sauté until slightly golden, about 1 minute. Sprinkle the fish with lemon juice, almonds and parsley and serve.
Makes 2 servings.

One serving: 264 calories, 28g protein,
4g carbohydrate, 17g fat (2g saturated),
60mg cholesterol, 98mg sodium, 1g fibre

butter beans

450g (1lb) butter beans
2 teaspoons olive oil
Salt and freshly ground black
  pepper to taste

Heat the beans in a small pan, then drain. Add the oil to the same frying pan used for the fish and heat on high. Sauté the beans for 1 minute. Add salt and pepper to taste.
Makes 2 servings.

One serving: 154 calories, 7g protein,
21g carbohydrate, 5g fat (1g saturated),
0mg cholesterol, 3mg sodium, 4g fibre

grilled tomatoes

2 medium tomatoes, halved
Salt and freshly ground black
  pepper to taste

Preheat the grill. Season the tomato halves with salt and pepper to taste. Grill for 4 minutes and serve with the fish and butter beans.
Makes 2 servings.

One serving: 25 calories, 2g protein,
5g carbohydrate, 0g fat (0g saturated),
0mg cholesterol, 10mg sodium, 0g fibre

helpful hints

● *Any type of non-oily fish fillet can be used.*
● *To save washing another pan, use the same pan for the fish and butter beans.*

countdown

● *Preheat grill.*
● *Make fish.*
● *Make butter beans.*
● *Make salad.*

shopping list

SEAFOOD
  350g (12oz) sole fillet
GROCERY
  1 small packet flaked
    almonds (25g/1oz needed)
  450g (1lb) tinned butter
    beans
FRUIT AND VEG
  1 lemon
  1 small bunch parsley
    (optional)
  2 medium tomatoes
STAPLES
  Olive oil
  Salt
  Black peppercorns

five-spice tuna tataki

Tataki – beef or fish that has been seared, thinly sliced, chilled and served with a dipping sauce – is a tangy, Japanese recipe. Traditional tataki accompaniments are grated daikon (white radish), ginger, chopped spring onions and a dipping sauce.

Japanese and Chinese rice vinegars are made from fermented rice. They're milder than most Western vinegars. White vinegar can be used in this recipe. Add a few drops of water to soften the strength.

Brown rice takes about 45 minutes to cook. There are several brands of quick-cooking brown rice available. Their cooking time ranges from 10 to 30 minutes. I find the 30-minute rice has more flavour, but any quick-cooking rice will work for this dinner.

helpful hints

- Coarse-ground black pepper and five-spice powder can be bought in the spice section of the supermarket.
- Red radishes can be used instead of the daikon or white radish.

countdown

- Sear tuna and let cool slightly.
- Make rice.
- While rice cooks, prepare sauce.
- Make dessert just before serving.

five-spice tuna tataki

2 x 175g (6oz) tuna steaks
1 tablespoon coarse-ground black pepper
1½ tablespoons sesame oil
2 tablespoons low-sodium soy sauce
2 medium garlic cloves, crushed
½ teaspoon five-spice powder
1 small daikon (white) radish, grated (optional)

Roll tuna steaks in black pepper. Heat ½ tablespoon sesame oil in a small non-stick frying pan over high heat. Sear tuna for 2 minutes. Turn and sear second side for 2 minutes. Remove to a chopping board and thinly slice.

Mix soy sauce, remaining tablespoon sesame oil, garlic and five-spice powder together in a small bowl. Serve sliced tuna on 2 individual dinner plates and spoon sauce on top. Sprinkle with grated daikon radish.

Makes 2 servings.

Per serving: 335 calories, 37.3 grams protein, 2.5 grams carbohydrate, 18.0 grams fat (3.4 saturated), 59 milligrams cholesterol, 677 milligrams sodium, 0 grams fibre

japanese brown rice

50g (2oz) 30-minute quick-
cooking brown rice

110g (4oz) button mushrooms,
sliced

110g (4oz) fresh mange tout,
trimmed

115ml (4fl oz) fat-free, low-sodium
chicken stock

1 tablespoon rice vinegar

2 tablespoons low-sodium soy
sauce

Salt and freshly ground black
pepper

Bring a large saucepan with 2–3 litres (4–5 pints) of water to the boil. Add rice and boil for 25 minutes. Add mushrooms and mange tout and continue to boil for 5 minutes. Drain. Mix chicken stock, vinegar and soy sauce together and toss with rice and vegetables. Add salt and pepper to taste.

Makes 2 servings.

Per serving: 125 calories, 6.1 grams protein, 22.1 grams carbohydrate, 1.1 grams fat (0.1 saturated), 0 milligrams cholesterol, 750 milligrams sodium, 2.4 grams fibre

raspberry banana cooler

110g (4oz) frozen raspberries
(not in sugar syrup)

1/2 medium banana, sliced

225ml (8fl oz) diet lemon-lime

225ml (8fl oz) ice cubes

Artificial sweetener equivalent to
2 teaspoons sugar

Place raspberries, banana, diet lemon-lime, ice cubes and sweetener in a blender or food processor and blend until smooth. Serve in tall glasses.

Makes 2 servings.

Per serving: 66 calories, 1.1 grams protein, 16.4 grams carbohydrate, 0.6 grams fat (0.1 saturated), 0 milligrams cholesterol, 1 milligram sodium, 3.5 grams fibre

shopping list

SEAFOOD

2 x 175g/6oz tuna steaks

GROCERY

1 small jar five-spice powder

1 small pack frozen
raspberries (not in sugar
syrup)

1 small can/bottle diet
lemon-lime

1 small bottle rice vinegar

1 small jar coarse-ground
black pepper

1 small bottle sesame oil

FRUIT AND VEG

1 small daikon (white) radish

1 medium banana

110g (4oz) button
mushrooms

110g (4oz) fresh mange tout

STAPLES

Garlic

Quick-cooking brown rice

Artificial sweetener

Fat-free, low-sodium chicken
stock

Low-sodium soy sauce

Salt

Black peppercorns

chicken with black bean salsa and brown rice

helpful hints

● *Look for roasted chicken that is not marinated in honey or a barbecue sauce. These sauces usually contain sugar.*

● *This recipe calls for serving the chicken at room temperature. For a hot meal, microwave chicken on high for 2 minutes.*

countdown

● *Start rice.*
● *Make salsa.*
● *Assemble salad.*

Roasted chicken served over rice with a black bean and corn salsa dresses up shop-bought roasted or rotisserie chicken breasts.

Sweet vermouth gives this black bean and corn salsa an intriguing flavour. Use the salsa dressing in the recipe or add vermouth and cumin to a bottled low-fat vinaigrette dressing. Brown rice takes about 45 minutes to cook. There are several brands of quick-cooking brown rice available. Their cooking time ranges from 10 to 30 minutes. I find the 30-minute rice has more flavour, but any quick-cooking rice will work for this dinner.

brown rice

4oz (110g) 30-minute quick-cooking brown rice
1 tablespoon plus 1 teaspoon rapeseed oil,
½ tablespoon plus 1 teaspoon sweet (rosso) vermouth
Salt and freshly ground black pepper

First, prepare the brown rice. Bring a large saucepan with 2–3 litres (4–5 pints) of water to the boil. Add rice and boil, uncovered, for about 30 minutes (or follow packet instructions). Drain into a sieve in the sink. Run hot water through rice and stir with a fork. Return rice to saucepan and add 1 teaspoon rapeseed oil, 1 teaspoon vermouth and salt and pepper to taste.

chicken with black bean salsa

1 teaspoon ground cumin

Several drops hot pepper sauce

50g (2oz) tinned black beans, rinsed and drained

50g (2oz) frozen corn kernels, defrosted

350g (12oz) roasted chicken breast, bones and skin removed

15g (1/2oz) chopped fresh coriander

2 small tomatoes, cut into wedges

Salt and freshly ground black pepper

While rice cooks, mix 1 tablespoon rapeseed oil, tablespoon vermouth, cumin, hot pepper sauce and salt and pepper to taste in a medium-sized bowl. Add the black beans and corn. Toss well. Taste and add more seasoning if needed.
Spoon rice on to 2 dinner plates. Slice chicken and place on rice. Spoon salsa on top and sprinkle with coriander. Arrange tomatoes on the side of the dinner plates.
Makes 2 servings.

Per serving: 558 calories, 32.0 grams protein, 38.4 grams carbohydrate, 18.4 grams fat (3.2 saturated), 144 milligrams cholesterol, 146 milligrams sodium, 2.6 grams fibre

shopping list

MEAT

350g (12oz) roasted chicken breast, bones and skin removed

GROCERY

1 small bottle sweet (rosso) vermouth

1 small tin black beans

1 small pack frozen corn kernels

FRUIT AND VEG

1 small bunch coriander

2 small tomatoes

STAPLES

Quick-cooking brown rice

Rapeseed oil

Ground cumin

Hot pepper sauce

Salt

Black peppercorns

veal piccata

Tender veal escalopes are sautéed in a wine and lemon sauce for this quick meal. Garlic courgettes and tomatoes take only minutes in the microwave oven.

helpful hints

● The vegetables can be sautéed instead of cooking them in a microwave oven. Heat the oil in a non-stick frying pan, add the vegetables, cover with a lid, and cook for 10 minutes.

countdown

● Boil water for orzo.
● Prepare all ingredients.
● Boil orzo.
● While orzo boils, microwave vegetables.
● Sauté veal.

shopping list

MEAT
　350g (12oz) veal escalopes
GROCERY
　1 small bottle dry vermouth
　1 small pack orzo
FRUIT AND VEG
　1 small bunch parsley (optional)
　225g (8oz) courgettes
　1 medium tomato
STAPLES
　Lemons
　Garlic
　Flour
　Olive oil
　Fat-free, low-sodium chicken stock
　Salt
　Black peppercorns

veal piccata

2 tablespoons flour
Salt and freshly ground black pepper
350g (12oz) veal escalopes
1 teaspoon olive oil
2 tablespoons fresh lemon juice
2 tablespoons dry vermouth
50ml (2fl oz) fat-free, low-sodium chicken stock
2 tablespoons chopped fresh parsley (optional)

Season flour with salt and pepper to taste. Dip veal in flour and shake off excess. Heat oil in a medium-sized non-stick frying pan on medium-high heat. When oil is very hot, brown veal on both sides, about 1 minute per side. Sprinkle lemon juice on top. Remove veal to a plate and cover with foil to keep warm. Raise heat to high and add vermouth and chicken stock to the pan. Reduce the liquid by half, takes about 3 minutes. Add salt and pepper to taste. Spoon sauce over veal and sprinkle with parsley.
Makes 2 servings.

Per serving: 424 calories, 44.2 grams protein, 12.4 grams carbohydrate, 19.1 grams fat (10.4 saturated),138 milligrams cholesterol, 177 milligrams sodium, 0.6 grams fibre

garlic courgettes and tomato orzo

50g (2oz) orzo (rice-shaped pasta)
225g (8oz) courgettes, cut into 2.5cm (1in) pieces
1 medium tomato, cut into 2.5cm (1in) pieces
2 medium garlic cloves, crushed
2 teaspoons olive oil
Salt and freshly ground black pepper

Bring a large saucepan filled with 3–4 litres (5–7 pints) water to the boil. Add orzo and boil for 8 minutes. Drain. Meanwhile, place courgettes, tomatoes and garlic in a microwave-safe bowl. Cover with clingfilm or a plate and microwave on high for 3 minutes. Stir and microwave on high for 1 minute. Remove and add orzo, olive oil and salt and pepper to taste. Toss well.
Makes 2 servings.

Per serving: 157 calories, 4.5 grams protein, 23.3 grams carbohydrate, 5.1 grams fat (0.7 saturated), 0 milligrams cholesterol, 6 milligrams sodium, 1.2 grams fibre

stir-fry bok choy with shiitake noodles

50g (2oz) wholemeal thin
    spaghetti

2 tablespoons low-sodium soy
    sauce

2 tablespoons dry sherry

2 tablespoons water

4 medium-sized garlic cloves,
    crushed

5cm (2in) piece fresh ginger,
    peeled and chopped
    (2 tablespoons)

2 teaspoons olive oil

110g (4oz) bok choy, sliced

110g (4oz) shiitake mushrooms,
    sliced

4 spring onions, sliced

Salt and freshly ground black
    pepper to taste

Bring a large saucepan filled with water to a boil.
Add the spaghetti and boil for 5 minutes, or
according to the packet's instructions. Do not
overcook. Drain.

Combine the soy sauce, sherry, water, garlic
and ginger in a small bowl. Make sure all
ingredients are prepared and ready for the wok.

Heat the oil until smoking in the same wok or
frying pan used for tuna. Add the spaghetti, bok
choy and mushrooms. Stir-fry for 2 minutes.
Draw to the sides of the wok, leaving a well in
the middle. Add the sauce and toss with the
vegetables for 2 minutes. Add the spring onions
and season with salt and pepper to taste. Toss
well. Spoon onto plates with the tuna.

Makes 2 servings.

One serving: 273 calories, 10g protein,
38g carbohydrate, 6g fat (1g saturated),
0mg cholesterol, 629mg sodium, 6g fibre

countdown

● *Prepare all ingredients.*
● *Boil pasta.*
● *Make tuna in wok and*
remove.
● *Stir-fry bok choy and*
pasta.

shopping list

SEAFOOD
    275g (10oz) fresh tuna steak
GROCERY
    1 packet sesame seeds
        (white, black or
        combination)
    1 packet wholemeal thin
        spaghetti (50g/2oz
        needed)
    1 small bottle dry sherry
    1 small bok choy (110g/4oz
        needed)
    1 packet shiitake mushrooms
        (110g/4oz needed)
FRUIT AND VEG
    1 small bunch spring onions
        (4 needed)
    5cm (2in) piece fresh ginger
STAPLES:
    Garlic
    Olive oil
    Low-sodium soy sauce
    Salt
    Black peppercorns

spicy chicken legs

Aromatic flavours of Chinese 5-spice powder make this dish a winner. It takes a little longer to cook this dish – about 30 minutes – but the flavour is worth it.
● Boneless, skinless chicken legs and thighs are now available. With the skin removed, the fat content is greatly reduced. Their richer-flavoured meat make a nice alternative to boneless, skinless chicken breasts. ● This dish tastes great the second day. Make extra for another quick meal. ● Serve with a simple Chinese side dish or garlic bean sprouts and rice.

helpful hints

● *To save clean-up time, use the same wok or frying pan for the chicken and the rice with bean sprouts.*
● *If Chinese 5-spice powder is unavailable you can make it at home by mixing equal measures of ground cinnamon, cloves, fennel seeds, star anise and peppercorns.*
● *Distilled white vinegar diluted with a little water can be used instead of rice vinegar.*
● *To avoid having to look back at the recipe as you stir-fry, line up the ingredients on a board or plate in order so you know which ingredient to add next.*
● *For crisp, not steamed, stir-fried vegetables, start with a very hot wok or frying pan. Let the vegetables sit for a minute before tossing to allow the wok to regain its heat.*

spicy chicken legs

125ml (4fl oz) fat-free, low-sodium chicken stock
50ml (2fl oz) rice vinegar
1 teaspoon Chinese 5-spice powder
6 large garlic cloves
2 tablespoons low-sodium soy sauce
125ml (4fl oz) water
2 teaspoons sesame oil
275g (10oz) boneless, skinless chicken legs or thighs, visible fat removed
110g (4oz) broccoli florets
225g (8oz) sliced button mushrooms

Combine the chicken stock, vinegar, Chinese 5-spice, whole garlic cloves, soy sauce and water in a small bowl. Make sure all ingredients are prepped and ready for stir-frying. Heat the oil in a wok or frying pan over a high heat until smoking. Brown the chicken on all sides, about 2 minutes. Add the chicken stock mixture and reduce the heat to medium-low. Simmer gently for 15 minutes, turning the chicken several times. The liquid should be just at the bubbling stage. Add the broccoli and mushrooms and continue cooking for 5 minutes. The sauce will boil down to a glaze as the chicken cooks. Remove the garlic cloves. Spoon the completed dish into a bowl and cover with foil to keep warm.

Makes 2 servings.

One serving: 419 calories, 45g protein, 13g carbohydrate, 20g fat (4g saturated), 130mg cholesterol, 897mg sodium, 1g fibre

garlic bean sprouts and rice

75g (3oz) brown rice

Salt and freshly ground black
   pepper to taste

2 teaspoons sesame oil

110g (4oz) fresh bean sprouts

2 medium-sized garlic cloves,
   crushed

Rinse the rice and place in a large saucepan filled with water. Bring to a boil and cook for 30 minutes. Drain and season with salt and pepper to taste.

Again, make sure all ingredients are prepared and ready for stir-frying. Place the wok over a high heat and add the oil. Add the rice, bean sprouts and garlic and sauté for 2–3 minutes. Season with salt and pepper to taste. Place on 2 plates and spoon the stir-fried chicken and vegetables on top.

Makes 2 servings.

One serving: 207 calories, 11g protein,
25g carbohydrate, 9g fat (1g saturated),
0mg cholesterol, 10mg sodium, 1g fibre

countdown

- *Start rice.*
- *Place chicken on to cook.*
- *Complete bean sprouts and rice.*

shopping list

MEAT

   275g (10oz) boneless,
      skinless chicken legs or
      thighs

GROCERY

   1 small packet brown rice

   1 small bottle rice vinegar

   1 small bottle sesame oil

   1 jar Chinese 5-spice powder

FRUIT AND VEG

   1 small packet broccoli florets
      (110g/4oz needed)

   225g (8oz) sliced button
      mushrooms

   1 small container fresh bean
      sprouts

STAPLES:

   Garlic

   Fat-free, low-sodium chicken
      stock

   Low-sodium soy sauce

   Salt

   Black peppercorns

right carbs

Great food that's great for you is the goal of this third phase, which is designed to become your permanent lifestyle. This is an overall balanced approach to eating. The right-carb phase approximates to a 40–30–30 dietary profile. While there are differences of opinion, it is generally agreed that fat levels (primarily mono-unsaturated) should make up to 30 per cent of one's diet. Carbohydrate intake should be restricted to 30 per cent more than protein intake. So if the calories from protein are 30 per cent of one's diet, the correct carbohydrate level should be 40 per cent. Here in these recipes, high-fibre carbohydrates are incorporated into breakfast, lunch and dinner menus.

Following the Right Carbs 14-Day Menu Plans you will consume an average of 130–140 grams of carbohydrates per day. Carbohydrate percentage is based on carbohydrates less fibre consumed, which is the normal way of calculating carbohydrate consumption. The balance of these meals is 38 per cent of calories from carbohydrates, 30 per cent of calories from lean protein, 23 per cent of calories from mono-unsaturated and poly-unsaturated fats and 7 per cent of calories from unsaturated fat.

As with the other sections, I have organised the menus into two meal-at-a-glance charts with some easy and quick meals for mid-week and those that take a little more time for the weekends. They are arranged to give variety throughout the day and over the course of the week. Presentation is as ever important and the appeal of a beautiful plate of food adds to our eating experience. Celebrating events and holidays with friends and cooking for them is a pleasure and almost all the recipes here can be used for special occasions.

Breakfast

Western Omlette, Monte Cristo Sandwich or Mediterranean Platter – these are just some of the savoury breakfasts you can choose from the Right Carbs Menu Plans that follow. Try them all to add variety to your morning repertoire. Your body does need a boost of energy in the morning, especially during the week, to set you up for the day, both mentally and physically, so don't skimp here.

Lunch

Choose from the wide variety to fit every appetite. When you're in a hurry, grab Fish and Cheese on Toast, Chicory and Orange Salad with Swiss Turkey or Waldorf Salad with Roast Beef Sandwich. The quality of the ingredients is important with simply prepared food. When you have more time, enjoy the Blue Cheese and Beef Pasta Salad.

Dinner

Enjoy these meals without worrying about numbers or questioning what you eat. The old saying that you should breakfast like a King, lunch like a Prince and dine like a Pauper is one of the best pieces of nutritional advice ever given. Menus like Whisky-Soused Salmon and Turkey Gratinée will entice you to stay on this low-carbohydrate, balanced style of eating. Roasted Pepper and Olive Snapper certainly makes a delicious and rounded meal fit for a King!

For those days when you are really pressed for time, select Mock Hungarian Goulash or Black Bean Soup with Rice from the Super Speed Suppers section of the book. For weekends when you have more time and want something special, try the Pan-Seared Tuna with Mango Salsa, or Indian-Spiced Chicken from the Weekends section of the book.

right carbs 14-day menu plan (1)

week 1	breakfast	lunch	dinner
sunday	Smoked Salmon Omelettes 165	Waldorf Salad with Roast Beef Sandwich 193	Japanese Beef Sukiyaki 209
monday	Grilled Ham and Cheddar Sandwich 166	Turkey and Asparagus Penne Salad 192	Aromatic Poached Sole 204
tuesday	Spinach and Parmesan Omelette 167	Prawn Caesar Wrap 186	Chicken with Parmesan, and Tomato Sauce 207
wednesday	Ranchero Burrito 174	Turkey-avocado Pitta 189	Cioppino 205
thursday	Western Omelette . . .171	Fresh Salmon Burgers 196	Pork Souvlaki 215
friday	Mediterranean Platter 172	Fish and Cheese on Toast 198	Mediterranean Veal and Olives 212
saturday	Vietnamese Pancakes 175	Caribbean Prawn Salad 190	Country Minestrone with Meatballs 213

week 2	breakfast	lunch	dinner
sunday	French Toast with Ham 176	Ham and Mushroom Pitta Pizza 195	Curried Prawns and Vegetables 221
monday	Shiitake and Swiss Scramble 177	Prawn Caesar Wrap . .186	Chicken Fajitas 223
tuesday	Goat's Cheese and Palm Hearts Omelette 180	Turkey-Avocado Pitta 189	Roast Beef and Shiitake Hash 225
wednesday	Cottage Cheese and Cucumber Sandwich 179	Turkey and Asparagus Penne Salad 192	Cioppino 205
thursday	Warm Turkey Sandwich 182	Waldorf Salad with Roast Beef Sandwich 193	Summer-and-winter Chicken Casserole 227
friday	Egg-in-toast 173	Fish and Cheese on Toast 198	Beef Stir-fry with Oyster Sauce 228
saturday	Frittata Primavera 170	Chicken Sandwich with Sun-dried Tomato Sauce 199	Roasted Pork and Peach Salsa 220

right carbs 14-day menu plan (2)

week 1	breakfast	lunch	dinner
sunday	Ham and Pepper Frittata 169	Mulligatawny Soup 185	Pan-Seared Tuna with Mango Salsa..............264
monday	Smoked Salmon Sandwich...................168	BLT Sandwich on Rye............................188	Chicken Creole..........242
tuesday	Strawberry Splash with Cottage Cheese-Stuffed Chicory 183	Layered Antipasto Salad 187	Mahi Mahi Satay with Thai Peanut Sauce.............202
wednesday	Shiitake Swiss Scramble 177	Blue Cheese and Beef Pasta Salad...........................194	Turkey Gratinée with Basil Linguine....................210
thursday	Western Omelette 171	Chicory and Orange Salad with Swiss Turkey 191	Parmesan Sole...........241
friday	Monte Cristo Sandwich 178	Fish and Cheese on Toast...........................198	Mexican Sopes...........201
saturday	Provençal Omelette 181	Danish Prawn Smorrebrod 197	Indian-Spiced Chicken....................263

week 2	breakfast	lunch	dinner
sunday	Ham and Pepper Frittata 169	Mulligatawny Soup 185	Whisky-Soused Salmon 216
monday	Smoked Salmon Sandwich.....................168	BLT Sandwich on Rye............................188	Roasted Pepper and Olive Snapper 218
tuesday	Strawberry Splash with Cottage Cheese-Stuffed Chicory 183	Layered Antipasto Salad 187	Chicken Creole...........242
wednesday	Shiitake Swiss Scramble 177	Blue Cheese and Beef Pasta Salad........................194	Black Bean Soup with Rice...........................244
thursday	Western Omlette........................171	Chicory and Orange Salad with Swiss Turkey 191	Mock Hungarian Goulash....................245
friday	Monte Cristo Sandwich 178	Fish and Cheese on Toast...........................198	Mexican Sopes 201
saturday	Provençal Omelette 181	Danish Prawn Smorrebrod 197	Pork Chops with Apple Relish........................266

right carbs
breakfasts

smoked salmon omelettes

This is perfect for a weekend breakfast or, served at room temperature, for parties.

smoked salmon omelettes

2 whole eggs

4 egg whites

25g (1oz) snipped fresh dill or 3 tablespoons dried

Salt and freshly ground black pepper to taste

Olive oil spray

110g (4oz) sliced smoked salmon

1 medium tomato, sliced

2 tablespoons reduced-fat soured cream

Several sprigs fresh dill for garnish (optional)

Preheat the grill. Whisk the eggs, egg whites and dill in a medium-sized bowl. Season with salt and pepper to taste. Set a 20.5–23cm (8–9in) non-stick frying pan over a medium-high heat. Spray with olive oil. Add half the egg mixture and swirl in the pan to form a thin layer. Cook for 1 minute and place under the grill for 1 minute, or until the omelette is cooked on top. Remove from the grill. Slide the omelette onto a plate and repeat for the second one. Place the smoked salmon and tomato slices on one half of each omelette, letting some of the salmon overlap the edge. Spoon soured cream over the salmon and add sprigs of dill, again letting them peek out from the omelettes. Fold the omelettes in half once and then in half again to form a triangle. Serve hot or at room temperature. *Makes 2 servings.*

bran cereal

50g (2oz) high-fibre, no-sugar-added bran cereal

225ml (8fl oz) skimmed milk

1 sliced banana

Divide the cereal between 2 bowls and add the milk and banana to each.
Makes 2 servings.

Total breakfast one serving: 428 calories, 33g protein, 61g carbohydrate, 15g fat (4g saturated), 237mg cholesterol, 832mg sodium, 15g fibre

helpful hint

● *If using dried dill, make sure the herb is less than 6 months old. The leaves should be green, not grey.*

countdown

● *Preheat grill.*

● *Make omelettes and fill.*

● *Assemble cereal.*

shopping list

DAIRY

1 small pot reduced-fat soured cream

FISH

110g (4oz) sliced smoked salmon

FRUIT AND VEG

1 medium tomato

1 small bunch fresh dill or 1 jar dried

1 banana

STAPLES

Eggs

Olive oil spray

High-fibre, no-sugar-added bran cereal

Skimmed milk

Salt

Black peppercorns

grilled ham and cheddar sandwich

This is a simple breakfast that can be made in 5 minutes and taken with you for breakfast-on-the-run.

grilled ham and cheddar sandwich

4 slices wholemeal bread

Olive oil spray

225g (8oz) sliced lean ham (about 4 slices)

25g (1oz) grated, reduced-fat mature Cheddar cheese

2 small tomatoes, sliced

Preheat the grill. Line a baking tray with foil. Place the bread on the tray and spray with olive oil. Place under the grill for 1 minute. Turn each slice, top with ham and sprinkle with cheese. Return to the grill for 2 minutes, or until the cheese melts. Serve as an open-faced sandwich with a sliced tomato on the side. Or, if taking it with you, place the tomato slices on one slice and cover with another slice to make a complete sandwich.

Makes 2 servings.

oatmeal

110g (4oz) oatmeal

450ml (16fl oz) water

225ml (8fl oz) skimmed milk

2g (1/16oz) artificial sweetener (optional)

To prepare in the microwave, combine the oatmeal and water in a microwave-safe bowl. Microwave on high for 4 minutes. Stir in the milk and artificial sweetener, divide between 2 bowls and serve warm.

Alternatively, to prepare on the hob, combine the oatmeal and water in a small saucepan over a medium-high heat, and bring to a boil. Reduce the heat to medium and cook for about 5 more minutes, stirring occasionally. Stir in the milk and sweetener, divide between 2 bowls and serve warm.

Makes 2 servings.

Total breakfast one serving: 488 calories, 39g protein, 60g carbohydrate, 14g fat (5g saturated), 52mg cholesterol, 116mg sodium, 10g fibre

helpful hint

● *Any type of whole-grain bread can be used.*

countdown

● *Preheat grill.*
● *Make sandwich.*
● *Assemble cereal.*

shopping list

DAIRY

1 small packet grated, reduced-fat mature Cheddar cheese

DELI

225g (8oz) sliced lean ham

FRUIT AND VEG

2 small tomatoes

STAPLES

Oatmeal

Skimmed milk

Wholemeal bread

Olive oil spray

Artificial sweetener

spinach and parmesan omelette

My husband made this breakfast one very hurried morning before going to work. His comment? 'I can't believe it took me only 15 minutes – start to finish!'

spinach and parmesan omelette

2 whole eggs

4 egg whites

Salt and freshly ground black pepper to taste

2 large handfuls washed, ready-to-eat fresh spinach

2 teaspoons olive oil

2 tablespoons freshly grated Parmesan cheese

Preheat the oven to 200°C/400°F/gas mark 6. Lightly beat the whole eggs and egg whites together in a medium-sized bowl. Season with salt and pepper to taste. Set a medium-sized non-stick ovenproof frying pan over a medium heat. Add the spinach and sauté for 3 minutes, or until wilted. Stir the cooked spinach into the egg mixture. In the same pan, heat the oil over a medium heat. Pour the egg mixture into pan and let set for 1 minute. Sprinkle with Parmesan and place in the oven for 3 minutes, or until eggs are set to desired consistency. Serve immediately.
Makes 2 servings.

bran-yoghurt parfait

275g (10oz) blueberries

2g (1/16oz) artificial sweetener

225g (8oz) light blueberry-flavoured yoghurt

50g (2oz) high-fibre, no-sugar-added bran cereal

Purée blueberries in a food processor or press through a sieve. Stir in the sweetener. Divide half of the yoghurt between 2 bowls or parfait glasses and sprinkle each with bran. Pour some blueberry purée over the bran in each bowl. Spoon the remaining yoghurt over the purée and drizzle with the remaining blueberry purée before serving.
Makes 2 servings.

> Total breakfast one serving: 366 calories, 26g protein, 53g carbohydrate, 14g fat (3g saturated), 220mg cholesterol, 564mg sodium, 20g fibre

helpful hints

- *Buy good-quality Parmesan cheese and grate it yourself or chop it in the food processor. Freeze the extra: you can spoon out what you need and leave the rest frozen.*
- *Washed, ready-to-eat fresh spinach is available in most supermarkets. It makes using fresh spinach a dream.*

countdown

- *Preheat oven to 200°C/400°F/gas mark 6.*
- *Prepare all ingredients.*
- *Make omelette.*
- *Assemble cereal.*

shopping list

DAIRY

1 pot light blueberry-flavoured yoghurt

FRUIT AND VEG

1 bag washed, ready-to-eat fresh spinach

1 small punnet blueberries

STAPLES

Eggs

Olive oil

Parmesan cheese

Artificial sweetener

High-fibre, no-sugar-added bran cereal

Salt

Black peppercorns

smoked salmon sandwich

Buttery, smooth smoked salmon is a special breakfast treat.

smoked salmon sandwich

helpful hint

● *Smoked salmon can be frozen. Scottish, Norwegian or Atlantic salmon can be used.*

countdown

● *Make oatmeal.*
● *Assemble smoked salmon sandwich.*

shopping list

DAIRY
    1 small carton reduced-fat cream cheese
FISH
    175g (6oz) smoked salmon
FRUIT AND VEG
    1 medium tomato
STAPLES
    Rye bread
    Skimmed milk
    Oatmeal
    Artificial sweetener

2 slices rye bread
2 tablespoons reduced-fat cream cheese
175g (6oz) smoked salmon
1 medium tomato, sliced

Toast rye bread and spread with cream cheese. Divide smoked salmon in half and place over cream cheese on each piece of toast. Serve sandwiches with sliced tomato on the side.
Makes 2 servings.

oatmeal

75g (3oz) oatmeal
450ml (16fl oz) water
225ml (8fl oz) skimmed milk
Artificial sweetener equivalent to 2 teaspoons sugar (optional)

To prepare in the microwave, combine oatmeal and water together. Microwave on high for 4 minutes. Stir in milk and sweetener. Alternatively, combine oatmeal and water in a small saucepan. Bring to the boil. Cook for about 5 minutes over medium heat, stirring occasionally. Stir in milk and sweetener.
Makes 2 servings.

Per serving: 416 calories, 28.7 grams protein, 50.7 grams carbohydrate, 11.0 grams fat (4.9 saturated), 39 milligrams cholesterol, 985 milligrams sodium, 5.6 grams fibre

ham and pepper frittata

Plump, juicy frittatas take about 10 minutes to make. They can be made ahead and eaten at room temperature. They differ from omelettes. An omelette is cooked quickly over high heat, making it creamy and runny, while a frittata is cooked slowly over low heat, making it firm and set. A frittata needs to be cooked on both sides. It can be flipped over in the pan, but a much easier way is to place it in the oven or under a grill for half a minute to finish cooking.

ham and pepper frittata

Olive oil spray
225g (8oz) sliced onion
175g (6oz) sliced lean ham, cut into bite-sized pieces
1 medium red pepper, sliced
225ml (8fl oz) egg substitute
Salt and freshly ground black pepper

Pre-heat grill. Heat an ovenproof medium-sized non-stick frying pan on medium-high heat and spray with olive oil spray. Add onion, ham and red pepper. Cook for 2 minutes. Mix egg substitute with salt and pepper to taste. Reduce heat to low and add egg mixture. Cook, without browning the bottom, for 10 minutes. The eggs will be set, but the top a little runny. Place pan under the grill for ½–1 minute until the top is set, but not brown. Remove and cut in half. Slide halves on to 2 plates.
Makes 2 servings.

bran cereal

225ml (8fl oz) skimmed milk
75g (3oz) high-fibre, no-sugar-added bran cereal

Divide ingredients between 2 cereal bowls.
Makes 2 servings.

vegetable juice

350ml (12fl oz) low-sodium, no-sugar-added tomato or V-8 juice

Divide between 2 glasses.
Makes 2 servings.

Per serving: 366 calories, 38.1 grams protein, 50.6 grams carbohydrate, 7.6 grams fat (2.3 saturated), 42 milligrams cholesterol, 1178 milligrams sodium, 14.5 grams fibre

helpful hint

● *Be careful when removing the frying pan from the grill. The handle will be very hot and remain hot for several minutes after it is removed. Place a pot holder or oven glove over the handle for safety.*

countdown

● *Pre-heat the grill.*
● *Make frittata.*
● *While frittata cooks, assemble cereal.*

shopping list

DELI
175g (6oz) sliced lean ham
FRUIT AND VEG
1 medium red pepper
STAPLES
Onion
Egg substitute
Olive oil spray
Skimmed milk
High-fibre, no-sugar-added bran cereal
Low-sodium, no-sugar-added tomato or V-8 juice
Salt
Black peppercorns

frittata primavera

This frittata is as colourful as it is tasty, and makes a welcome vegetarian option. Green basil can be substituted for purple.

helpful hint

● *2 whole eggs and 4 egg whites can be used instead of egg substitute.*

countdown

● *Start frittata.*
● *While frittata cooks, assemble cereal.*

shopping list

DAIRY
  1 small packet grated, reduced-fat mature Cheddar cheese
FRUIT AND VEG
  1 medium-sized yellow courgette
  225g (8oz) whole portobello mushrooms
  1 small bunch asparagus
  1 packet purple basil
STAPLES
  Egg substitute
  Red onion
  Olive oil
  High-fibre, no-sugar-added bran cereal
  Skimmed milk
  Salt
  Black peppercorns

frittata primavera

225ml (8fl oz) egg substitute
50g (2oz) fresh purple basil leaves
Salt and freshly ground black pepper to taste
8 large spears asparagus or 16 thin (50g/2oz)
4 teaspoons olive oil
150g (5oz) yellow courgettes, sliced
110g (4oz) sliced red onion
225g (8oz) whole portobello mushrooms, sliced thinly
25g (1oz) grated, reduced-fat, mature Cheddar cheese

Combine the egg substitute and basil in a medium-sized bowl. Season with salt and pepper to taste. Cut or snap off the 2.5cm (1in) fibrous stem on the asparagus and discard. Slice the remaining asparagus into 2.5cm (1in) pieces. Heat the oil in a medium-sized non-stick frying pan over a medium-high heat and add the courgettes, onion, mushrooms and asparagus. Sauté for 5 minutes. Pour the egg mixture into the pan, and swirl around the vegetables. Sprinkle the frittata with cheese. Cover, reduce the heat to low and cook for 10 minutes more before serving.
Makes 2 servings.

bran cereal

50g (2oz) high-fibre, no-sugar-added bran cereal
225ml (8fl oz) skimmed milk

Divide the cereal and milk between 2 bowls.
Makes 2 servings.

Total breakfast one serving: 359 calories, 25g protein, 45g carbohydrate, 14g fat (3g saturated), 12mg cholesterol, 542mg sodium, 15g fibre

western omelette

Also known as a Denver omelette, this dish was created in kitchen wagons on the cattle trail in the Wild West. Apparently they used plenty of onions to disguise old eggs. This is a modern version that takes about 10 minutes to make.

western omelette

225ml (8fl oz) egg substitute

1/4 teaspoon cayenne pepper

Salt to taste

2 teaspoons olive oil

110g (4oz) diced onion

450g (1lb) green pepper, diced

175g (6oz) roasted red pepper, drained and diced

110g (4oz) sliced lean ham, diced

Preheat the grill. Season the egg substitute with cayenne and salt to taste. Heat the oil in a medium-sized non-stick frying pan over a medium-high heat. Add the onion and green pepper and sauté for 2 minutes. Add the roasted red pepper and ham and sauté for another minute. Add the egg mixture and let set for 2 minutes. Place under the grill for 5 minutes, or until set to the desired consistency. Slide out of the pan and serve.

Makes 2 servings.

oatmeal

110g (4oz) oatmeal

450ml (16fl oz) water

225ml (8fl oz) skimmed milk

2g (1/16oz) artificial sweetener (optional)

To prepare in the microwave, combine the oatmeal and water in a microwave-safe bowl. Microwave on high for 4 minutes. Stir in the milk and sweetener, divide between 2 bowls and serve warm.

Alternatively, to prepare on the hob, combine the oatmeal and water in a small saucepan over a medium-high heat and bring to a boil. Reduce the heat to medium and cook for about 5 more minutes, stirring occasionally. Stir in the milk and sweetener, divide between 2 bowls and serve warm.

Makes 2 servings.

> Total breakfast one serving: 385 calories,
> 31g protein, 54g carbohydrate, 12g fat (4g saturated),
> 93mg cholesterol, 782mg sodium, 16g fibre

helpful hints

- *Use a frying pan with an ovenproof handle.*
- *2 whole eggs and 4 egg whites can be used instead of egg substitute.*

countdown

- *Preheat grill.*
- *Make oatmeal.*
- *Make omelette.*

shopping list

DELI

　110g (4oz) sliced lean ham

GROCERY

　1 jar or tin roasted red pepper (175g/6oz needed)

STAPLES

　Olive oil

　Egg substitute

　Frozen, diced onion

　Frozen, diced green pepper

　Cayenne pepper

　Artificial sweetener

　Oatmeal

　Skimmed milk

　Salt

mediterranean platter

countdown

- Make platter.
- Assemble cereal.

shopping list

DAIRY
    1 pot low-fat ricotta cheese
DELI
    110g (4oz) sliced roasted
        boneless chicken breast
GROCERY
    1 small jar sun-dried tomatoes
FRUIT AND VEG
    half a cucumber
    1 small punnet strawberries
    2 medium oranges
STAPLES
    High-fibre, no-sugar-added
        bran cereal
    Skimmed milk
    Low-carbohydrate wholemeal
        bread

Sun-dried tomatoes, oranges and strawberries bring thoughts of a sunny Mediterranean morning. Better yet, it takes only a few minutes to assemble this breakfast.

mediterranean platter

110g (4oz) low-fat ricotta cheese
35g (1½oz) sun-dried tomatoes, drained and sliced
half a cucumber, peeled and sliced
2 medium oranges, peeled and sliced
110g (4oz) sliced roasted boneless chicken breast
2 slices low-carbohydrate wholemeal bread

Combine the ricotta cheese with the sun-dried tomatoes. Place on 2 plates. Arrange the cucumber, oranges and chicken slices around the ricotta mixture. Toast the bread and serve on the side.
Makes 2 servings.

bran cereal and fresh berries

50g (2oz) high-fibre, no-sugar-added bran cereal
225ml (8fl oz) skimmed milk
2 good handfuls strawberries, sliced

Divide the cereal between 2 bowls and add milk to each. Sprinkle with the strawberries.
Makes 2 servings.

Total breakfast one serving: 428 calories, 40g protein, 69g carbohydrate, 13g fat (5g saturated), 80mg cholesterol, 443mg sodium, 22g fibre

egg-in-toast

We used to call it 'Hole-in-the-Middle'. Some call it 'Egg-in-the-Hole'. Regardless, it's an old American favourite. I remember my father making this for breakfast; my job was to tear the hole out of the bread. Somehow I never got the hole to be the same size as the egg, but it was still very delicious. Whether the egg neatly fits the hole or runs over the bread, this is a quick, easy and fun breakfast.

egg-in-toast

2 slices low-carbohydrate wholemeal bread
Olive oil spray
2 eggs
35g (1½oz) reduced-fat Swiss or Gruyère cheese, sliced
Salt and freshly ground black pepper to taste

Tear a hole in each slice of bread about 5cm (2in) in diameter. Heat a non-stick frying pan over a low heat and spray with olive oil. Add the bread and the cutout pieces to the pan. Cook until golden, about 2 minutes. Turn the bread and cutouts over and break one egg into each hole. Cook for 1 minute, turn over and place the cheese slices over the eggs. Season with salt and pepper to taste. Cover with a lid and cook for 2–3 minutes, or until the eggs have set to the desired consistency.
Makes 2 servings.

bran cereal

50g (2oz) high-fibre, no-sugar-added bran cereal
225ml (8fl oz) skimmed milk

Divide the cereal and milk between 2 bowls.
Makes 2 servings.

grapefruit

1 medium grapefruit, halved

With a serrated knife, cut around the edge of the grapefruit to separate the flesh from the skin. Cut between the segments and serve on 2 plates.
Makes 2 servings.

Total breakfast one serving: 340 calories, 25g protein, 51g carbohydrate, 13g fat (4g saturated), 226mg cholesterol, 414mg sodium, 17g fibre

helpful hints

● *It doesn't matter if the egg spills over onto the bread or pan.*
● *To determine the weight of each slice of cheese, divide the packet weight by the number of slices.*
● *If you like your egg yolk firm, gently flip the bread and egg over before adding the cheese. Place the cheese on the top side.*

countdown

Prepare grapefruit.
Make egg.
Assemble cereal.

shopping list

DAIRY
1 small packet sliced, reduced-fat Swiss or Gruyère cheese (35g/1½oz needed)
FRUIT AND VEG
1 grapefruit
STAPLES
Olive oil spray
Eggs
High-fibre, no-sugar-added bran cereal
Skim milk
Low-carbohydrate wholemeal bread
Salt
Black peppercorns

ranchero burrito

This burrito is quick to make and easy to eat. Black bean pâté, grated Cheddar cheese and smoked turkey breast – all supermarket products designed to make our life easier – make this a 5-minute meal. ● Black bean pâté is usually found in the snack section near the nachos and dips in the supermarket. You can choose hot, medium or mild. Look for one that does not have added sugar.

ranchero burrito

2 x 15cm (6in) wholemeal tortillas
50g (2oz) black bean pâté
110g (4oz) sliced smoked turkey breast
50g (2oz) grated, reduced-fat Cheddar cheese
1 medium tomato, sliced

Warm the tortillas in a microwave oven for 10 seconds, or in a warm oven for 15–20 seconds, to make them easier to roll. Spread the warmed tortillas with the black bean pâté, top with turkey and sprinkle with Cheddar cheese. Roll up and microwave for 45 seconds on high, or until the cheese melts. Or, place in a warm oven for 2 minutes. Cut in half crosswise and serve with tomato slices on the side.
Makes 2 servings.

bran cereal

50g (2oz) high-fibre, no-sugar-added bran cereal
225ml (8fl oz) skimmed milk

Divide the cereal and milk between 2 bowls.
Makes 2 servings.

tomato juice

225ml (8fl oz) low-sodium tomato juice

Divide between 2 glasses.
Makes 2 servings.

Total breakfast one serving: 353 calories, 34g protein, 51g carbohydrate, 9g fat (4g saturated), 52mg cholesterol, 939mg sodium, 14g fibre

vietnamese pancakes

This paper-thin crêpe is topped with mushrooms, onion, smoked bacon joint and bean sprouts. When you are looking for a delicious variation from more traditional omelettes and frittatas, this version will fit the bill. It takes about 10 minutes to make and is worth every minute.

vietnamese pancakes

2 eggs
4 egg whites
2 tablespoons wholemeal flour
2 tablespoons low-sodium soy sauce
4 spring onions, thinly sliced
2 teaspoons rapeseed oil
110g (4oz) lean smoked pork joint, cut into thin strips
225g (8oz) portobello mushrooms, sliced
110g (4oz) yellow onion, diced
110g (4oz) bean sprouts

With a wire whisk, mix the eggs, egg whites, wholemeal flour and soy sauce together in a small bowl until smooth. Add the spring onions and set aside. Heat the oil in 23–25.5cm (9–10in) non-stick frying pan over a medium heat Add the pork, mushrooms, onion and bean sprouts. Sauté until the onion turns golden, about 4 minutes. Remove to a bowl and add half the egg mixture to the hot pan. Swirl the mixture around the pan to form a thin crêpe. Cook for 3 minutes, or until the centre is cooked and the sides of the pancake start to curl up. Slide onto a plate. Repeat with the second half of the mixture. Divide the pork and vegetable mixture between both crêpes and serve.
Makes 2 servings.

bran cereal

50g (2oz) high-fibre, no-sugar-added bran cereal
225ml (8fl oz) skimmed milk

Divide cereal between 2 bowls and add milk to each.
Makes 2 servings.

Total breakfast one serving: 349 calories, 29g protein, 50g carbohydrate, 9g fat (2g saturated), 55mg cholesterol, 851mg sodium, 15g fibre

helpful hints

- If pressed for time, use pre-sliced mushrooms and onion.
- Lean ham can be substituted if smoked bacon joint is unavailable.

countdown

- Prepare ingredients.
- Make pancakes.
- Assemble cereal.

shopping list

MEAT
110g (4oz) lean smoked bacon joint
FRUIT AND VEG
225g (8oz) portobello mushrooms
1 container bean sprouts
1 bunch spring onions (4 needed)
STAPLES
Eggs
Yellow onion
Skimmed milk
Wholemeal flour
High-fibre, no-sugar-added bran cereal
Rapeseed oil
Low-sodium soy sauce

french toast with ham

For a change from scrambled eggs or omelettes, try this delicious French Toast. You can cook it with cheese or meat to vary the flavour, and it takes only minutes to make.

french toast with ham

125ml (4fl oz) egg substitute

Salt and freshly ground black
    pepper to taste

2 slices low-carbohydrate
    wholemeal bread

2 teaspoons olive oil

110g (4oz) sliced lean ham, cubed

Pour the egg substitute into a small bowl and season with salt and pepper to taste. Add the bread and let soak.

Heat the olive oil in a small frying pan over a medium heat. Remove the bread from the egg substitute and add to the pan. Cook for 1 minute, then turn. Add the ham to the cooked sides, cover with a lid and cook for 2 more minutes before serving.

Makes 2 servings.

bran cereal

50g (2oz) high-fibre, no-sugar-
    added bran cereal

225ml (8fl oz) skimmed milk

Divide the cereal and milk between 2 bowls.

Makes 2 servings.

vegetable juice

350ml (12fl oz) low-sodium, no-
    sugar-added tomato juice

Divide between 2 glasses.

Makes 2 servings.

Total breakfast one serving: 340 calories,
28g protein, 49g carbohydrate, 10g fat (2g saturated),
29mg cholesterol, 1019mg sodium, 17g fibre

helpful hint

● 1 egg can be used instead of egg substitute.
● Look for low-sodium tomato juice

countdown

● Pour juice.
● Make French toast.
● Assemble cereal.

shopping list

DELI

1 small packet sliced lean ham
    (110g/4oz needed)

GROCERY

1 bottle low-sodium, no-
    sugar-added tomato juice

STAPLES

Egg substitute

Olive oil

Low-carbohydrate wholemeal
    bread

High-fibre, no-sugar-added
    bran cereal

Skimmed milk

Salt

Black peppercorns

shiitake and swiss scramble

*Shiitake mushrooms and sautéed onions form the base for these scrambled eggs.
Although originally from Japan and Korea, shiitakes are now available in most supermarkets.*
● *If possible, buy ready-diced onion to save preparation time, or keep diced onion in
your freezer.*

shiitake and swiss scramble

2 teaspoons olive oil
110g (4oz) onion, diced
50g (2oz) shiitake mushrooms,
  sliced
2 eggs
4 egg whites
Salt and freshly ground black
  pepper to taste
25g (1oz) grated, reduced-fat
  Swiss or Gruyère cheese
2 slices low-carbohydrate
  wholemeal bread

Heat the oil in a medium-sized non-stick frying
pan over a medium heat. Add the onion and
mushrooms and sauté for 3 minutes. Whisk the
eggs and egg whites together lightly and season
with salt and pepper to taste. Add the eggs to
the pan and scramble with the vegetables, about
1 minute. Sprinkle with the cheese, cover and
allow to sit until the cheese melts, about 30
seconds. Toast the bread and place on 2 plates.
Top each piece of toast with the scrambled eggs
and serve immediately.
Makes 2 servings.

spiced oatmeal

110g (4oz) oatmeal
450ml (16fl oz) water
2g (¹/₁₆oz) artificial sweetener
  (optional)
½ teaspoon ground ginger
225ml (8fl oz) skimmed or semi-
  skimmed milk

To prepare in the microwave, combine the
oatmeal and water in a microwave-safe bowl.
Microwave on high for 4 minutes. Stir in the
sweetener and ginger. Stir in the milk, divide
between 2 bowls and serve warm.

   Alternatively, to prepare on the hob, combine
the oatmeal and water in a small saucepan over a
medium-high heat and bring to a boil. Reduce
the heat to medium and cook for about 5 more
minutes, stirring occasionally. Stir in the
sweetener and ginger. Stir in the milk, divide
between 2 bowls and serve warm.
Makes 2 servings.

Total breakfast one serving: 446 calories,
33g protein, 49g carbohydrate, 17g fat (4g saturated),
223mg cholesterol, 377mg sodium, 7g fibre

helpful hint
● *Any type of mushroom
can be substituted.*

countdown
● *Make oatmeal.*
● *Make eggs.*

shopping list
DAIRY
  *1 small packet grated,
    reduced-fat Swiss or
    Gruyère cheese*
FRUIT AND VEG
  *1 small packet shiitake
    mushrooms (25g/1oz
    needed)*
STAPLES
  Diced onion
  Eggs
  Olive oil
  Oatmeal
  Skimmed milk
  *Low-carbohydrate
    wholemeal bread*
  Ground ginger
  Artificial sweetener
  Salt
  Black peppercorns

monte cristo sandwich

helpful hint

- Buy turkey breast without added sugar. Honey-coated and barbecued turkey should be avoided as the glazes are sugar based.

countdown

- Make sandwich.
- Assemble cereal.

shopping list

DAIRY

1 small packet reduced-fat Swiss or Gruyère cheese (50g/2oz needed)

DELI

1 small packet sliced turkey breast

STAPLES

Egg substitute

Olive oil spray

Wholemeal bread

High-fibre, no-sugar-added bran cereal

Skimmed milk

Salt

Black peppercorns

Here's a quick version of an old American staple made with cheese and turkey, dipped in batter and fried or baked.

monte cristo sandwich

2 slices reduced-fat Swiss or
    Gruyère cheese (50g /2oz)
2 slices turkey breast (25g/1oz)
4 slices wholemeal bread
225ml (8fl oz) egg substitute
Salt and freshly ground black
    pepper to taste
Olive oil spray

Place 1 slice Swiss cheese and 1 slice turkey on 1 slice of bread. Cover with second slice of bread. Repeat with remaining cheese, turkey and bread. Beat egg substitute with salt and pepper to taste. Dip closed sandwiches into egg mixture. Place a large non-stick frying pan over medium heat and spray with olive oil spray. Remove sandwiches from egg mixture and place in frying pan. Brown for 2 minutes and turn. Cover with a lid and cook for2 minutes more. Remove to 2 plates, cut sandwiches in half, and serve.
Makes 2 servings.

bran cereal

225ml (8fl oz) skimmed milk
75g (3oz) high-fibre, no-sugar-
    added bran cereal

Divide ingredients between 2 cereal bowls.
Makes 2 servings.

Per serving: 372 calories, 40.2 grams protein,
52.5 grams carbohydrate, 8.9 grams fat
(3.1 saturated), 27 milligrams cholesterol,
707 milligrams sodium, 19 grams fibre

cottage cheese and cucumber sandwich

This is a quick and simple breakfast to make. Be sure to read the label on the cottage cheese, making sure it is low-fat with no sugar added.

cottage cheese and cucumber sandwich

2 slices rye bread
Olive oil spray
225ml (8fl oz) low-fat cottage cheese
half a cucumber, sliced

Toast the bread. Spray with olive oil. Place the toast on 2 plates, spread each toast with cottage cheese and top with cucumber slices. Serve the remaining cucumber slices on the side.
Makes 2 servings.

yoghurt crunch

225ml (8fl oz) light fruit-flavoured yoghurt
50g (2oz) high-fibre, no-sugar-added bran cereal

Divide the yoghurt between 2 bowls. Sprinkle with the bran cereal and stir together.
Makes 2 servings.

Total breakfast one serving: 285 calories, 24g protein, 51g carbohydrate, 6g fat (2g saturated), 13mg cholesterol, 651mg sodium, 17g fibre

helpful hint

● *Any type of wholemeal bread can be used.*

countdown

● *Make sandwich.*
● *Assemble cereal.*

shopping list

DAIRY
   1 small pot light fruit-flavoured yoghurt
   1 small pot low-fat cottage cheese
FRUIT AND VEG
   half a cucumber
STAPLES
   Olive oil spray
   High-fibre, no-sugar-added bran cereal
   Rye bread

goat's cheese and palm hearts omelette

Palm hearts are the tender heart of the Sabal palm tree. If you can find fresh palm hearts, they're a real treat. Otherwise, they are sold in cans or jars in the supermarket.

goat's cheese and palm hearts omelette

Olive oil spray
350g (12oz) sliced palm hearts
225ml (8fl oz) egg substitute
50g (2oz) herbed goat's cheese, broken into small pieces
Salt and freshly ground black pepper to taste
2 slices wholemeal bread

Set a medium-sized non-stick frying pan over a medium-high heat and spray with olive oil. Add the palm hearts. Combine the egg substitute with the goat's cheese. Pour into the pan, cover with a lid and cook for 3–4 minutes. Sprinkle with salt and pepper to taste. Cut the omelette in half and slide onto 2 plates with a spatula. Serve with toasted wholemeal bread.
Makes 2 servings.

oatmeal

110g (4oz) oatmeal
450ml (16fl oz) water
225ml (8fl oz) skimmed milk
2g (1/16oz) artificial sweetener, (optional)

To prepare in the microwave, combine the oatmeal and water in a microwave-safe bowl. Microwave on high for 4 minutes. Stir in the milk and sweetener, divide between 2 bowls and serve warm.

Alternatively, to prepare on the hob, combine the oatmeal and water in a small saucepan over a medium-high heat and bring to a boil. Reduce the heat to medium and cook for about 5 more minutes, stirring occasionally. Stir in the milk and artificial sweetener, divide between 2 bowls and serve warm.
Makes 2 servings.

Total breakfast one serving: 461 calories, 35g protein, 53g carbohydrate, 15g fat (7g saturated), 24mg cholesterol, 1166mg sodium, 11g fibre

helpful hint

- 2 whole eggs and 4 egg whites can be used instead of egg substitute.
- Any type of goat's cheese can be used.
- Artichoke hearts can be used instead of palm hearts.

countdown

- Make oatmeal.
- Make omelette.

shopping list

DAIRY
1 packet herbed goat's cheese (50g/2oz needed)

GROCERY
1 large tin or jar of palm hearts (350g/12oz needed)

STAPLES
Egg substitute
Olive oil spray
Artificial sweetener
Oatmeal
Skim milk
Wholemeal bread
Salt
Black peppercorns

provençal omelette

The flavours of this omelette remind me of sunny Provence where thyme, parsley, peppers and tomatoes grow abundantly under the hot sun.

provençal omelette

2 slices multi-grain bread
Olive oil spray
½ teaspoon dried thyme
50g (2oz) chopped fresh parsley
115ml (4 fl oz) low-sodium, no-sugar-added tomato sauce
2 whole eggs
4 egg whites
⅛ teaspoon cayenne pepper
Salt and freshly ground black pepper

Toast bread, spray with olive oil spray, and set aside. Mix thyme, parsley and tomato sauce together and set aside. Heat a medium-sized non-stick frying pan over medium-high heat. Place eggs in a bowl and stir in cayenne pepper and salt and pepper to taste. Pour the mixture into the frying pan. Let the eggs set for about 30 seconds. Tip the pan and lightly move the eggs so that they all set. Cook for 1½ minutes or until eggs are set. Cook a few seconds longer for firmer eggs. Spoon tomato sauce on half the omelette and fold the omelette in half. Slide out of the pan by tipping the pan and holding a plate vertically against the side of the pan. Turn the pan and plate to invert the omelette on to the plate. Cut in half and serve on 2 plates with the toast.
Makes 2 servings.

oatmeal

75g (3oz) oatmeal
450ml (16fl oz) water
225ml (8fl oz) skimmed milk
Artificial sweetener equivalent to 2 teaspoons sugar (optional)

To prepare in the microwave, combine oatmeal and water together. Microwave on high for 4 minutes. Stir in milk and sweetener. Alternatively, combine oatmeal and water in a small saucepan. Bring to the boil. Cook about 5 minutes over medium heat, stirring occasionally. Stir in milk and sweetener.
Makes 2 servings.

Per serving: 380 calories, 28.9 grams protein, 50.1 grams carbohydrate, 11.2 grams fat (2.6 saturated), 215 milligrams cholesterol, 373 milligrams sodium, 7.8 grams fibre

helpful hints

● *Dried thyme is called for. If using dried spices, make sure the bottle is less than 6 months old.*

countdown

● *Make oatmeal.*
● *Make omelette.*

shopping list

DELI
110g (4oz) smoked turkey breast
FRUIT AND VEG
110g (4oz) portobello mushrooms
1 medium tomato
STAPLES
Eggs (6 needed)
Olive oil spray
Dried tarragon
Salt
Black peppercorns

warm turkey sandwich

Sliced smoked turkey, tomato and cream cheese on toast make a quick, 10-minute breakfast.

countdown

- Preheat grill.
- Prepare grapefruit.
- Make sandwich.
- Assemble cereal.

shopping list

DAIRY
1 small packet reduced-fat
cream cheese
DELI
110g (4oz) sliced lean smoked
turkey breast
FRUIT AND VEG
1 medium tomato
1 medium grapefruit
STAPLES
Olive oil spray
Low-carbohydrate wholemeal
bread
High-fibre, no-sugar-added
bran cereal
Skimmed milk
Salt
Black peppercorns

warm turkey sandwich

2 slices low-carbohydrate
wholemeal bread
Olive oil spray
2 tablespoons reduced-fat cream
cheese
110g (4oz) sliced lean smoked
turkey breast
1 medium tomato, sliced
Salt and freshly ground black
pepper to taste

Preheat the grill. Spray the bread with olive oil and toast until golden brown. Spread the toast with cream cheese and top with the turkey and tomato slices. Season with salt and pepper to taste. Serve on 2 plates.
Makes 2 servings.

grapefruit

1 medium grapefruit, halved

With a serrated knife, cut around the edge of the grapefruit to separate the flesh from the skin. Cut between the segments and serve on 2 plates.
Makes 2 servings.

bran cereal

50g (2oz) high-fibre, no-sugar-
added bran cereal
225ml (8fl oz) skimmed milk

Divide the cereal between 2 bowls and add milk to each.
Makes 2 servings.

Total breakfast one serving: 338 calories,
29g protein, 53g carbohydrate, 9g fat (3g saturated),
53mg cholesterol, 411mg sodium, 17g fibre

strawberry splash

Sweet strawberries flavour this quick shake that you can make and take on the run.

strawberry splash

225ml (8fl oz) soya milk
275g (10oz) strawberries
1 teaspoon vanilla essence
Artificial sweetener equivalent to
    2 teaspoons sugar

Place soya milk, strawberries, vanilla essence and sweetener in a blender and blend until smooth. Divide between 2 glasses.
Makes 2 servings.

cottage cheese-stuffed chicory

225g (8oz) low-fat cottage cheese
2 tablespoons pecan pieces
2 tablespoons snipped dill or
    ½ teaspoon dried
1 small head chicory

Mix cottage cheese, pecans and dill together. Remove leaves from chicory and fill with cottage cheese mixture. Divide between 2 plates.
Makes 2 servings.

bran cereal

225ml (8fl oz) skimmed milk
75g (3oz) high-fibre, no-sugar-
    added bran cereal

Divide ingredients between 2 cereal bowls.
Makes 2 servings.

Per serving: 387 calories, 24.6 grams protein, 54.8 grams carbohydrate, 13.7 grams fat (2.6 saturated), 12 milligrams cholesterol, 610 milligrams sodium, 16.9 grams fibre

helpful hints

- Frozen or fresh strawberries can be used. Make sure frozen ones are not packed in sugar syrup.
- Use any type of berries.
- The stuffed chicory can be made the night before and wrapped in clingfilm.
- The easiest way to chop dill leaves is to snip them right off the stem with scissors.
- Dried dill can be used.

countdown

- Make shake.
- Assemble stuffed chicory.

shopping list

DAIRY
    1 small carton soya milk
    (225ml/8fl oz needed)
    225g (8oz) low-fat cottage
        cheese
GROCERY
    1 small bottle vanilla essence
    1 small packet pecan pieces
FRUIT AND VEG
    1 punnet strawberries
        (275g/10oz needed)
    1 small bunch fresh dill (or
        dried dill in a jar)
    1 small head chicory
STAPLES
    Skimmed milk
    Artificial sweetener
    High-fibre, no-sugar-added
        bran cereal

right carbs
lunches

mulligatawny soup

Curry powder and ginger give mulligatawny soup a pungent flavour, while chicken and freshly diced crunchy apple provide a contrast in textures.

Authentic curry powder is a blend of freshly ground spices and herbs such as cardamom, chillies, cinnamon, cloves, coriander and cumin and is made fresh every day. Commercial curry powder comes in two forms: standard and Madras, the hotter one.

This soup tastes great the second day. If you have time, make double the recipe and reheat when you want to use it.

mulligatawny soup

2 teaspoons rapeseed oil
225g (8oz) sliced onion
1 medium carrot, sliced
1 celery stalk, sliced
1/2 tablespoon curry powder
1 tablespoon flour
1cm (1/2in) piece fresh ginger, chopped or 1 teaspoon ground ginger
350ml (12fl oz) fat-free, low-sodium chicken stock
225ml (8fl oz) water
115ml (4fl oz) 'light' coconut milk
225g (8oz) roasted boneless, skinless chicken breast pieces
Salt and freshly ground black pepper
1 medium apple, cored and cubed
2 tablespoons chopped fresh coriander (optional)
4 lemon wedges

Heat oil on medium-high heat in a large non-stick saucepan. Add onion, carrot and celery. Sauté for 5 minutes. Add the curry powder, flour and ginger and sauté for about 30 seconds. Stir in chicken stock, water and coconut milk and simmer for 5 minutes. Add chicken and continue to simmer for another 5 minutes. Add salt and pepper to taste. Spoon into 2 bowls. Sprinkle with chopped apple and coriander. Place lemon wedges on side.
Makes 2 servings.

Per serving: 337 calories, 32.5 grams protein, 28.8 grams carbohydrate, 12.5 grams fat (3.5 saturated), 72 milligrams cholesterol, 547 milligrams sodium, 2.7 grams fibre

dessert

2 medium pears

Divide between 2 dessert plates.
Makes 2 servings.

Per serving: 98 calories, 0.7 grams protein, 25.1 grams carbohydrate, 0.7 grams fat (0 saturated), 0 milligrams cholesterol, 1 milligram sodium, 4.1 grams fibre

helpful hints

● Curry powder can be found in the spice section of the supermarket. It loses its freshness after 2–3 months.
● The soup tastes even better after letting it stand. Leave it for about 5–10 minutes and reheat if you have time.

countdown

● Make soup.
● Assemble dessert.

shopping list

DELI
225g (8oz) roasted boneless, skinless chicken breast pieces
GROCERY
1 small jar curry powder
1 tin 'light' coconut milk (115ml/4fl oz needed)
FRUIT AND VEG
1 medium apple
1 small bunch fresh coriander (optional)
1 small piece fresh ginger (or ground ginger)
2 medium pears
STAPLES
Carrot
Celery
Lemon
Onion
Rapeseed oil
Flour
Fat-free, low-sodium chicken stock
Salt
Black peppercorns

prawn caesar wrap

This is one of America's most popular salads, said to have been created in 1924 in Tijuana, Mexico, by a restaurateur named Caesar Cardini. Eighty years on, his combination of garlic, anchovies, lemon juice, croûtons and lettuce is on nearly every restaurant menu in the US.

prawn caesar wrap

8 anchovies, rinsed

2 small garlic cloves, crushed

2 tablespoons freshly squeezed lemon juice

4 teaspoons olive oil, divided

4 teaspoons Worcestershire sauce

225g (8oz) large raw prawns, peeled and deveined

2 x 32cm (12in) wholemeal tortillas

6 large cos lettuce leaves, torn into bite-sized pieces

2 tablespoons freshly grated Parmesan cheese

Freshly ground black pepper to taste

To make the dressing, put the anchovies, garlic, lemon juice, 2 teaspoons of the olive oil and the Worcestershire sauce in a food processor and blend thoroughly, or mix and mash together well by hand. Heat the remaining 2 teaspoons of olive oil in a small non-stick frying pan over a medium-high heat. Add the prawns and sauté for 2 minutes. Remove the pan from the heat, leaving the prawns in the pan to finish cooking.

Wrap the tortillas in kitchen paper and microwave on high for 20 seconds to soften. Remove from the microwave, discard the kitchen paper and place the tortillas on a work surface. Spread the dressing over each tortilla. Place lettuce evenly over the dressing and sprinkle with Parmesan cheese. Cut the prawns in half and place on the lettuce, making sure to add any juices from the pan. Season with black pepper to taste. Fold up the top and bottom edges of the tortilla, then roll up tightly to make a neat parcel. Slice in half and serve.

Makes 2 servings.

> One serving: 333 calories, 33g protein, 18g carbohydrate, 15g fat (3g saturated), 178mg cholesterol, 1076mg sodium, 5g fibre

dessert

225ml (8fl oz) light fruit-flavoured yoghurt

2 medium pears, cored and sliced

Spoon the yoghurt into 2 dessert bowls and top with the pear slices.

Makes 2 servings

> One serving: 148 calories, 5g protein, 34g carbohydrate, 1g fat (0g saturated), 3mg cholesterol, 59mg sodium, 4g fibre

helpful hints

- 1 tablespoon low-sugar (less than 0.5g per 2 tablespoons) Caesar salad dressing can be substituted for this dressing.
- *Buy peeled prawns.*
- *Use any type of lettuce.*
- *Buy good quality Parmesan cheese and grate it yourself. Freeze extra for quick use later – you can spoon out what you need and leave the rest frozen.*

countdown

- *Make dressing.*
- *Make wrap.*
- *Assemble yoghurt and pear.*

shopping list

DAIRY

   1 pot light fruit-flavoured yoghurt

SEAFOOD

   225g (8oz) large raw prawns

GROCERY

   1 small tin anchovies packed in olive oil

   1 packet 30cm (12in) wholemeal tortillas

FRUIT AND VEG

   1 small head cos lettuce

   1 lemon

   2 medium pears

STAPLES

   Garlic

   Olive oil

   Worcestershire sauce

   Parmesan cheese

   Black peppercorns

layered antipasto salad

Prawns, Parmesan curls, tomatoes, roasted red pepper, rocket and lettuce form colourful layers for this antipasto salad that is topped with a flavourful Italian dressing.

layered antipasto salad

2 medium tomatoes

2 tablespoons no-sugar-added oil and vinegar dressing

275g (10oz) washed, ready-to-eat Italian-style salad leaves

2 medium green peppers, cut into rings

450g (16oz) sweet pepper, drained and cut into strips

40g (1¹/₂oz) rocket, torn into large pieces

2 tablespoons Parmesan curls

225g (8oz) peeled, deveined and cooked prawns

225g (8oz) red onion rings

Quarter 1 tomato and place in food processor with oil and vinegar dressing. Process to make a sauce. Place salad leaves in a salad bowl. Cover with a layer of sliced green pepper. Spread the sweet pepper on top of the green pepper and layer the rocket on top. Slice the second tomato and place it over the rocket. Make Parmesan curls by scraping a potato peeler over the cheese. Place prawns and Parmesan curls over rocket. Sprinkle with onion rings and dressing mixture. *Makes 2 servings.*

Per serving: 387 calories, 33.3 grams protein, 31.8 grams carbohydrate, 13.5 grams fat (3.5 saturated), 181 milligrams cholesterol, 466 milligrams sodium, 0.4 grams fibre

dessert

1 grapefruit

Cut grapefruit in half with a serrated knife and cut around edge and between segments. Place each half on a dessert plate and serve. *Makes 2 servings.*

Per serving: 39 calories, 0.8 grams protein, 9.9 grams carbohydrate, 0.1 gram fat (0 saturated), 0 milligrams cholesterol, 0 milligrams sodium, 1.3 grams fibre

helpful hints

● *Buy cooked, peeled prawns from the fish counter or frozen food section. Make sure they are of good quality.*

● *Look for washed, ready-to-eat salad selections with many different-coloured leaves.*

● *Any type of bowl can be used for the salad. A glass one shows off the coloured layers.*

● *Make Parmesan strips by peeling thin strips from the cheese with a potato peeler.*

countdown

● *Prepare ingredients.*
● *Make salad.*

shopping list

SEAFOOD

225g (8oz) peeled, deveined and cooked prawns

GROCERY

1 jar sweet peppers

FRUIT AND VEG

2 medium tomatoes

1 bag washed, ready-to-eat Italian-style salad leaves

2 medium green peppers

1 small bunch rocket

1 grapefruit

STAPLES

Parmesan cheese

No-sugar-added oil and vinegar dressing

Red onion

BLT sandwich on rye

This bacon, rocket and tomato on rye bread is a modern version of the classic American bacon, lettuce and tomato sandwich.

BLT sandwich on rye

225g (8oz) back bacon, cut into 5cm (2in) strips
2 slices rye bread
2 tablespoons reduced-fat mayonnaise
1 tablespoon frozen chopped onion, defrosted
75g (3oz) fresh rocket, torn into bite-sized pieces
1 medium tomato, sliced

Heat a medium-sized non-stick frying pan on medium-high heat and add bacon strips. Sauté for 2–3 minutes. Remove to a plate. Meanwhile, toast bread and mix mayonnaise with onion. Spread toast with mayonnaise mixture. Divide rocket into 2 servings and place on toast. Place tomato slices on the rocket. Top with bacon strips. Serve as open sandwiches.
Makes 2 servings.

> Per serving: 305 calories, 26.6 grams protein, 22.5 grams carbohydrate, 11.9 grams fat (3.2 saturated), 58 milligrams cholesterol, 1321 milligrams sodium, 1.9 grams fibre

dessert

550g (1¼lb) watermelon cubes

Divide between 2 dessert bowls.
Makes 2 servings.

> Per serving: 99 calories, 1.9 grams protein, 22.1 grams carbohydrate, 1.3 grams fat (0.2 saturated), 0 milligrams cholesterol, 6 milligrams sodium, 1.5 grams fibre

helpful hints

- *Any type of salad leaves can be used instead of rocket.*
- *Bacon can be cooked in microwave for 1 minute.*
- *Frozen onion can be defrosted in the microwave for 2 minutes.*
- *Fresh-cut watermelon cubes can be found in the fruit and veg section of some supermarkets.*

countdown

- *Sauté bacon.*
- *Toast bread.*
- *Assemble sandwich.*

shopping list

DELI
  225g (8oz) back bacon
FRUIT AND VEG
  1 container fresh watermelon cubes
  1 bunch rocket
  1 medium tomato
STAPLES
  Rye bread
  Reduced-fat mayonnaise
  Frozen chopped onion

turkey-avocado pitta

Turkey, crunchy alfalfa sprouts and nutty avocado blend together for a fresh taste in this pitta sandwich. It's sometimes hard to find a ripe avocado, but you can ripen one quickly by removing the small stem and storing in a paper bag in a warm spot until soft to the touch.

turkey-avocado pitta

1 wholemeal pitta bread, halved

110g (4oz) sliced smoked turkey breast, cut into 1cm (½in) strips

Half a small ripe avocado, stoned, peeled and sliced

2 handfuls alfalfa sprouts, tops only

1 small tomato, sliced

1 tablespoon no-sugar-added oil and vinegar dressing

Grill or toast the pitta halves for 1 minute, or until the bread is warm. Place the turkey, avocado slices, alfalfa sprouts and tomato slices in the pockets of the pitta bread and spoon dressing over the turkey and vegetables before serving.

Makes 2 servings.

One serving: 339 calories, 25g protein, 29g carbohydrate, 15g fat (3g saturated), 40mg cholesterol, 154mg sodium, 6g fibre

dessert

225ml (8fl oz) light mixed berry-flavoured yoghurt

3 good handfuls fresh raspberries

Place the yoghurt in 2 small dessert dishes and sprinkle with the berries.

Makes 2 servings.

One serving: 81 calories, 5g protein, 16g carbohydrate, 0.5g fat (0g saturated), 3mg cholesterol, 58mg sodium, 3g fibre

helpful hints

- *Any type of sprouts can be used.*
- *Any flavour of light yoghurt can be used.*

countdown

- *Preheat grill.*
- *Peel avocado.*
- *Make sandwich.*
- *Assemble yoghurt.*

shopping list

DAIRY

1 pot light mixed berry-flavoured yoghurt

DELI

110g (4oz) sliced smoked turkey breast

GROCERY

1 small packet wholemeal pitta bread

FRUIT AND VEG

1 small ripe avocado

1 punnet alfalfa sprouts

1 small tomato

1 small punnet fresh raspberries

STAPLES

No-sugar-added oil and vinegar dressing

caribbean prawn salad

Emerald waters and crystal-clear blue skies create the backdrop for this tropical lunch. Prawns, hot pepper sauce and black beans are staples throughout the Caribbean. ● Based on total worldwide consumption, mangoes are second in popularity only to bananas. They can be found in many supermarkets. They can be messy to cube, but I offer an easy method below.

helpful hint

- *Any type of bean, such as haricot or kidney beans can be used.*

countdown

- *Make yoghurt cup.*
- *Make prawn salad.*

shopping list

DAIRY
  1 pot light tropical fruit-
    flavoured yoghurt
SEAFOOD
  225g (8oz) cooked prawns
FRUIT AND VEG
  1 medium-sized green pepper
  1 small tomato
  1 small head lettuce
  1 mango
  2 limes
STAPLES
  Red onion
  Celery
  Mayonnaise made with olive
    or soya bean oil
  1 small tin black beans
    (75g/3oz needed)
  Hot pepper sauce
  Salt
  Black peppercorns

caribbean prawn salad

2 tablespoons mayonnaise made
  with olive or soya bean oil
2 tablespoons warm water
Several drops hot pepper sauce
2 tablespoons freshly squeezed
  lime juice
75g (3oz) tinned black beans,
  rinsed and drained
1 medium-sized green pepper, diced
2 celery stalks, diced
110g (4oz) red onion, diced
1 small tomato, diced
225g (8oz) cooked prawns, cubed
Salt and freshly ground black
  pepper to taste
Several lettuce leaves, washed and
  torn into bite-sized pieces

Combine the mayonnaise, water, hot pepper sauce and lime juice in a medium-sized bowl. Add the black beans, green pepper, celery, onion, tomato and prawns. Toss well. Season with salt and pepper to taste. Place the lettuce leaves on a plate and spoon the prawn salad on top of the lettuce to serve.

Makes 2 servings.

One serving: 346 calories, 31g protein, 27g carbohydrate, 14g fat (2g saturated), 178mg cholesterol, 341mg sodium, 3g fibre

dessert

1 mango
125ml (4fl oz) light tropical fruit-
  flavoured yoghurt

Slice off each side of the mango as close to the stone as possible. Take the mango half in your hand, skin- side down. Score the fruit in a cross-hatch pattern through to the skin. Bend the skin backwards so that the cubes pop up like a porcupine. Slice the cubes off the skin. Score and slice any fruit left on the stone.

   Divide the yoghurt between 2 cups and top with the mango cubes.

Makes 2 servings.

One serving: 117 calories, 5g protein, 26g carbohydrate, 0.3g fat (0g saturated), 3mg cholesterol, 60mg sodium, 1g fibre

chicory and orange salad with swiss turkey

Chicory and orange segments make a colourful and quick salad. To make this ahead, assemble the salad and the Swiss Turkey, but add the dressing and melt the cheese on the sandwiches just before serving.

chicory and orange salad

2 medium heads chicory
2 medium oranges
1 tablespoon pinenuts
2 tablespoons olive oil and vinegar
    dressing

Wipe chicory with damp kitchen paper. Cut 2.5cm (1in) from the base end of the chicory. Slice the chicory crossways and place in a bowl. Peel oranges and break or cut into segments. Add to bowl. Place pinenuts on a small foil-lined baking tray and toast under grill. Sprinkle over salad. Drizzle with dressing. Divide between 2 plates. *Makes 2 servings.*

Per serving: 165 calories, 1.7 grams protein, 18.3 grams carbohydrate, 8.9 grams fat (2.2 saturated), 0 milligrams cholesterol, 93 milligrams sodium, 3.2 grams fibre

swiss turkey

110g (4oz) sliced turkey breast
2 slices multi-grain bread
25g (1oz) sliced reduced-fat Swiss
    or Gruyère cheese
1 medium tomato, sliced

Place turkey on bread and place sliced cheese on top. Place on foil-lined baking tray under a grill for 2 minutes or until cheese melts. Divide between 2 plates and place tomato slices on the side. Serve with chicory salad. *Makes 2 servings.*

Per serving: 193 calories, 26 grams protein, 12.8 grams carbohydrate, 5.1 grams fat (1.9 saturated), 48 milligrams cholesterol, 181 milligrams sodium, 3 grams fibre

dessert

425g (15oz) melon cubes

Divide melon cubes between 2 dessert bowls. *Makes 2 servings.*

Per serving: 86 calories, 2.1 grams protein, 20.1 grams carbohydrate, 0.6 grams fat (0 saturated), 0 milligrams cholesterol, 21 milligrams sodium, 0.8 grams fibre

helpful hints

- *Any type of salad leaf can be used instead of the chicory.*
- *Cubed fresh melon can be found in the fruit and veg section of most supermarkets.*

countdown

- *Pre-heat grill.*
- *Make salad.*
- *Spoon melon into dessert bowls.*
- *Make sandwich.*

shopping list

DAIRY
    1 small packet sliced reduced-fat Swiss or Gruyère cheese (25g/1oz needed)
DELI
    110g (4oz) sliced turkey breast
GROCERY
    1 small packet pinenuts
    Multi-grain bread
FRUIT AND VEG
    2 medium heads chicory
    1 tomato
    2 medium oranges
    425g (15oz) melon cubes
STAPLES
    Olive oil and vinegar dressing

turkey and asparagus penne salad

This turkey, asparagus, tomato and basil penne salad can be assembled in the time it takes to boil water and cook the penne. My first experience with wholemeal pasta was a surprise. It has a nutty flavour, very good texture and can be used like regular pasta.

turkey and asparagus penne salad

50g (2oz) wholemeal penne or
   macaroni
110g (4oz) asparagus
75g (3oz) sliced carrots
1 medium tomato, cut into 2.5cm
   (1in) cubes
110g (4oz) sliced smoked turkey
   breast
25g (1oz) fresh basil, snipped with
   scissors
3 tablespoons no-sugar-added oil
   and vinegar dressing
Salt and freshly ground black
   pepper to taste

Bring a large saucepan filled with water to the boil. Add the pasta and cook for 10 minutes, or according to the packet's instructions. Do not overcook. While the pasta is cooking, cut or snap off the 2.5cm (1in) fibrous stem on the asparagus and discard. Slice the remaining asparagus into 2.5cm (1in) pieces. Add the asparagus and carrots for the last 2 minutes of cooking time. Drain. Place the pasta, asparagus, carrots, tomato, turkey and basil in a bowl. Add the dressing and toss well. Season with salt and pepper if needed and serve warm.
Makes 2 servings.

> One serving: 334 calories, 23g protein,
> 26g carbohydrate, 15g fat (3g saturated),
> 40mg cholesterol, 170mg sodium, 5g fibre

dessert

225ml (8fl oz) light orange-
   flavoured yoghurt
2 medium clementines, peeled
   and segmented

Divide the yoghurt into 2 dessert bowls and top with clementine slices.
Makes 2 servings.

> One serving: 87 calories, 5g protein,
> 18g carbohydrate, 0.2g fat (0g saturated),
> 3mg cholesterol, 59mg sodium, 0g fibre

whisky pork chops p142

frittata primavera p170

waldorf salad and roast beef sandwich

Salad greens with crisp apples and nuts were first served at the Waldorf Astoria Hotel in Manhattan in 1893; since then the Waldorf Salad has been a standard on menus. Add an open-faced roast beef sandwich to the spread and enjoy an all-American lunch.

waldorf salad

1 tablespoon mayonnaise made with olive or soya bean oil

1 tablespoon freshly squeezed lemon juice (about ½ lemon)

Salt and freshly ground black pepper to taste

4 pecan halves, broken into pieces (1 tablespoon)

2 celery stalks, sliced

1 small red apple, cored and cut into 1cm (½ in) cubes

Several cos lettuce leaves, washed and dried

Combine the mayonnaise and lemon juice in a medium-sized bowl. Season with salt and pepper to taste. Toast the pecans under the grill for 1 minute, or until brown, to bring out their flavour (optional). Be careful: they burn easily. Toss the celery, apple and pecans in the mayonnaise mixture. Place the lettuce leaves on 2 plates and spoon the salad onto the leaves to serve.
Makes 2 servings.

One serving: 151 calories, 2g protein, 16g carbohydrate, 10g fat (1g saturated), 3mg cholesterol, 116mg sodium, 4g fibre

roast beef sandwich

2 slices rye bread

1 tablespoon Dijon mustard

110g (4oz) sliced lean roast beef, sliced

1 small tomato, sliced

Spread the bread with mustard. Divide the roast beef between each slice of bread. Top with the tomato slices. Serve any extra tomato slices on the side.
Makes 2 servings.

One serving: 179 calories, 22g protein, 13g carbohydrate, 6g fat (2g saturated), 46mg cholesterol, 337mg sodium, 3g fibre

dessert

225ml (8fl oz) light fruit-flavoured yoghurt

Divide the yoghurt between 2 dessert bowls.
Makes 2 servings.

One serving: 50 calories, 4g protein, 9g carbohydrate, 0g fat (0g saturated), 51mg cholesterol, 511mg sodium, 6g fibre

helpful hints

- *Any type of lettuce can be used.*
- *Toasting pecans can be tricky, as they burn quickly. Watch them carefully.*

countdown

- *Make salad.*
- *Make sandwich.*
- *Assemble yoghurt.*

shopping list

DAIRY
  1 pot light fruit-flavoured yoghurt

DELI
  110g (4oz) sliced lean roast beef

GROCERY
  1 small packet pecan halves (10g/½oz needed)

FRUIT AND VEG
  1 small tomato
  1 small head cos lettuce
  1 lemon
  1 small red apple

STAPLES
  Celery
  Mayonnaise made with olive or soya bean oil
  Dijon mustard
  Rye bread
  Salt
  Black peppercorns

blue cheese and beef pasta salad

Pasta tossed with sweet ripe pears, tangy blue cheese and juicy roast beef makes this colourful and tasty lunch.

blue cheese and beef pasta salad

75g (3oz) wholemeal penne pasta

1 medium pear, cored and sliced into 2.5cm (1in) pieces

110g (4oz) cubed roast beef

250g (9oz) cherry tomatoes

2 tablespoons no-sugar-added oil and vinegar dressing

Salt and freshly ground black pepper

3 tablespoons crumbled blue cheese

Bring a large saucepan filled with water to the boil. Add the pasta and cook for 10 minutes, or according to packet instructions. Do not overcook. Drain into a colander in the sink and run under cold water. Place in a bowl and add pear slices, roast beef and tomatoes. Add dressing and salt and pepper to taste. Toss well. Sprinkle blue cheese on top.

Makes 2 servings.

Per serving: 393 calories, 25.0 grams protein, 37.0 grams carbohydrate, 17.4 grams fat (5.6 saturated), 57 milligrams cholesterol, 318 milligrams sodium, 5.6 grams fibre

dessert

1 small bunch grapes

Divide the grapes between 2 dessert bowls.

Makes 2 servings.

Per serving: 58 calories, 0.6 grams protein, 15.8 grams carbohydrate, 0.3 grams fat (0.1 saturated), 0 milligrams cholesterol, 2 milligrams sodium, 0 grams fibre

helpful hints

- Any short-cut pasta can be used.
- Ask the deli counter to slice the roast beef in one thick slice. It is easier to cut into cubes this way.

countdown

- Boil water.
- While pasta cooks, prepare remaining ingredients.

shopping list

DAIRY

1 packet blue cheese

DELI

110g (4oz) roast beef

GROCERY

1 small packet wholemeal penne pasta or other short-cut pasta (75g/3oz needed)

FRUIT AND VEG

1 medium pear

1 small bunch grapes

1 packet cherry tomatoes

STAPLES

No-sugar-added oil and vinegar dressing

Salt

Black peppercorns

ham and mushroom pitta pizza

This dish is covered with onion, mushrooms, peppers and ham – and it can be made faster than ordering out pizza. ● *A secret to cooking the pizza fast is to preheat the baking tray.*

ham and mushroom pitta pizza

Olive oil spray

1 medium-sized green pepper, sliced

4 slices red onion

2 small portobello mushrooms, sliced

1 wholemeal pitta bread

1 medium tomato sliced

110g (4oz) sliced lean ham, torn into bite-sized pieces

110g (4oz) reduced-fat mozzarella cheese, sliced

Preheat the grill. Line a baking tray with foil and place under the grill. Set a non-stick frying pan over a medium-high heat and spray with olive oil. Add the pepper, onion and mushrooms and sauté for 5 minutes. Slice open the pitta bread so that you have 2 round pizza bases. Remove the baking tray from the grill and place the pitta halves on the foil, cut-side up. Spray the pitta bread with olive oil and place the tomato slices on top. Spoon the pepper mixture over the tomatoes and top with the ham and cheese. Grill for 3 minutes, or until the cheese is bubbly. Serve hot. *Makes 2 servings.*

> One serving: 354 calories, 36g protein, 35g carbohydrate, 8g fat (3g saturated), 35mg cholesterol, 1009mg sodium, 5g fibre

fennel salad

1 small fennel bulb, sliced

1 tablespoon no-sugar-added oil and vinegar dressing

Salt and freshly ground black pepper to taste

Remove the stem and fern-like leaves from the fennel. Wash and reserve the leaves. Thinly slice the fennel. Toss the fennel with the dressing. Snip small pieces from the fennel leaves with scissors (about 4 tablespoons) and sprinkle on top as a garnish. Season with salt and pepper to taste. Serve with the pizza. *Makes 2 servings.*

> One serving: 53 calories, 0g protein, 0g carbohydrate, 4g fat (1g saturated), 0mg cholesterol, 38mg sodium, 0g fibre

dessert

1 medium banana

Slice the banana in half and serve. *Makes 2 servings.*

> One serving: 70 calories, 1g protein, 18g carbohydrate, 0.5g fat (0g saturated), 0mg cholesterol, 1mg sodium, 1g fibre

helpful hint

● *The fennel bulb can be sliced with a mandoline or in a food processor fitted with a thin-slicing blade.*

countdown

● *Preheat grill.*
● *Prepare all ingredients.*
● *Make pizza.*
● *While pizza bakes, make salad.*

shopping list

DAIRY

1 ball reduced-fat mozzarella cheese (110g/4oz needed)

DELI

110g (4oz) lean ham

GROCERY

1 small packet wholemeal pitta bread

FRUIT AND VEG

1 medium-sized green pepper

2 portobello mushrooms (50g/2oz needed)

1 medium tomato

1 small fennel bulb

1 medium banana

STAPLES

Olive oil spray

Red onion

No-sugar-added oil and vinegar dressing

Salt

Black peppercorns

fresh salmon burgers

My sons have given me a strong warning, 'Don't mess with my burgers.' The fact is that this all-American dish is changing. I've recently noticed salmon burgers on several menus and decided to create this quick lunch. The flavourful salmon meat requires very little fish for a rich-tasting burger. ● The salmon can be chopped in a food processor. However, it is very soft and takes only a few minutes to chop by hand if you don't have a food processor.

countdown

- Make salmon burgers.
- Assemble cantaloupe and yoghurt cup.

shopping list

DAIRY
1 pot light fruit-flavoured
  yoghurt
FISH
175g (6oz) salmon fillet
GROCERY
1 small container wholemeal
  bread crumbs
1 tube no-salt-added tomato
  purée
FRUIT AND VEG
1 small bunch spring onions
  (8 needed)
1 small tomato
1 small cantaloupe
STAPLES
Eggs
Multi-grain bread
Mayonnaise made with olive
  or soya bean oil
Salt
Black peppercorns

fresh salmon burgers

175g (6oz) salmon fillet
8 spring onions, sliced
25g (1oz) wholemeal bread
  crumbs
1 tablespoon no-salt-added
  tomato purée
2 egg whites
Salt and freshly ground black
  pepper to taste
2 tablespoons mayonnaise made
  with olive or soya bean oil
2 slices multi-grain bread
1 small tomato, sliced

Remove any fat or dark meat from the salmon. Cut the pink meat into 5cm (2in) cubes and chop in food processor or by hand. Add half the spring onions to the salmon along with the bread crumbs, tomato purée and egg whites. Season with salt and pepper to taste. Form into 2 burgers about 10cm (4in) in diameter and 1cm ($\frac{1}{2}$in) thick. Set a non-stick frying pan over a medium-high heat and brown the burgers on one side, about 1 minute. Reduce the heat to medium and cook for 3 minutes. Turn over, raise the heat to medium-high and cook for another 2 minutes. Meanwhile, mix the mayonnaise and remaining spring onions together in a small bowl. Season with salt and pepper to taste. Toast the bread. To serve, place the salmon burgers on the toasted bread and top with mayonnaise. Serve tomato slices alongside the salmon burger.
Makes 2 servings.

One serving: 350 calories, 31g protein, 19g carbohydrate, 17g fat (3g saturated), 65mg cholesterol, 1341mg sodium, 3g fibre

dessert

225ml (8fl oz) light fruit-flavoured
  yoghurt
1 cantaloupe, cubed

Spoon the yoghurt into 2 dessert bowls and top with the cantaloupe.
Makes 2 servings.

One serving: 127 calories, 6g protein, 27g carbohydrate, 1g fat (0g saturated), 3mg cholesterol, 77mg sodium, 3g fibre

danish prawn smorrebrod

Pretty Danish open sandwiches are attractive and good to eat too.

danish prawn smorrebrod

1 tablespoon mayonnaise

1 tablespoon freshly squeezed
   lemon juice

225g (8oz) peeled, deveined and
   cooked prawns, sliced

Salt and freshly ground black
   pepper

2 slices rye bread

2 red-leaf lettuce leaves

150g (5oz) diced tomato

Mix mayonnaise and lemon juice together. Add prawns and salt and pepper to taste. Toss well. Place rye bread on 2 plates. Place a lettuce leaf on each slice. Spoon prawns on top. Sprinkle diced tomatoes on prawns.

Makes 2 servings.

Per serving: 263 calories, 26.5 grams protein, 18.8 grams carbohydrate, 8.6 grams fat (1.4 saturated), 176 milligrams cholesterol, 423 milligrams sodium, 1.9 grams fibre

scandinavian cucumber salad

Artificial sweetener equivalent to
   1 teaspoon sugar

6 tablespoons hot water

2 tablespoons distilled white
   vinegar

2 tablespoons fresh dill, chopped,
   or 1 teaspoon dried

1 teaspoon freshly ground black
   pepper

1 medium cucumber, peeled and
   thinly sliced

Dissolve the artificial sweetener in hot water. When thoroughly dissolved, add vinegar, dill and black pepper. Mix well. Pour over cucumber and leave to marinate for 10 minutes. Serve with sandwich.

Makes 2 servings.

Per serving: 26 calories, 0.9 grams protein, 6.1 grams carbohydrate, 0.3 grams fat (0 saturated), 0 milligrams cholesterol, 4 milligrams sodium, 0.9 grams fibre

dessert

350g (12oz) blueberries

Divide blueberries between 2 dessert bowls.

Makes 2 servings.

Per serving: 82 calories, 1 gram protein, 20 grams carbohydrate, 0.5 grams fat (0 saturated), 0 milligrams cholesterol, 9 milligrams sodium, 4.4 grams fibre

helpful hints

● *The quickest way to chop fresh dill is to snip the leaves from the stem with scissors.*

● *Any type of leaf lettuce can be used.*

● *Slice cucumber in a food processor fitted with a thin slicing blade. Or thinly slice with a mandoline.*

countdown

● *Make cucumber salad and leave to marinate while preparing sandwich.*

● *Make sandwich.*

shopping list

SEAFOOD

   225g (8oz) peeled, deveined
      and cooked prawns

FRUIT AND VEG

   1 medium cucumber

   1 medium tomato

   1 small head red-leaf lettuce

   1 small bunch fresh dill (or
      dried dill)

   1 small punnet blueberries

STAPLES

   Lemon

   Rye bread

   Mayonnaise

   Artificial sweetener

   Distilled white vinegar

   Salt

   Black peppercorns

fish and cheese on toast

helpful hints

- Any type of firm, non-oily white fish can be used – turbot, halibut or monkfish.
- To determine the weight of each slice of cheese, divide the packet weight by the number of slices.

countdown

- Make tomato tapenade.
- Make fish.

shopping list

DAIRY
  1 pot light vanilla-flavoured yoghurt
  1 small packet sliced, reduced-fat Cheddar cheese (35g/1½oz needed)
FISH
  175g (6oz) fish fillet
GROCERY
  1 small bottle capers
  1 small jar or tin stoned green olives
FRUIT AND VEG
  1 medium tomato
  2 medium oranges
STAPLES
  Garlic
  Red onion
  Olive oil
  Balsamic vinegar
  Wholemeal bread
  Salt
  Black peppercorns

This dish of fresh fish sautéed with onions and served over cheese on toast reminds me of the lunches we have while sitting on the docks and watching the boats come in with their fresh catch. ● A tapenade is a thick paste usually made from capers, olives, oil and vinegar. It is a great hors d'oeuvre or topping, in this case, to dress fresh sliced tomatoes.

fish and cheese on toast

175g (6oz) fish fillet
2 teaspoons olive oil
Salt and freshly ground black pepper to taste
110g (4oz) red onion, diced
2 slices wholemeal bread
2 slices reduced-fat Cheddar cheese (35g/1½oz)

Rinse the fillet and pat dry with kitchen paper. Heat the oil in a small non-stick frying pan over a medium-high heat. Add the fillet and sauté for 5 minutes. Turn and season the cooked side. Add the onion to the pan and sauté for 3 more minutes. Toast the bread on one side, turn, cover with cheese and return to the grill until the cheese melts. Divide the fish in half, place on top of the melted cheese and spoon the onion over the fillet to serve.
Makes 2 servings.

One serving: 249 calories, 26g protein, 13g carbohydrate, 11g fat (4g saturated), 46mg cholesterol, 341mg sodium, 3g fibre

tomato tapenade salad

2 medium-sized garlic cloves, crushed
2 tablespoons drained capers
4 stoned green olives
2 teaspoons balsamic vinegar
1 medium tomato, sliced
Salt and freshly ground black pepper to taste

Place garlic, capers, olives and balsamic vinegar in a food processor and purée. Alternatively, finely chop by hand. Divide the tomato slices between 2 plates. Sprinkle with salt and pepper to taste and spoon the tapenade on top. Serve at room temperature.
Makes 2 servings.

One serving: 27 calories, 1g protein, 4g carbohydrate, 1g fat (0g saturated), 0mg cholesterol, 410mg sodium, 0g fibre

dessert

2 medium-sized oranges
225ml (8fl oz) light vanilla-flavoured yoghurt

Peel and segment the oranges. Divide the yoghurt between 2 dessert bowls and top with the orange segments.

One serving: 174 calories, 6g protein, 39g carbohydrate, 0.5g fat (0g saturated), 3mg cholesterol, 0mg sodium, 6g fibre

chicken sandwich with sun-dried tomato sauce

Sun-dried tomatoes and capers make a great sauce for chicken breasts. The chicken can be sautéed in minutes in garlic and lemon juice, or buy roasted chicken to save time. ● People often ask me what a caper is. Capers are small, unopened flowers from a bush that grows in the Mediterranean region. Capers are picked, dried and pickled in a vinegar brine. There are many types of capers in the supermarket. They vary from the small, nonpareil type from southern France to larger versions. The flavour depends largely on the brining and pickling process. Buy a good-quality, well-known brand for the best results.

chicken sandwich with sun-dried tomato sauce

2 x 75g (3oz) boneless, skinless chicken breasts

2 teaspoons freshly squeezed lemon juice (½ small lemon)

4 medium-sized garlic cloves, crushed

¼ teaspoon freshly ground black pepper

2 slices multi-grain bread

2 tablespoons sun-dried tomatoes, drained and diced

3 tablespoons capers, drained

2 tablespoons mayonnaise made with olive or soya bean oil

Several leaves red-leaf lettuce

Remove any visible fat from the chicken and pound it flat to about 0.5cm (¼ in) with a meat mallet or the bottom of a sturdy frying pan. Combine the lemon juice, garlic and black pepper in a small bowl. Set a medium-sized non-stick frying pan over a medium-high heat. Add the lemon mixture and chicken. Cook for 3 minutes. Turn and cook for 3 more minutes. Toast the bread. Combine the sun-dried tomatoes and capers with the mayonnaise. (Use the same bowl as for the lemon mixture.) Place the bread on 2 plates, cover with lettuce, top with chicken and spread with sauce to serve. Makes 2 servings.

One serving: 327 calories, 32g protein, 16g carbohydrate, 17g fat (2g saturated), 77mg cholesterol, 596mg sodium, 4g fibre

dessert

225ml (8fl oz) light fruit-flavoured yoghurt

2 apples, cored and sliced

Divide the yoghurt between 2 bowls and top with the apple slices.

One serving: 131 calories, 4g protein, 30g carbohydrate, 0.5g fat (0g saturated), 3mg cholesterol, 58mg sodium, 4g fibre

helpful hint

● The sauce can be made several days ahead and refrigerated.

countdown

● Make chicken.
● Assemble dessert.

shopping list

DAIRY

1 pot light fruit-flavoured yoghurt

MEAT

2 x 75g (3oz) boneless, skinless chicken breasts

GROCEERY

1 small jar sun-dried tomatoes in olive oil

1 small jar capers

1 small loaf multi-grain bread

FRUIT AND VEG

1 small head red-leaf lettuce

1 lemon

2 apples

STAPLES

Garlic

Mayonnaise made with olive or soya bean oil

Salt

Black peppercorns

right carbs
dinners

mexican sopes

mexican sopes

2 teaspoons rapeseed oil
110g (4oz) diced red onion
110g (4oz) rinsed and drained tinned black beans
Several drops hot pepper sauce
Salt and freshly ground black pepper
225g (8oz) roasted or rotisserie chicken breast, skin and bones removed
4 x 15cm (6in) corn tortillas
75g (3oz) washed, ready-to-eat, shredded lettuce
25g (1oz) grated reduced-fat Cheddar cheese
225ml (8fl oz) medium-heat no-sugar-added tomato salsa

Heat 1 teaspoon oil in a large non-stick frying pan on medium-high heat. Add half the diced onion and sauté until it starts to shrivel, about 3 minutes. Remove to the bowl of a food processor. Add beans, remaining oil and hot pepper sauce and purée. If you do not have a food processor, mash the beans with a fork and mix with the onion, oil and hot pepper sauce. If the beans are dry, add a few tablespoons of water. Add salt and pepper to taste. Set aside. Shred chicken into bite-sized pieces.

Place the same frying pan over medium-low heat. Add the tortillas and warm for 30 seconds. Turn them over and top each tortilla with the black bean mixture. Sprinkle with the remaining onion. Layer lettuce, cheese and chicken over each one. Cover with a lid for 1 minute. Remove to 2 dinner plates. Serve with the salsa.
Makes 2 servings.

oranges in cherry coulis

2 oranges
275g (10oz) frozen sweet, dark cherries

Peel oranges and slice, reserving the juice. Defrost cherries for 1 minute in a microwave oven. Purée cherries in a food processor, adding juice from peeled oranges, or press cherries through a food mill. Spoon cherry coulis on to 2 dessert plates. Place orange slices on top.
Makes 2 servings.

Per serving: 228 calories, 31.5 grams protein, 4.7 grams carbohydrate, 9.3 grams fat (2.5 saturated), 253 milligrams cholesterol, 215 milligrams sodium, 0 grams fibre

helpful hints

- If 4 tortillas don't fit into your pan, cook in batches.
- If pressed for time, buy a jar of spicy black bean dip instead of making it.

countdown

- Make Oranges in Cherry Coulis and set aside.
- Make black bean spread.
- Shred chicken and prepare ingredients.
- Make sopes.

shopping list

DAIRY
1 packet grated reduced-fat Cheddar cheese
DELI
225g (8oz) roasted or rotisserie chicken breast
GROCERY
1 bag frozen sweet, dark cherries
4 x 15cm (6in) corn tortillas
FRUIT AND VEG
1 bag washed, ready-to-eat shredded lettuce
2 oranges
STAPLES
Rapeseed oil
Red onion
Tinned black beans
Hot pepper sauce
Medium-heat, no-sugar-added tomato salsa
Salt
Black peppercorns

mahi mahi satay with thai peanut sauce

Fresh fish, quickly cooked and served with a spicy, peanut sauce, brings back memories of the enticing aroma of satay (Asian kebabs) cooking on small grills in the street markets of South-east Asia. I've used peanut butter as a base for the spicy peanut sauce to shorten the preparation time.

If using wooden skewers, be sure to soak them in water for about 30 minutes before use. This keeps them from burning under the grill.

The fish only takes 4 minutes to cook. Brown rice takes about 45 minutes to cook. There are several brands of quick-cooking brown rice available. Their cooking time ranges from 10 to 30 minutes. I find the 30-minute rice has more flavour, but any quick-cooking rice will work for this dinner.

mahi mahi satay with thai peanut sauce

1 teaspoon rapeseed oil
1½ tablespoon rice vinegar
1 garlic clove, bruised
Salt and freshly ground black pepper
350g (12oz) mahi mahi
2 x 20cm (8in) wooden or metal skewers
2 tablespoons crunchy peanut butter
1 tablespoon low-sodium soy sauce
Artificial sweetener equivalent to 2 teaspoons sugar
6 drops hot pepper sauce

Pre-heat grill. Mix oil, 1 tablespoon rice vinegar and garlic together. Add salt and pepper to taste. Slice fish into strips about 1cm (½ in) thick and 10cm (4in) long. Place in the marinade and set aside for 10 minutes, turning after 5 minutes to make sure all sides are marinated. Remove from marinade and thread the fish strips on to the skewers. I find that threading in a wave pattern allows more even cooking. Place on a foil-lined baking tray and grill for 2 minutes on each side.

To make the peanut sauce: In a small bowl, mix peanut butter, soy sauce and remaining ½ tablespoon rice vinegar together until blended to a smooth consistency. Add artificial sweetener and hot pepper sauce.

Serve the skewers on a plate with a little of the sauce poured over the fish and the rest on the side for dipping.

Makes 2 servings.

Per serving: 259 calories, 33.8 grams protein, 4.6 grams carbohydrate, 11.6 grams fat (2.1 saturated), 116 milligrams cholesterol, 446 milligrams sodium, 0 grams fibre

helpful hints

● *Any firm fish – monkfish, swordfish or cod – can be used.*

● *Rice vinegar can be bought in the Asian section of the supermarket. Half a tablespoon water mixed with tablespoon distilled white vinegar may be used as a substitute.*

● *An easy way to marinate the fish is to place the marinade and fish in a self-closing plastic bag. You can easily turn the bag halfway through the marinade time to make sure all of the fish is marinated.*

countdown

● *Pre-heat grill.*
● *Marinate fish.*
● *Start rice.*
● *Make sauce for fish.*
● *Grill fish.*
● *Finish rice dish.*

mange tout and rice

50g (2oz) 30-minute quick-
   cooking brown rice
110g (4oz) mange tout, trimmed
2 teaspoons rapeseed oil
Salt and freshly ground black
   pepper

Bring a large saucepan filled with 2–3 litres (4–5 pints) of water to the boil. Add the rice, stir once or twice, and let boil for 25 minutes. Add the mange tout and continue to boil for 2 minutes. Test a grain; rice should be cooked through, but not soft. Drain into a sieve in the sink and return to the pan. Mix in oil and salt and pepper to taste.

Makes 2 servings.

Per serving: 153 calories, 4.3 grams protein,
22.3 grams carbohydrate, 5.5 grams fat
(0.8 saturated), 0 milligrams cholesterol,
3 milligrams sodium, 2.6 grams fibre

dessert

350g (12oz) tinned, drained
   lychees

Divide between 2 dessert bowls.

Makes 2 servings.

Per serving: 126 calories, 2 grams protein, 32 grams
carbohydrate, 0.5 grams fat (0 saturated), 0 milligrams
cholesterol, 2 milligrams sodium, 4 grams fibre

shopping list

FISH
   350g (12oz) mahi mahi
GROCERY
   1 small bottle rice vinegar
   1 small jar crunchy peanut
      butter
   1 small packet 20cm (8in)
      wooden or metal skewers
   1 tin lychees
FRUIT AND VEG
   110g (4oz) mange tout
STAPLES
   Rapeseed oil
   Garlic
   30-minute quick-cooking
      brown rice
   Low-sodium soy sauce
   Artificial sweetener
   Hot pepper sauce
   Salt
   Black peppercorns

aromatic poached sole

The ingredients are folded in a piece of foil. The natural juices are sealed in as the fish steams, and a burst of aroma escapes when you open the foil parcel. You can assemble the parcel about an hour in advance and then place it in the oven when needed. ● There's a large variety of flavoured or infused olive oils available. Using them is an easy way to add flavour to a dish.

helpful hints

- Use snapper or bream instead of sole if you prefer.
- If possible, buy diced sun-dried tomatoes to save the time spent dicing whole ones.
- Olive oil with a small crushed garlic clove works fine as a substitute for garlic-infused oil.
- For optimum flavour, make sure the dried thyme is less than 6 months old.
- Fat-free, low-sodium chicken stock can be used in place of the dry white wine.

countdown

- Preheat grill.
- Make fish.
- While fish cooks, make couscous.

shopping list

FISH
  2 x 150g (5oz) thin fish fillet
GROCERY
  1 jar diced sun-dried tomatoes
  1 small bottle dry white wine
    (or chicken stock)
  1 packet couscous
  1 bottle garlic-infused olive oil
FRUIT AND VEG
  1 small packet sliced
    mushrooms (75g/3oz
    needed)
  225g (8oz) courgettes
  1 small bunch grapes
STAPLES
  Dried thyme
  Foil
  Salt
  Black peppercorns

aromatic poached sole

2 x 150g (5oz) fillets of sole, skinned
2 x 2.5cm (10in) squares foil
Salt and freshly ground black pepper to taste
75g (3oz) sliced mushrooms
75g (3oz) diced and drained sun-dried tomatoes
1/2 teaspoon dried thyme
50ml (2fl oz) dry white wine or fat-free, low-sodium chicken stock

Preheat the grill. Line a baking tray with foil and place under the grill about 12.5cm (5in) from the heat. Centre the fish on the foil squares. Season with salt and pepper. Spread the mushrooms and sun-dried tomatoes over the fish. Sprinkle with the thyme and pour the wine or chicken stock on top. Fold the edges of foil together, sealing tightly to prevent them from leaking. Place the parcels on the baking tray and grill for 15 minutes. Serve the fish in the pouch or remove to plates and spoon the sauce and vegetables on top.
Makes 2 servings.

One serving: 213 calories, 31g protein, 6g carbohydrate, 6g fat (0g saturated), 52mg cholesterol, 169mg sodium, 2g fibre

garlic-courgette couscous

225ml (8fl oz) water
225g (8oz) courgettes, sliced
110g (4oz) couscous
4 teaspoons garlic-infused olive oil
Salt and freshly ground black pepper to taste

Combine the water and courgette in a medium saucepan, and bring to the boil over a high heat. Remove from the heat, add the couscous, cover and set aside for 5 minutes. Add the infused oil and toss with a fork. Season to taste and serve.
Makes 2 servings.

One serving: 263 calories, 8g protein, 38g carbohydrate, 10g fat (1g saturated), 0mg cholesterol, 8mg sodium, 2g fibre

dessert

30 grapes

Divide the grapes between 2 dessert plates.
Makes 2 servings.

One serving: 58 calories, 1g protein, 16g carbohydrate, 0g fat (0g saturated), 0mg cholesterol, 2mg sodium, 0g fibre

cioppino (seafood stew)

Cioppino is a 20-minute, one-pot meal that is great in winter or summer. Italian immigrants are credited with bringing this soup – a hearty combination of seafood and vegetables – to San Francisco.

cioppino

225g (8oz) fresh sea scallops

175g (6oz) fish fillet

3 teaspoons olive oil

Salt and freshly ground black
  pepper to taste

225g (8oz) red onion, sliced

2 medium-sized green peppers,
  sliced

5 medium-sized garlic cloves,
  crushed

110g (4oz) unpeeled red potatoes,
  washed, halved and sliced

450ml (16fl oz) low-sodium, no-
  sugar-added tinned whole
  tomatoes (including juice)

450ml (16fl oz) bottled clam juice

¼ teaspoon red pepper flakes

2 tablespoons balsamic vinegar

25g (1oz) chopped fresh basil

2 slices multi-grain bread

Olive oil spray

Wash the scallops and fish and pat dry with kitchen paper. Cut the fish into 2.5cm (1in) pieces about the same size as the scallops. Heat the olive oil in a medium-sized non-stick frying pan over a high heat. Add the fish and scallops and sauté for 2 minutes. Remove to a large soup bowl and season with salt and pepper to taste. In the same frying pan and sauté the onion, pepper and 4 garlic cloves over a high heat for 3 minutes. Add the potatoes, tomatoes, clam juice and red pepper flakes, breaking up the whole tomatoes with a spoon. Bring to a simmer, cover and simmer for 15 minutes. Add the balsamic vinegar and season with salt and pepper to taste. Spoon the mixture over the fish and sprinkle with the basil.

Spray the bread with olive oil. Cut the remaining garlic clove in half and rub the bread with the cut sides of the garlic. Toast beneath the grill and serve with the cioppino.
Makes 2 servings.

One serving: 502 calories, 46g protein,
50g carbohydrate, 14g fat (2g saturated),
67mg cholesterol, 966mg sodium, 8g fibre

helpful hints

- *Any type of firm, non-oily white fish can be used – turbot, halibut or monkfish.*
- *If clam juice is unavailable, use fish stock instead.*
- *Several drops hot pepper sauce can be substituted for red pepper flakes.*
- *Look for watermelon cut into cubes in the fruit and veg section of the supermarket.*
- *If pressed for time, omit the Watermelon Spritzer and just serve the watermelon cubes.*

countdown

- *Make stew.*
- *While stew simmers, make salad.*
- *Make watermelon spritzer.*

cioppino continued

shopping list

SEAFOOD

   225g (8oz) fresh sea scallops

   175g (6oz) fish fillet

GROCERY

   1 bottle no-sugar-added
     lemon-lime or citrus-
     flavoured sparkling water

   1 small bottle red pepper
     flakes

   1 tin no-sugar-added whole
     tomatoes

   2 bottles clam juice
     (500ml/18fl oz needed)

FRUIT AND VEG

   1 packet cooked beetroots
     (450g/1lb needed)

   2 medium-sized green
     peppers

   110g (4oz) red potatoes

   1 small bunch fresh basil

   1 packet watermelon cubes
     or ¼ whole watermelon
     (275g/10oz needed)

   2 limes

STAPLES

   Red onion

   Garlic

   Olive oil

   Olive oil spray

   Balsamic vinegar

   No-sugar-added oil and
     vinegar dressing

   Multi-grain bread

   Artificial sweetener

   Salt

   Black peppercorns

beetroot and onion salad

450g (1lb) cooked beetroots,
   sliced

110g (4oz) sliced red onion

2 tablespoons no-sugar-added oil
   and vinegar dressing

Salt and freshly ground black
   pepper to taste

Divide the sliced beetroot between 2 plates. Sprinkle with the onion and drizzle with the dressing. Season with salt and pepper to taste and serve with the cioppino.

Makes 2 servings.

One serving: 129 calories, 2g protein, 13g carbohydrate, 9g fat (1g saturated), 0mg cholesterol, 159mg sodium, 0g fibre

watermelon spritzer

450ml (16fl oz) no-sugar-added
   lemon-lime or citrus-flavoured
   sparkling water, chilled

2 tablespoons freshly squeezed
   lime juice

2g (¹⁄₁₆oz) artificial sweetener

275g (10oz) watermelon cubes

Place the sparkling water, lime juice, sweetener and watermelon cubes in a blender. Blend until smooth. Pour into 2 glasses and serve immediately.

Makes 2 servings.

One serving: 53 calories, 1g protein, 13g carbohydrate, 0.6g fat (0g saturated), 0mg cholesterol, 3mg sodium, 1g fibre

chicken with parmesan and tomato sauce

This quick dinner takes only 20 minutes to make. The pasta and broccoli are cooked in the same saucepan to save washing an extra pan.

chicken with parmesan and tomato sauce

Olive oil spray

225g (8oz) boneless, skinless chicken breast, visible fat removed

Salt and freshly ground pepper to taste

125ml (4fl oz) low-sugar, low-fat tomato sauce for pasta

2 tablespoons freshly grated Parmesan cheese

Set a medium-sized non-stick frying pan over a medium-high heat. Spray with olive oil and brown the chicken for 2 minutes on each side. Season each cooked side with salt and pepper to taste. Add the pasta sauce and simmer for 4 minutes. Sprinkle with Parmesan cheese, cover with a lid and set aside for 1 minute. Divide between 2 plates and serve with the pasta and broccoli.

Makes 2 servings.

> One serving: 248 calories, 39g protein, 4g carbohydrate, 9g fat (3g saturated), 100mg cholesterol, 390mg sodium, 1g fibre

pasta and broccoli

50g (2oz) wholemeal spaghetti

110g (4oz) broccoli florets

2 teaspoons olive oil

Salt and freshly ground black pepper to taste

Bring a large pan of water to the boil and add the pasta. Cook for 5 minutes, add the broccoli and continue to cook for 4 minutes. Drain and toss with the olive oil. Season with salt and pepper to taste.

Makes 2 servings.

> One serving: 206 calories, 9g protein, 30g carbohydrate, 6g fat (1g saturated), 0mg cholesterol, 28mg sodium, 6g fibre

helpful hints

● *Buy good quality Parmesan cheese and grate it yourself. Freeze extra for quick use later – simply spoon out what you need and leave the rest frozen.*

● *When draining pasta, leave a little water on the pasta for added sauce.*

● *If pressed for time, omit the poached spiced pears and serve 1 medium pear per person.*

countdown

● *Place water for pasta on the hob to boil.*

● *Make poached spiced pears.*

● *Make pasta and broccoli.*

● *Make chicken.*

shopping list

MEAT
  *225g (8oz) boneless, skinless
    chicken breast*
GROCERY
  1 jar whole cloves
  *1 small bottle low-sugar, low-
    fat, tomato pasta sauce
    (125ml/4fl oz needed)*
  *1 small packet wholemeal
    spaghetti (50g/2oz needed)*
  1 small bag frozen sweetcorn
FRUIT AND VEG
  *1 small packet broccoli florets
    (110g/4oz needed)*
  *1 bag washed, ready-to-eat,
    Italian-style salad leaves*
  1 small bunch fresh mint
  2 ripe pears
  1 lemon
STAPLES
  Olive oil spray
  Olive oil
  *No-sugar-added salad
    dressing*
  Parmesan cheese
  Artificial sweetener
  Salt
  Black peppercorns

chicken with parmesan and tomato sauce continued

italian-style salad

*350g (12oz) washed, ready-to-eat,
  Italian-style salad leaves*
175g (6oz) frozen sweetcorn
*2 tablespoons no-sugar-added
  salad dressing*

Toss the salad and corn with the dressing.
Makes 2 servings.

> One serving: 151 calories, 3g protein,
> 19g carbohydrate, 9g fat (1g saturated),
> 0mg cholesterol, 85mg sodium, 2g fibre

poached spiced pears

450ml (16fl oz) water
2g (¹/₁₆oz) artificial sweetener
8 whole cloves
8 strips lemon peel from 1 lemon
2 ripe pears
2 sprigs fresh mint

Place the water, sweetener, cloves and lemon peel in a medium-sized saucepan. Peel the pears over the pan to catch the juice. Core and slice the pears. Add the pear slices to the saucepan. Bring to a simmer and poach gently for 10 minutes. Remove the pear slices and arrange in a circle on 2 dessert plates. Place a sprig of mint in the centre of each plate.
Makes 2 servings.

> One serving: 98 calories, 1g protein,
> 26g carbohydrate, 1g fat (0g saturated),
> 0mg cholesterol, 1mg sodium, 4g fibre

Smoked Salmon Sandwich   **p168**

Strawberry Splash   p183

japanese beef sukiyaki

This is a fun beef dish that's cooked at the table with an electric frying pan or wok. Alternatively, you can cook the entire meal in the kitchen and bring it to the table. The recipe for beef sukiyaki is for two servings, but can easily be doubled or tripled.

japanese beef sukiyaki

50g (2oz) vermicelli or thin wholemeal spaghetti

50ml (2fl oz) fat-free, low-sodium chicken stock

50ml (2fl oz) low-sodium soy sauce

125ml (4fl oz) dry sherry

2g (1/16oz) artificial sweetener

4 teaspoons sesame oil

225g (8oz) yellow onion, sliced

4 celery stalks, sliced

175g (6oz) beef sirloin, cut into strips about 10cm (4in) long and 2.5cm (1in) wide

110g (4oz) mushrooms, sliced

150g (5oz) washed, ready-to-eat fresh spinach

175g (6oz) sliced water chestnuts drained

8 spring onions, sliced

Freshly ground black pepper to taste

Bring a large saucepan filled with water to a boil. When the water boils, add the noodles and boil for 5 minutes, or according to the packet's instructions. Do not overcook. Drain and divide between 2 plates.

Combine the chicken stock, soy sauce, sherry and sweetener in a small bowl. Make sure all ingredients are prepared and ready for stir-frying. Heat the sesame oil in non-stick frying pan or wok. Add the onion and celery and cook for 3 minutes. Add the beef and cook for 1 minute, tossing constantly. Add half of the sauce and stir. Add the mushrooms and cook for 30 seconds. Add the spinach, water chestnuts and spring onions and cook for 1 minute. Add the remaining sauce and cook for 30 seconds more, continuing to stir. Season with black pepper to taste. Remove immediately from the pan and serve over the noodles. Spoon the sauce on top. Makes 2 servings.

> One serving: 666 calories, 46g protein, 68g carbohydrate, 18g fat (6g saturated), 76mg cholesterol, 1604mg sodium, 14g fibre

fresh peaches in kirsch

2 medium peaches, stoned and sliced

2 tablespoons kirsch

Divide the peach slices between 2 dessert bowls and sprinkle with kirsch.
Makes 2 servings.

> One serving: 69 calories, 1g protein, 10g carbohydrate, 0g fat (0g saturated), 0mg cholesterol, 0mg sodium, 1g fibre

helpful hints

- Any liqueur or brandy can be substituted for the kirsch
- To avoid having to look back at the recipe as you stir-fry, line up the ingredients on a board or plate in order so you know which ingredient to add next.

countdown

- Cook noodles.
- Prepare remaining ingredients.
- Bring to table and cook.

shopping list

MEAT
  175g (6oz) beef sirloin
GROCERY
  1 tin sliced water chestnuts
  1 bottle sesame oil
  1 small packet wholemeal vermicelli or thin spaghetti (50g/2oz needed)
  1 small bottle dry sherry
  1 small bottle kirsch
FRUIT AND VEG
  1 packet sliced mushrooms (110g/4oz needed)
  1 bunch spring onions (8 needed)
  1 bag washed, ready-to-eat fresh spinach (150g/5oz needed)
  2 medium peaches
STAPLES
  Celery
  Yellow onion
  Fat-free, low-sodium chicken stock
  Low-sodium soy sauce
  Artificial sweetener
  Black peppercorns

turkey gratinée with basil linguine

A golden, cheesy crust tops this quick turkey and mushroom sauté. The grilled grated cheese and breadcrumb crust is called a gratin. This meal takes about 10 minutes to complete. Or you can make it ahead and then place it under the grill just before you need it.
The turkey breast escalopes called for in the recipe are cut about 0.5cm (¼in) thick. They only need to be cooked for 1 minute on each side. Watch them carefully. They become dry and tough if overdone.

helpful hints

- Buy good-quality Parmesan cheese and grate it yourself or chop it in the food processor. Freeze extra for quick use. You can spoon out what you need and leave the rest frozen.
- Chicken escalopes can be substituted for turkey.
- Any green herb can be substituted for the basil.
- Fresh pineapple cubes can be found in the fruit and veg section of many supermarkets.

countdown

- Pre-heat grill.
- Make dessert.
- Boil water for pasta.
- Make turkey.
- Make pasta.

turkey gratinée

1 teaspoon olive oil
225g (8oz) turkey breast escalopes (about 0.5cm/¼ inch thick)
Salt and freshly ground black pepper
225g (8oz) frozen chopped onion
2 medium garlic cloves, crushed
225g (8oz) portobello mushrooms, sliced
1 tablespoon flour
115ml (4fl oz) skimmed milk
25g (1oz) plain breadcrumbs
2 tablespoons grated Parmesan cheese

Pre-heat grill. Heat oil in a medium-sized non-stick ovenproof frying pan over medium-high heat. Brown turkey for 1 minute, then turn and brown second side for 1 minute. Remove to a plate and sprinkle with salt and pepper to taste. Add onion, garlic and mushrooms to pan and sauté for 2 minutes. Add flour and continue to sauté for 30 seconds. Add milk and stir for 2 minutes to thicken sauce. Push mushrooms to sides of frying pan and return turkey to the pan. Cover turkey with mushrooms and sprinkle with breadcrumbs and Parmesan cheese. Add salt and pepper to taste. Place under grill for 2 minutes.
Makes 2 servings.

Per serving: 355 calories, 41.3 grams protein, 18.7 grams carbohydrate, 10.2 grams fat (3.5 saturated), 88 milligrams cholesterol, 312 milligrams sodium, 0 grams fibre

basil linguine

110g (4oz) fresh linguine
2 teaspoons olive oil
15g (1oz) chopped fresh basil
Salt and freshly ground black
pepper

Bring a large saucepan filled with 3–4.5 litres (5–8 pints) of water to the boil. When water comes to the boil, add pasta and cook 3 minutes for fresh pasta or 9 minutes for dried. Drain, leaving about 2 tablespoons pasta water with the pasta. Add olive oil to pasta and toss well. Add basil and salt and pepper to taste.
Makes 2 servings.

Per serving: 219 calories, 5.8 grams protein, 35.7 grams carbohydrate, 5.4 grams fat (0.7 saturated), 0 milligrams cholesterol, 1 milligram sodium, 2.1 grams fibre

spiced pineapple

teaspoon ground allspice
Artificial sweetener equivalent to
2 teaspoons sugar
275g (10oz) pineapple cubes

Mix allspice and sweetener together. Place pineapple cubes in a microwave-safe bowl. Sprinkle spice mixture on top and toss to make sure all cubes are coated with the mixture. Place in microwave oven and microwave on high for 1 minute. Remove and divide between 2 dessert bowls.
Makes 2 servings.

Per serving: 77 calories, 0.6 grams protein, 20.2 grams carbohydrate, 0.7 grams fat (0 saturated), 0 milligrams cholesterol, 1 milligrams sodium, 2.4 grams fibre

shopping list

MEAT
  225g (8oz) turkey breast escalopes (about 0.5cm/¼in thick)
GROCERY
  1 small jar ground allspice
  110g (4oz) fresh linguine
  1 small packet plain breadcrumbs
FRUIT AND VEG
  1 small bunch fresh basil
  225g (8oz) sliced portobello mushrooms
  1 container pineapple cubes
STAPLES
  Olive oil
  Garlic
  Frozen chopped onions
  Skimmed milk
  Flour
  Parmesan cheese
  Artificial sweetener
  Salt
  Black peppercorns

mediterranean veal and olives

Olives and pinenuts give this 20-minute veal stew a rich Mediterranean flavour. ● *Warm, bright sunshine, rolling hills touched with varying shades of green from the rows of olive trees, good food, thoughts of Italy and Greece … these memories inspired this quick, veal dinner and accompanying dish of orange-flavoured pearl barley.*

helpful hints

● *Veal stewing meat can be ordered from your butcher, or you can used pork tenderloin instead. Remove as much fat from the meat as possible before you cook it.*

● *Freeze any leftover pinenuts.*

countdown

● *Prepare veal.*

● *While veal cooks, make pearl barley.*

shopping list

MEAT

225g (8oz) veal stewing meat

GROCERY

1 tin low-sodium, no-sugar-added crushed tomatoes (225ml/8fl oz needed)

1 small jar stoned black olives

1 small packet pinenuts

1 small packet quick cook pearl barley

1 small bottle dry white wine

1 small carton orange juice

FRUIT AND VEG

225g (8oz) broccoli florets

1 small bunch fresh basil

STAPLES

Yellow onion

Garlic

Olive oil

Olive oil spray

Fat free, low-sodium chicken stock

Salt

Black peppercorns

mediterranean veal and olives

Olive oil spray

225g (8oz) veal stewing meat, visible fat trimmed and meat cut into 2.5cm (1in) cubes

225g (8oz) diced yellow onion

2 medium-sized garlic cloves, crushed

125ml (4fl oz) dry white wine

225g (8fl oz) low-salt, no-sugar-added tinned crushed tomatoes

225g (8oz) broccoli florets

8 black olives, stoned and halved

2 tablespoons pinenuts

25g (1oz) fresh basil, torn into bite-sized pieces

Salt and freshly ground black pepper to taste

Set a non-stick frying pan over a medium-high heat and spray with olive oil. Brown the veal on all sides for 3 minutes. Remove the veal, add the onion and garlic to the pan and cook for 2 minutes. Add the wine and cook for another minute. Add the tomatoes and broccoli. Reduce the heat to medium-low and return the veal to the pan. Cover and simmer for 15 minutes. Add the olives and pinenuts. Cook for 5 more minutes. Add the basil, season with salt and pepper to taste and serve.

Makes 2 servings.

One serving: 409 calories, 38g protein, 22g carbohydrate, 13g fat (4g saturated), 100mg cholesterol, 497mg sodium, 5g fibre

orange pearl barley

125ml (4fl oz) fat-free, low-sodium chicken stock

110g (4oz) quick cook pearl barley

2 teaspoons olive oil

1 tablespoon orange juice

Salt and freshly ground black pepper to taste

Bring the stock to the boil in a medium saucepan and add the pearl barley. Boil for 10 minutes, uncovered. Drain and add the oil and orange juice. Season with salt and pepper to taste and serve with the veal.

Makes 2 servings.

One serving: 222 calories, 5g protein, 41g carbohydrate, 5g fat (1g saturated), 0mg cholesterol, 142mg sodium, 0g fibre

country minestrone with meatballs

'Minestra' is Italian for soup, and minestrone is a hearty vegetable soup. This meatball minestrone is a complete meal in one pot. The recipe can be doubled easily so, if you have time, make extra to use another time. ● Spices can add exciting flavours with very little effort. Fennel seeds are oval, green-brown seeds that come from the common fennel plant. They have an anise taste and are used in many liqueurs. They can be found in health food shops or the spice section of your supermarket, and they will keep for 6 months. Here, combined with oregano, they give the meatballs a unique flavour. ● Follow this comforting main course with a second helping of soul food – ginger-spiced apple sauce.

country minestrone with herbed meatballs

2 teaspoons fennel seeds

1 teaspoon dried oregano

110g (4oz) lean minced beef sirloin

Salt and freshly ground black pepper to taste

2 teaspoons olive oil

110g (4oz) yellow onion, sliced

2 celery stalks, sliced

4 medium-sized garlic cloves, crushed

225ml (8fl oz) tinned low-sodium, no-sugar-added diced tomatoes

450ml (16fl oz) fat-free, low-sodium chicken stock

450ml (16fl oz) water

50g (2oz) wholemeal spaghetti or linguine, broken into small pieces

275g (10oz) washed, ready-to-eat fresh spinach

110g (4oz) tinned small haricot beans, rinsed and drained

2 tablespoons freshly grated Parmesan cheese

Mix the fennel seeds and oregano into the minced beef. Add a little salt and pepper to taste. Form into meatballs about 4–5cm (1½–2in) in diameter. Heat the oil in a medium-sized non-stick saucepan over a medium-high heat. Brown the meatballs on all sides, about 5 minutes, or until cooked through. Remove to a plate. Add the onion and celery to the saucepan. Sauté for 3 minutes without letting them brown. Add the garlic, tomatoes, chicken stock and water. Bring to a boil. Add the pasta and cook gently for 8–9 minutes, stirring once or twice to make sure the pasta rolls freely in the liquid. Add the spinach and beans to the cooking pasta. Return the meatballs to the soup and cook until heated through, about 2 minutes. Season to taste and serve in 2 large soup bowls with Parmesan cheese sprinkled on top.
Makes 2 servings.

One serving: 510 calories, 45g protein, 62g carbohydrate, 14g fat (5g saturated), 55mg cholesterol, 965mg sodium, 21g fibre

helpful hints

● If you are not serving the soup immediately or are making some to freeze later, cook the pasta in a separate pan of water for 10 minutes. Drain, reserving 3 tablespoons of the cooking liquid. Add ½ teaspoon olive oil to the liquid and toss with the pasta to keep it from sticking. Add the pasta to the soup a few minutes before serving to warm through. The pasta will absorb the soup liquid if left to sit for any length of time.

● Cannellini beans or chickpeas can be substituted for haricot beans.

● Frozen spinach can be used instead of fresh. Defrost and squeeze dry before using.

● Buy good quality Parmesan cheese and grate it yourself. Freeze extra for quick use later – spoon out what you need and leave the rest frozen.

● If pressed for time, omit the Ginger-spiced Apple Sauce and serve 1 medium apple per person.

countdown

● Make minestrone.
● Core, peel and cook apples.
● Assemble salad.
● Complete apple sauce.

shopping list

MEAT

110g (4oz) lean minced beef
sirloin

GROCERY

1 tin low-sodium, no-sugar-
added diced tomatoes
(225ml/8fl oz needed)

1 small tin haricot beans
(110g/4oz needed)

1 jar fennel seeds

1 packet wholemeal spaghetti
or linguine (50g/2oz needed)

FRUIT AND VEG

1 bag washed, ready-to-eat
fresh spinach (275g/10oz
needed)

1 bag washed, ready-to-eat,
Italian-style salad leaves

2.5cm (1in) piece fresh ginger

2 Granny Smith apples

1 lemon

STAPLES

Celery

Yellow onion

Garlic

Parmesan cheese

Olive oil

No-sugar-added oil and
vinegar dressing

Dried oregano

Fat-free, low-salt chicken
stock

Ground cinnamon

Artificial sweetener

Salt

Black peppercorns

country minestrone with meatballs continued

italian salad

150g (5oz) washed, ready-to-eat,
Italian-style salad leaves

2 tablespoons no-sugar-added oil
and vinegar dressing

Toss the salad with the dressing and serve.
Makes 2 servings.

One serving: 79 calories, 0g protein,
1g carbohydrate, 8g fat (1g saturated),
0mg cholesterol, 78mg sodium, 0g fibre

ginger-spiced apple sauce

2 Granny Smith apples, cored and
cut into eighths

125ml (4fl oz) water

2 tablespoons freshly squeezed
lemon juice (1 lemon)

2g (1/16oz) artificial sweetener

2 tablespoons grated fresh ginger

1/2 teaspoon ground cinnamon

Place the apples and water in a medium
saucepan. Cover with a lid and bring to a boil.
Cook for 10 minutes. Alternatively, place the
apples and water in a microwave-safe bowl.
Cover and microwave on high for 5 minutes. Let
stand for 2 to 3 minutes.

Place the cooked apples and water in the bowl
of a food processor and add the lemon juice and
sweetener. Grate the ginger over the bowl,
making sure to catch any ginger juice. Process
until thoroughly mixed. Spoon into 2 dessert
bowls. Sprinkle the apple sauce with a little
cinnamon and serve.
Makes 2 servings.

One serving: 90 calories, 0.5g protein,
24g carbohydrate, 0.5g fat (0g saturated),
0mg cholesterol, 1mg sodium, 4g fibre

pork souvlaki

Barbecued, skewered meats called souvlaki are sold as a quick meal on many street corners in Athens. A simple Greek marinade of lemon juice, olive oil, oregano and garlic flavours the meat. ● *Bulghur is wheat kernels that have been steamed, dried and crushed. It has a chewy texture and tastes delicious in salads.*

pork souvlaki

50ml (2fl oz) freshly squeezed lemon juice (2 lemons)

2 teaspoons olive oil

2 teaspoons dried oregano

2 medium-sized garlic cloves, crushed

225g (8oz) pork tenderloin, visible fat removed and meat cut into 4cm (1½in) cubes

2 small green peppers, cut into 5cm (2in) square pieces

half a small yellow onion, cut into pieces 1cm (½in) wide and 5cm (2in) long

2 kebab skewers

Preheat the grill. Combine the lemon juice, oil, oregano and garlic in a medium-sized bowl or large freezer bag. Add the pork and marinate for 15 minutes. Remove the pork from the marinade and thread onto skewers, alternating with the green pepper and onion pieces. Line a baking tray with foil and place the souvlaki on the tray. Place beneath the pre-heated grill and grill for 5 minutes. Turn and cook for 5 more minutes. Serve over the bulghur wheat.
Makes 2 servings.

One serving: 299 calories, 36g protein, 16g carbohydrate, 10g fat (3g saturated), 106mg cholesterol, 82mg sodium, 1g fibre

bulghur wheat salad

225ml (8fl oz) fat-free, low-sodium chicken stock

75g (3oz) coarse bulghur or cracked wheat

Salt and freshly ground black pepper to taste

50g (2oz) raisins

25g (1oz) pine nuts

2 teaspoons olive oil

Pour the stock into a small saucepan and bring to the boil over a high heat. Add the bulghur wheat and a pinch of salt and pepper. Lower the heat, stir and cover with a lid. Gently simmer for 10 minutes, or until the liquid is absorbed. Stir the raisins, pine nuts and olive oil into the cooked bulghur. Season with additional salt and pepper to taste.
Makes 2 servings.

One serving: 245 calories, 5g protein, 32g carbohydrate, 5g fat (1g saturated), 0mg cholesterol, 553mg sodium, 4g fibre

dessert

8 medium-sized fresh apricots

Divide between 2 plates.
Makes 2 servings.

One serving: 67 calories, 2g protein, 16g carbohydrate, 0.5g fat (0g saturated), 0mg cholesterol, 1mg sodium, 3g fibre

helpful hints

● *If using wooden skewers, soak in water before using.*

● *To make marinating the pork easier, place it in self-seal freezer bags. Flip the bag over to turn the meat in the marinade – and there's no bowl to wash.*

countdown

● *Preheat grill.*
● *Marinate pork.*
● *Make salad.*
● *Cook souvlaki.*

shopping list

MEAT

   225g (8oz) pork tenderloin

GROCERY

   1 packet bulghur or cracked wheat

   1 small packet pine nuts

   1 small packet raisins

FRUIT AND VEG

   2 small green peppers

   2 lemons

   8 medium-sized fresh apricots

STAPLES

   Yellow onion

   Garlic

   Olive oil

   Dried oregano

   Fat free, low-salt chicken stock

   Salt

   Black peppercorns

whisky-soused salmon

Salmon, potatoes and whisky combine to star in this quick dinner. Salmon can be bought as thick steaks with the bone in or as thin fillets.

whisky-soused salmon

2 x 175g (6oz) salmon steaks
450ml (16fl oz) water
Pinch salt
50ml (2 fl oz) reduced-fat mayonnaise
1 tablespoon fresh lemon juice
1 tablespoon whisky
Several sprigs of watercress

Rinse salmon. Bring water to the boil and add salt. Place salmon in water. Liquid should completely cover salmon. Add more water, if needed. Bring to a simmer and gently cook for 5 minutes. Salmon will be opaque. Remove to individual plates. Whisk mayonnaise, lemon juice and whisky together in a small bowl and spoon over salmon. Place several sprigs of watercress on the side.
Makes 2 servings.

Per serving: 286 calories, 38.6 grams protein, 0.8 grams carbohydrate, 9.8 grams fat (2.3 saturated), 111 milligrams cholesterol, 114 milligrams sodium, 0 grams fibre

helpful hints

● *The quickest way to wash watercress is to place it leaves first into a bowl of water. Leave for a minute, then lift out and shake dry.*
● *A quick way to chop chives is to cut them with scissors.*

countdown

● *Make dessert*
● *Boil potatoes.*
● *Make salmon sauce.*
● *Poach salmon.*
● *Add broccoli and finish potatoes.*

broccoli and potatoes

*225g (8oz) new potatoes, washed
   and cut into 3.5cm (1¹/₂in)
   pieces*
110g (4oz) broccoli florets
2 teaspoons olive oil
*Salt and freshly ground black
   pepper*
2 tablespoons snipped chives

Place potatoes in a large saucepan and cover
with cold water. Cover with a lid and bring to the
boil. Lower heat to medium and simmer for 5
minutes. Add the broccoli florets and continue
to cook, covered, for 5 minutes. Drain, remove
to a bowl, and toss with olive oil and salt and
pepper to taste. Sprinkle with chives. Toss well.
Makes 2 servings.

> Per serving: 159 calories, 5.1 grams protein,
> 25.2 grams carbohydrate, 5.1 grams fat
> (0.6 saturated), 0 milligrams cholesterol, 27 milligrams
> sodium, 3.0 grams fibre

deep dish blueberry cream

1 tablespoon cornflour
*Artificial sweetener equivalent to
   2 teaspoons sugar*
350g (12oz) blueberries
225ml (8fl oz) water
*225ml (8fl oz) non-fat vanilla
   yoghurt*

In a small cup, mix cornflour and sugar. Stir this
mixture into water placed in a medium-sized
saucepan. Bring to the boil over high heat and
allow to thicken. Add 50g (2oz) blueberries and
boil for 3 minutes. Remove from heat. Divide
yoghurt between 2 ramekins. Spoon the
remaining berries on top. Spoon sauce over
berries. Refrigerate until needed.
Makes 2 servings.

> Per serving: 192 calories, 6.5 grams protein,
> 41.6 grams carbohydrate, 0.6 grams fat (0 saturated),
> 3 milligrams cholesterol, 104 milligrams sodium,
> 4.4 grams fibre

shopping list

DAIRY
   1 pot non-fat vanilla yoghurt
SEAFOOD
   2 x 175g (6oz) salmon steaks
GROCERY
   1 small bottle whisky
FRUIT AND VEG
   225g (8oz) new potatoes
   1 small packet broccoli florets
   1 small bunch fresh chives
   1 small bunch watercress
   1 small punnet blueberries
STAPLES
   Olive oil
   Reduced-fat mayonnaise
   Lemon
   Cornflour
   Artificial sweetener
   Salt
   Black peppercorns

roasted pepper and olive snapper

helpful hints

- *Any type of olive can be used.*
- *Any type of fish fillet can be used. Allow 10 minutes cooking time for each 2.5cm (1in) of thickness.*

countdown

- *Make eggs.*
- *Arrange salad on 2 plates.*

Fresh snapper, roasted red peppers and Greek olives are grilled for only 8 minutes for this simple Greek meal. This quick meal was inspired by a trip to Greece. We drove to Delphi along a road bordered by an endless sea of olive trees. These amazing groves contained over a million trees. The view over this olive carpet leading to the blue sea was spectacular. Brown rice takes about 45 minutes to cook. There are several brands of quick-cooking brown rice available. Their cooking time ranges from 10 to 30 minutes. I find the 30-minute rice has more flavour, but any quick-cooking rice will work for this dinner.

roasted pepper and olive snapper

2 x 175g (6oz) snapper fillets
1 tablespoon olive oil
Salt and freshly ground black pepper
350g (12oz) sliced sweet pepper, drained
8 stoned black olives, cut in half

Pre-heat grill. Wash fish fillets and pat dry with kitchen paper. Place in a small, shallow ovenproof dish. Drizzle olive oil on top. Sprinkle with salt and pepper to taste. Place pimiento slices and olives around fish. Grill for 8 minutes. If fillet is 2.5cm (1in) thick, grill for 10 minutes. Serve fish on 2 plates and spoon roasted peppers and olives on top.
Makes 2 servings.

Per serving: 296 calories, 33.6 grams protein, 15.2 grams carbohydrate, 11.5 grams fat (1.5 saturated), 57 milligrams cholesterol, 694 milligrams sodium, 3 grams fibre

lemon-braised celery hearts and rice

225ml (8fl oz) fat-free, low-sodium chicken stock

225ml (8fl oz) water

6 medium celery stalks, tender lower sections only, cut into 5cm (2in) pieces

50g (2oz) 30-minute quick-cooking brown rice

1 tablespoon freshly squeezed lemon juice

2 teaspoons olive oil

40g (1¹/₂oz) raisins

Salt and freshly ground black pepper

Pour chicken stock and water into a saucepan and bring to the boil on high heat. Add celery and rice and reduce heat to medium. Cover with a lid and simmer for 30 minutes until stalks are tender but still firm. Drain, reserving 3 tablespoons liquid. Remove to a shallow bowl. Mix lemon juice, olive oil and cooking liquid together and add raisins, salt and pepper to taste. Pour over rice and celery.

Makes 2 servings.

Per serving: 184 calories, 3.4 grams protein, 33.1 grams carbohydrate, 5.5 grams fat (0.8 saturated), 0 milligrams cholesterol, 54 milligrams sodium, 1 gram fibre

peach crumble

3 medium peaches, stones removed and sliced

2 tablespoons flour

Artificial sweetener equivalent to 2 teaspoons sugar

1 tablespoon butter

Place peach slices in an oven-to-table bowl that can also be used in a microwave oven. Microwave fruit on high for 2 minutes. Mix flour and sweetener together. Cut in butter, and rub with fingertips to make a crumbly mixture. Spoon over fruit and place under grill for 5 minutes, or until topping is golden.

Makes 2 servings.

Per serving: 138 calories, 1.8 grams protein, 21.6 grams carbohydrate, 5.7 grams fat (3.5 saturated), 16 milligrams cholesterol, 58 milligrams sodium, 0.8 grams fibre

shopping list

FISH

    2 x 175g (6oz) snapper fillets

GROCERY

    1 jar sweet peppers

    1 container stoned black olives (8 olives needed)

    1 small packet raisins

FRUIT AND VEG

    1 bunch celery hearts

    3 medium peaches

STAPLES

    Olive oil

    Butter

    Flour

    30-minute quick-cooking brown rice

    Fat-free, low-sodium chicken stock

    Artificial sweetener

    Lemon

    Salt

    Black peppercorns

roasted pork and peach salsa

For best results, the peaches should be ripe. Look for tree-ripened peaches, which have more flavour. ● *Both the pork and pasta salad can be served warm or at room temperature.*

roasted pork and peach salsa

helpful hints

- *If peaches are not available, use fresh pear or papaya.*
- *Shop-bought salsa can be used instead of fresh peach salsa. Make sure there is no sugar added.*

countdown

- *Preheat oven to 200°C/400°F/gas mark 6.*
- *Start pork.*
- *Start pasta.*
- *Make salsa.*
- *Finish pasta.*

shopping list

MEAT
225g (8oz) pork tenderloin
GROCERY
1 packet wholemeal fusilli or macaroni pasta (50g/2oz needed)
FRUIT AND VEG
225g (8oz) courgettes
2 jalapeño peppers
1 small bunch fresh coriander
2 ripe peaches
1 lime
1 cantaloupe
STAPLES
Carrots
Olive oil
Olive oil spray
Dried oregano
Ground cumin
Artificial sweetener
Salt
Black peppercorns

225g (8oz) pork tenderloin
Olive oil spray
½ teaspoon dried oregano
½ teaspoon ground cumin
2 ripe peaches, washed, halved and stoned
2 teaspoons freshly squeezed lime juice
2g (1/16oz) artificial sweetener
2 tablespoons chopped fresh coriander leaves
2 jalapeño peppers, deseeded and chopped (2 tablespoons)
Salt and freshly ground black pepper to taste

Preheat the oven to 200°C/400°F/gas mark 6. Line a baking tray with foil. Remove any visible fat from the pork, place on the foil and spray both sides with olive oil. Sprinkle the pork with the oregano and cumin. Place in the oven and roast for 25 minutes.

While the pork roasts, dice the peaches. Combine the lime juice and sweetener in a small bowl. Add the peaches, coriander and jalapeños. Toss well and season with salt and pepper to taste.

When the pork is cooked, slice and serve immediately, or let cool to room temperature and then slice. Serve with the salsa on the side.
Makes 2 servings.

> One serving: 278 calories, 35g protein, 19g carbohydrate, 8g fat (3g saturated), 106mg cholesterol, 83mg sodium, 1g fibre

pasta salad

50g (2oz) wholemeal fusilli or macaroni pasta
225g (8oz) sliced carrots
275g (10oz) sliced courgettes
4 teaspoons olive oil
Salt and freshly ground black pepper to taste

Fill a large saucepan with water and bring to the boil. Add the pasta and boil for 7 minutes. Add the carrots and courgettes. Continue to boil for 2 minutes, or until the pasta is cooked through but firm. Drain the pasta and vegetables and toss with the olive oil. Season with salt and pepper to taste. Serve with the pork.
Makes 2 servings.

> One serving: 285 calories, 9g protein, 40g carbohydrate, 10g fat (2g saturated), 0mg cholesterol, 51mg sodium, 7g fibre

dessert

1 cantaloupe, cubed

Divide the cantaloupe between 2 dessert bowls.
Makes 2 servings.

> One serving: 77 calories, 2g protein, 18g carbohydrate, 1g fat (0g saturated), 0mg cholesterol, 20mg sodium, 2g fibre

curried prawns and vegetables

This meal takes a little more time, about 30 minutes, but is very much worth the effort. Juicy prawns cooked in a light curry sauce produce a flavour-packed, ethnic meal – try it when you want something with a zing. ● *Authentic curries are made with a blend of about 15 spices. I have used shop-bought curry powder to shorten the preparation time for this meal. This type of powder loses its flavour quickly and should be not used if more than 3–4 months old.*

curried prawns and vegetables

1 tablespoon olive oil

2 medium-sized garlic cloves, crushed

2.5cm (1in) piece fresh ginger, chopped (2 tablespoons)

2 tablespoons wholemeal flour

2 teaspoons ground cumin

1½ tablespoons curry powder

225ml (8fl oz) fat-free, low-sodium chicken stock

225g (8oz) broccoli florets

110g (4oz) sliced red onion

50g (2oz) raisins

350g (12oz) large raw prawns, peeled and deveined

Salt and freshly ground black pepper to taste

2 tablespoons crème fraîche

Heat the olive oil in a non-stick frying pan over a medium heat. Add the garlic, ginger, wholemeal flour, cumin and curry, stirring to blend well. Add the chicken stock. Cook until the sauce begins to thicken, about 1 minute. Add the broccoli florets, onion and raisins. Cover and simmer for 5 minutes. Add the raw prawns and cook uncovered for 2 minutes, or until the prawns are cooked. Season with salt and pepper to taste. Remove from the heat and blend in the crème fraîche. Divide between 2 plates and serve. *Makes 2 servings.*

One serving: 451 calories, 42g protein, 36g carbohydrate, 17g fat (5g saturated), 281mg cholesterol, 564mg sodium, 1g fibre

helpful hints

● *Buy peeled raw prawns – it is well worth the time otherwise spent shelling them yourself.*

● *If only cooked prawns are available, add them to at the end of the cooking time, just long enough to heat them through.*

● *To chop fresh ginger quickly, cut it into small cubes and press through a garlic press with large holes. If using a press with small holes, just catch the juice that is squeezed out; it will give enough flavour for the recipe.*

● *Lentil salad can be made a day ahead and served warm or at room temperature. Make extra if you have time for a great lunch or snack*

● *To shorten preparation time for this meal, omit the lentil salad and serve a quick-cooking brown rice instead.*

countdown

● *Start lentil salad.*
● *Prepare ingredients for curried prawns.*
● *Cook curried prawns.*
● *Finish lentil salad.*

shopping list

DAIRY

1 small pot crème fraîche

SEAFOOD

350g (12oz) large raw prawns, peeled

GROCERY

1 tin lychees

1 jar curry powder

1 small packet dried lentils

1 small packet raisins
(50g/2oz needed)

FRUIT AND VEG

1 packet broccoli florets
(225g/8oz needed)

1 small bunch spring onions
(4 needed)

2.5cm (1in) piece fresh ginger

STAPLES

Olive oil

No-sugar-added oil and
vinegar dressing

Red onion

Garlic

Wholemeal flour

Fat-free, low-sodium chicken
stock

Ground cumin

Salt

Black peppercorns

curried prawns and vegetables continued

lentil salad

225ml (8fl oz) fat-free, low-sodium chicken stock

225ml (8fl oz) water

110g (4oz) green lentils

2 whole garlic cloves

4 spring onions, thinly sliced

2 tablespoons no-sugar-added oil and vinegar dressing

Salt and freshly ground black pepper to taste

Bring the stock and water to the boil in a medium saucepan. Rinse the lentils and slowly pour into the boiling stock, so that the stock continues to boil. Add the garlic and reduce the heat to medium-low. Simmer for 20 minutes, or until lentils are cooked through but still firm. Meanwhile, mix the spring onions with the dressing. Add salt and pepper to taste. Drain the lentils and remove the garlic cloves. Mix the dressing with the lentils while still warm.
Makes 2 servings.

One serving: 147 calories, 6g protein, 13g carbohydrate, 9g fat (1g saturated), 0mg cholesterol, 357mg sodium, 2g fibre

dessert

150g (5oz) tinned lychees, drained

Divide the lychees between 2 dessert bowls and serve.
Makes 2 servings.

One serving: 63 calories, 1g protein, 16g carbohydrate, 0.5g fat (0g saturated), 0mg cholesterol, 1mg sodium, 1g fibre

chicken fajitas

Fajitas make deliciously light meals. Served with an array of colourful vegetables and wrapped in warm tortillas, these little Mexican sandwiches are an entire meal in themselves.

● *Enjoy grapefruit with a kick for dessert.*

chicken fajitas

50ml (2fl oz) freshly squeezed lemon juice (2 lemons)

3 teaspoons rapeseed oil, divided

1 teaspoon ground cumin

Pinch ground cayenne

225g (8oz) boneless, skinless chicken breast, very thinly sliced

4 x 20.5cm (8in) wholemeal tortillas

225g (8oz) red onion, sliced

2 medium-sized red peppers, sliced

2 medium-sized green peppers, sliced

4 garlic cloves, crushed

2 medium tomatoes, diced

50g (2oz) grated, reduced-fat Cheddar cheese

25g (1oz) chopped fresh coriander leaves

Preheat the oven to 180°C/350°F/gas mark 4. Mix the lemon juice, 1 teaspoon of the oil, the cumin and cayenne together in a microwave-safe bowl. Microwave for 30 seconds on high. Alternatively, place in a small saucepan, bring to the boil and then immediately remove from the heat. Place the chicken in the warm marinade for 15 minutes, stirring to make sure all of the chicken is covered. Tightly wrap the tortillas in 2 foil parcels and place in the preheated oven for 10 minutes. Remove and leave wrapped in foil.

Heat the remaining 2 teaspoons of oil in a medium-sized non-stick frying pan until the oil begins to smoke. Remove the chicken from the marinade, saving any marinade that remains (most will be absorbed by the chicken), and sauté the chicken for about 1 minute. Add the onion, peppers and garlic. Sauté for 2 minutes. Add the marinade and toss with the chicken and vegetables for another minute, or until the sauce reduces and just coats the chicken.

To serve, arrange the diced tomatoes, grated cheese and chopped coriander in small bowls. Spoon the chicken and vegetables onto a warm serving dish along with the wrapped tortillas. Fill the tortillas with the chicken and vegetables, sprinkle with the tomatoes, grated cheese and coriander and fold to eat.

Makes 2 servings.

One serving: 630 calories, 63g protein, 56g carbohydrate, 23g fat (8g saturated), 116mg cholesterol, 614mg sodium, 2g fibre

helpful hints

● *Red, yellow and green peppers make this a colourful dish, but you can use one or any combination of peppers you like.*

● *Heating dried spices releases their oils, increasing their flavour.*

● *Triple Sec and other orange liqueurs can be bought in miniature bottles at many supermarkets and most off-licences.*

countdown

● *Preheat oven to 180°C/350°F/gas mark 4.*

● *Make fajitas.*

● *Make grapefruit.*

chicken fajitas continued

shopping list

DAIRY

　1 small packet grated,
　　reduced-fat Cheddar cheese

MEAT

　225g (8oz) boneless, skinless,
　　chicken breast

GROCERY

　1 small packet wholemeal
　　tortillas

　1 small bottle Triple Sec

FRUIT AND VEG

　2 medium-sized red peppers

　2 medium-sized green
　　peppers

　2 medium tomatoes

　1 small bunch fresh coriander

　2 lemons

　1 small grapefruit

STAPLES

　Red onion

　Garlic

　Rapeseed oil

　Ground cumin

　Cayenne pepper

tipsy grapefruit

1 grapefruit
1 tablespoon Triple Sec or other
　orange liqueur

Separate the grapefruit segments with a serrated knife and scoop out onto 2 dessert plates. Sprinkle with the Triple Sec and serve.
Makes 2 servings.

One serving: 101 calories, 1g protein, 17g carbohydrate, 0g fat (0g saturated), 0mg cholesterol, 1mg sodium, 1g fibre

ham and mushroom pitta pizza   p195

chicken sandwich with sun-dried tomato sauce **p199**

roast beef and shiitake hash

Roast beef, shiitake mushrooms and fresh thyme transform a 1950s-style American 'hash' to a modern version that takes only 20 minutes to make. I've shortened the cooking time by using lean roast beef from the deli and making a light gravy from chicken stock. The gravy just coats the hash. I've updated the flavour using shiitake mushrooms, pine nuts and fresh thyme. This hash keeps well, so make double if you have time.

roast beef and shiitake hash

2 teaspoons olive oil

110g (4oz) unpeeled red potatoes, washed and cut into 2.5cm (1in) cubes

110g (4oz) diced red onion

2 medium-sized red peppers, diced

110g (4oz) shiitake mushrooms, diced

225g (8oz) sliced lean roast beef, diced

2 tablespoons wholemeal flour

225ml (8fl oz) fat-free, low-sodium chicken stock

Salt and freshly ground black pepper to taste

Heat the oil in a non-stick frying pan over a medium-high heat. Add the potatoes and sauté for 5 minutes, tossing to turn halfway through. Add the onion, peppers and mushrooms. Sauté for 10 minutes, again tossing to turn halfway through. Add the roast beef and toss for 1 minute. Push the ingredients to the side of the pan, leaving a hole in the centre. Add the flour, then the stock and stir until the sauce thickens. Toss with the ingredients to lightly bind the hash. Season with salt and pepper to taste. Divide between 2 plates and serve.
Makes 2 servings.

One serving: 409 calories, 39g protein, 29g carbohydrate, 14g fat (4g saturated), 93mg cholesterol, 364mg sodium, 1g fibre

green salad

350g (12oz) washed, ready-to-eat mixed salad leaves

75g (3oz) cannellini beans

2 tablespoons no-sugar-added oil and vinegar salad dressing

Salt and freshly ground black pepper to taste

Place the salad leaves and beans in a bowl and drizzle with the dressing. Season with salt and pepper to taste and toss. Serve with the hash.
Makes 2 servings.

One serving: 136 calories, 4g protein, 14g carbohydrate, 9g fat (1g saturated), 0mg cholesterol, 82mg sodium, 3g fibre

helpful hints

● *Ask the deli to cut the roast beef in a single slice to make it easier to cube.*

● *Pecans or almonds can be substituted for the walnuts.*

● *If pressed for time, substitute 1 medium apple per person for the Cinnamon Walnut Baked Apples*

countdown

● *Make hash.*

● *While hash cooks, make salad.*

● *Make baked apples.*

shopping list

DELI

225g (8oz) sliced lean roast beef

GROCERY

1 tin cannellini beans (110g/4oz needed)

1 small packet broken walnuts (about 25g/1oz needed)

FRUIT AND VEG

110g (4oz) red potatoes

2 medium-sized red peppers

1 packet shiitake mushrooms (110g/4oz needed)

1 bag washed, ready-to-eat mixed salad leaves

2 Red Delicious apples

roast beef and shiitake hash continued

STAPLES
  Olive oil
  Red onion
  Wholemeal flour
  Fat-free, low-sodium chicken
    stock
  Ground cinnamon
  Artificial sweetener
  No-sugar-added oil and
    vinegar salad dressing
  Salt
  Black peppercorns

cinnamon-walnut baked apples

2 tablespoons broken walnuts
1 teaspoon ground cinnamon
2g (1/16oz) artificial sweetener
2 Red Delicious apples, cored

Chop the walnuts with the cinnamon and sweetener in a food processor. Place the apples in 2 small dessert bowls, and fill the core of each apple with the cinnamon-walnut mixture. (Some of the mixture may spill over the top. This is fine.) Cover each bowl with another bowl or microwave-safe cling film. Microwave on high 4 minutes. Remove and let stand, covered, 2 minutes. Serve in the dessert bowls.
Makes 2 servings.

One serving: 159 calories, 2g protein, 24g carbohydrate, 8g fat (0.8g saturated), 0mg cholesterol, 1mg sodium, 4g fibre

summer-and-winter chicken casserole

This flavourful casserole takes only 30 minutes to make and is a meal in a bowl, but light enough to enjoy year-round.

summer-and-winter chicken casserole

675ml (24fl oz) fat-free, low-sodium chicken stock

450ml (16fl oz) low-sodium, no-sugar-added, tinned diced tomatoes (including juice)

225g (8oz) red onion, sliced

2 celery stalks, sliced

75g (3oz) white cabbage, sliced

50g (2oz) wholemeal fusilli pasta

1 tablespoon horseradish

1 tablespoon balsamic vinegar

275g (10oz) washed, ready-to-eat fresh spinach

2 slices wholemeal bread

50g (2oz) grated, reduced-fat Swiss or Gruyère cheese

Salt and freshly ground black pepper to taste

Bring the chicken stock and tomatoes to the boil in a large saucepan over a medium-high heat. Add the onion and celery. Cover, lower the heat to medium and cook on a slow boil for 10 minutes. Add the cabbage and fusilli. Boil uncovered for 10 minutes. Combine the horseradish and vinegar. Add to the pan and stir in the spinach. Simmer for 2 minutes, until the spinach is just wilted. Toast the bread. Add the cheese to the casserole. Season with salt and pepper to taste. Serve with the toasted bread. *Makes 2 servings.*

One serving: 434 calories, 36g protein, 66g carbohydrate, 7g fat (3g saturated), 15mg cholesterol, 1289mg sodium, 22g fibre

grilled cinnamon oranges

2 medium oranges

½ teaspoon ground cinnamon

2 tablespoons flaked almonds

2g (¹⁄₁₆oz) artificial sweetener

Preheat the grill. Line a baking tray with foil or use a small oven-to-table dish. Peel the oranges over a bowl to catch the juice. With a serrated knife, cut the oranges into circular 1cm (½in) slices over the bowl. Place the orange slices in a single layer in the baking dish. Sprinkle with the cinnamon and almonds and grill for 3 minutes. Combine the sweetener with the reserved orange juice. Pour the juice over the grilled oranges and serve. *Makes 2 servings.*

One serving: 129 calories, 4g protein, 19g carbohydrate, 6g fat (0.5g saturated), 0mg cholesterol, 0mg sodium, 4g fibre

helpful hints

- *Use any type of short-cut wholemeal pasta.*
- *If pressed for time, omit the grilled cinnamon oranges and serve fresh orange.*

countdown

- *Preheat grill.*
- *Prepare all ingredients.*
- *Make casserole.*
- *While casserole cooks, toast bread.*
- *Make grilled oranges.*

shopping list

DAIRY
  1 small packet grated, reduced-fat Swiss or Gruyère cheese (50g/2oz needed)

GROCERY
  1 tin low-sodium, no-sugar-added, tinned diced tomatoes (450ml/16fl oz needed)
  1 small jar horseradish
  1 packet flaked almonds
  1 packet wholemeal fusilli pasta (50g/2oz needed)

FRUIT AND VEG
  ¼ head white cabbage
  1 bag washed, ready-to-eat fresh spinach
  2 medium oranges

STAPLES
  Celery
  Red onion
  Fat-free, low-sodium chicken stock
  Balsamic vinegar
  Wholemeal bread
  Ground cinnamon
  Artificial sweetener
  Salt
  Black peppercorns

beef stir-fry with oyster sauce

helpful hints

- Look for meat that has already been cut for stir-frying.
- Oyster sauce can be found in the Oriental section of the supermarket. Look for a low-sodium one, about 260 mg per tablespoon.
- I call for ordinary brown rice instead of quick-cooking brown rice because it contains more nutrients. If you're really pressed for time, the quick-cooking brown rice will work fine, but be careful not to buy the type that comes with a sachet of sauce or seasoning.
- Any type of mint (such as spearmint) can be used.
- I like to cook my rice like pasta, using a pan of boiling water that's large enough for the rice to roll freely. Use the method given here or follow the directions on the packet.
- To avoid having to look back at the recipe as you stir-fry the ingredients, line them up on a chopping board or plate in the order of use so you know which ingredient comes next.
- For crisp, not steamed, stir-fried vegetables, start with a very hot wok or frying pan. Let the vegetables sit for a minute before tossing to allow the wok to regain its heat.
- If pressed for time, omit the Minted Clementines and serve 1 clementine per person.

You can make a beef, broccoli and water chestnut stir-fry in less time than it takes to send out for Chinese food. The popularity of Chinese food in America has made this a classic 'American' dish.

beef stir-fry with oyster sauce

50ml (2fl oz) bottled oyster sauce
50ml (2fl oz) dry sherry or water
2 teaspoons sesame oil, divided
225g (8oz) broccoli florets
225g (8oz) lean beef (fillet, sirloin, flank or skirt) cut into 5 x 1cm (2 x ½ in) strips
250g (9oz) sliced water chestnuts
Salt and freshly ground black pepper to taste

Combine the oyster sauce, sherry and 1 teaspoon of the sesame oil in a small bowl. Make sure all ingredients are prepped and ready for stir-frying. Heat the remaining teaspoon of sesame oil in a non-stick wok or frying pan until smoking. Add the broccoli and stir-fry for 3 minutes. Add the beef, water chestnuts and sauce. Stir fry for 2 more minutes. Season with salt and pepper to taste and serve over brown rice.
Makes 2 servings.

One serving: 470 calories, 47g protein, 37g carbohydrate, 15g fat (5g saturated), 102mg cholesterol, 675mg sodium, 8g fibre

brown rice

75g (3oz) brown rice
8 spring onions, sliced
2 teaspoons sesame oil
Salt and freshly ground black pepper to taste

Fill a large saucepan with about 2–3 litres (4–5 pints) of water and bring to the boil. Place the rice in a strainer and rinse under cold water. Add to the saucepan, stir once or twice and boil for 30 minutes. Alternatively, follow the cooking instructions on the packet. Drain leaving about 3 tablespoons water on the rice. Toss the spring onions and sesame oil with the rice. Season with salt and pepper to taste.
Makes 2 servings.

One serving: 140 calories, 3g protein, 20g carbohydrate, 5g fat (1g saturated), 0mg cholesterol, 2mg sodium, 1g fibre

minted clementines

225ml (8fl oz) no-sugar-added
lemon-lime or citrus-flavoured
sparkling water, chilled
2 sprigs fresh mint
2g (¹/₁₆oz) artificial sweetener
2 medium clementines, peeled
and divided into segments

Pour the sparkling water into a small bowl and
add the mint sprigs, sweetener and clementine
segments. Stir to dissolve the sweetener. Let the
clementine segments marinate for 15 minutes,
then remove and arrange on 2 small plates. Pour
a little of the marinade over the segments and
garnish with a sprig of mint before serving.
Makes 2 servings.

One serving: 37 calories, 0.5g protein,
10g carbohydrate, 0.2g fat (0g saturated),
0mg cholesterol, 1mg sodium, 0g fibre

countdown

- Start rice.
- Marinate tangerines.
- Prepare beef ingredients.
- Stir-fry beef.
- Finish rice.

shopping list

MEAT
225g (8oz) lean beef (fillet,
sirloin, flank, or skirt)
GROCERY
1 tin sliced water chestnuts
(350g/12oz needed)
1 bottle oyster sauce
1 small bottle sesame oil
1 small packet brown rice
1 small bottle no-sugar-
added lemon-lime or citrus-
flavoured sparkling water
(225ml/8fl oz needed)
1 small bottle dry sherry
FRUIT AND VEG
225g (8oz) broccoli florets
1 small bunch spring onions
(8 needed)
1 small bunch fresh mint
2 medium clementines
STAPLES
Artificial sweetener
Salt
Black peppercorns

super speed suppers

These meals are for those nights when I haven't got the time to think about dinner, but don't want to send out for something that won't fit my low-carb lifestyle. At the end of the day, when I've just come in and the family needs to be fed, I need a repertoire of super speed suppers that can just be thrown together. It's a good idea to keep a stock of items that are the base of many super speed dishes – like fresh lettuce, from cos to romaine, and radicchio and rocket to add varied colour and flavour. I've based the recipes in this section on ingredients that I bought from the supermarket that can be assembled into a meal in 15 minutes or less.

Savoury Sage Chicken is one of my real favourites and I have made it time and again over the years since first moving to a low-carb lifestyle. It's based on roasted or rotisserie chicken that is jazzed up at home and you'd be surprised just how much zing it has from the addition of a little dry vermouth. It fits the Quick Start nutritional guidelines and takes about 10 minutes to make from start to finish. Delicious!

I love a good, hearty bowl of soup for supper, even in the summer. The Peasant Country Soup is perfect for a quick dinner. It takes only 10 minutes to make and fits the Which Carbs nutritional guidelines. Full of robust flavours, it is deeply satisfying.

When I brought the Mock Hungarian Goulash to the radio station studio for one of my programmes, all the staff lined up for seconds. It is made in 10 minutes, uses lean roast beef from the deli, and fits the Right Carbs nutritional guidelines.

Simply prepared food can be just as satisfying as something that's taken hours to make. Shopping is important and choosing the best ingredients you can afford will enhance the pleasure of eating good fresh dishes.

Look for ingredients which have not been covered in sauces and seasonings to cover up for poor quality. Try to select vegetables and fruits in season and ring the changes – one of the Super Speed menus includes melon for dessert and, if you look at the array of different melons in the supermarket, you will see that it is easy to choose a new variety for each day of the week.

These meals have been incorporated into the 2-week menu plans for the appropriate phase. Keep a good store of bottled ingredients on hand and you can throw a dinner together faster than getting into your car or phoning for a take-away. Jerk seasoning, tomato salsa, teriyaki sauce and Worcestershire sauce are just some of those handy ingredients to have around all the time; there is no end of low-carb ideas that can be made speedily using them.

When I give cooking classes and show these ideas, the response is always one of real surprise – that you can get such flavourful food in such a short time. I've served these meals at dinner parties, too, without telling anyone they were low-carb.

quick start

super speed

suppers

greek prawns with feta cheese

This meal fits the nutritional guidelines for the Quick Start phase. Greek feta cheese gives this prawn dish a tangy Mediterranean flavour.

greek prawns with feta cheese

2 teaspoons olive oil
110g (4oz) frozen chopped onion
2 garlic cloves, crushed
1 large tomato, diced
350g (12oz) large prawns, shelled and deveined
1 teaspoon dried oregano
50g (2oz) crumbled feta cheese
Salt and freshly ground black pepper

Heat olive oil in a medium-sized non-stick frying pan on medium-high heat and add the onion, garlic and tomato. Sauté for 3 minutes. Add prawns and oregano on top. Sauté for 3 minutes, turning prawns to make sure they are cooked on both sides. Add salt and pepper to taste. Sprinkle cheese on top and serve.
Makes 2 servings.

Per serving: 349 calories, 41.6 grams protein, 9.6 grams carbohydrate, 14.9 grams fat (6.2 saturated), 280 milligrams cholesterol, 638 milligrams sodium, 0.9 grams fibre

cos and fresh cabbage salad

175g (6oz) shredded, washed, ready-to-eat cabbage
175g (6oz) shredded, washed, ready-to-eat cos lettuce
2 spring onions, sliced
1 teaspoon dried dill
2 tablespoons olive oil and vinegar dressing

Combine cabbage, lettuce, spring onions and dill in a bowl. Add dressing and toss well.
Makes 2 servings.

Per serving: 104 calories, 1.4 grams protein, 6.1 grams carbohydrate, 8.7 grams fat (1.3 saturated), 0 milligrams cholesterol, 91 milligrams sodium, 1.2 grams fibre

helpful hints

● *Shredded cabbage can be bought ready-to-eat in the fruit and veg section of some supermarkets.*
● *Crumbled feta cheese can be found in the dairy section of the supermarket.*
● *Dried oregano and dill are used in this recipe. Replace dried herbs after 6 months. If they look grey and old, that's probably how they will taste.*

countdown

● *Assemble salad.*
● *Make prawns.*

shopping list

DAIRY
   1 small packet crumbled feta cheese
SEAFOOD
   350g (12oz) large prawns
FRUIT AND VEG
   1 bag shredded, washed, ready-to-eat cabbage
   1 bag shredded, washed, ready-to-eat cos lettuce
   1 small bunch spring onions
   1 large tomato
STAPLES
   Olive oil and vinegar dressing
   Olive oil
   Frozen chopped onion
   Garlic
   Dried dill
   Dried oregano
   Salt
   Black peppercorns

jamaican jerk pork

This meal fits the nutritional guidelines for the Quick Start phase.

'Jerking' is an ancient Jamaican method for preserving and cooking meat. In Jamaica the men who prepare the meat and sell it to the markets are called 'jerk men'. They use a long process involving marinating the meat and then slowly cooking it over a pimiento (allspice) wood fire. I've captured the flavours of jerk cooking for this quick dinner by using a prepared jerk seasoning.

jamaican jerk pork

2 x 175g (6oz) boneless pork chops, about 1cm (½in) thick
1 tablespoon jerk seasoning
1 teaspoon rapeseed oil

Remove fat from pork and rub with jerk seasoning. Heat oil in a medium-sized non-stick frying pan on medium-high heat. Add pork and brown for 2 minutes. Turn and brown second side for 2 minutes. Lower heat to medium and cook 2 more minutes. A meat thermometer should read 70ºC/160ºC. Makes 2 servings.
Makes 2 servings.

Per serving: 287 calories, 45.3 grams protein, 1.5 grams carbohydrate, 9.8 grams fat (3.0 saturated), 146 milligrams cholesterol, 107 milligrams sodium, 0 grams fibre

palm heart salad

400g (14oz) tin palm hearts
150g (5oz) washed, ready-to-eat salad
½ medium cucumber, peeled and sliced
2 tablespoons no-sugar-added oil and vinegar dressing
2 medium tomatoes, quartered

Drain palm hearts and cut into 2.5cm (1in) slices. Place prepared salad in a bowl and add cucumber and dressing. Toss well. Add tomato wedges along edge of bowl and sprinkle palm hearts on top.
Makes 2 servings.

Per serving: 160 calories, 6.8 grams protein, 15.9 grams carbohydrate, 9.5 grams fat (1.4 saturated), 0 milligrams cholesterol, 715 milligrams sodium, 4.3 grams fibre

helpful hints

● There are several jerk seasonings, liquid and dry, available. Choose whichever one suits your taste.

● If jerk seasoning is unavailable, make your own by mixing 1 teaspoon dried thyme, 1 teaspoon salt, ½ teaspoon allspice, ½ teaspoon cinnamon and a pinch of cayenne pepper together.

● If you are really pressed for time, serve the jerk pork with a washed, ready-to eat salad and 2 tablespoons of no-sugar-added salad dressing instead of the palm heart salad.

countdown

● Assemble salad.
● Make Jerk Pork.

shopping list

MEAT
2 x 175g (6oz) boneless pork chops
GROCERY
400g (14oz) tin palm hearts
1 small bottle jerk seasoning
FRUIT AND VEG
1 bag washed, ready-to-eat salad
1 medium cucumber
2 medium tomatoes
STAPLES
No-sugar-added oil and vinegar dressing
Rapeseed oil

savoury sage chicken

This is a tasty, 10-minute meal created by adding a quick sage and flour coating and a wine sauce to shop-bought roasted chicken.

savoury sage chicken

1 tablespoon flour

2 teaspoons dried ground sage

Salt and freshly ground black
    pepper

2 x 175g (6oz) roasted boneless,
    skinless chicken breasts

1 tablespoon olive oil

50ml (2fl oz) dry vermouth

50ml (2fl oz) water

Mix together flour, sage and salt and pepper to taste. Roll chicken in mixture, pressing flour into chicken on both sides. Heat a medium-sized non-stick frying pan on medium-high heat. Add chicken to pan and cook for 1 minute per side. Remove to a plate and raise heat to high. Add vermouth and water and reduce for 2 minutes. Pour sauce over chicken.

Makes 2 servings.

Per serving: 383 calories, 54.5 grams protein,
4.1 grams carbohydrate, 14.9 grams fat
(2.7 saturated), 144 milligrams cholesterol,
131 milligrams sodium, 0 grams fibre

italian courgettes and tomatoes

110g (4oz) courgettes, sliced

2 medium tomatoes, cut into
    wedges about same size as
    courgettes

1 teaspoon dried oregano

2 tablespoons grated semi-
    skimmed milk mozzarella
    cheese

Salt and freshly ground black
    pepper

Place courgettes and tomatoes in a microwave-safe bowl and microwave on high for 3 minutes. Add oregano, cheese and salt and pepper to taste. Toss well.

Makes 2 servings.

Per serving: 74 calories, 6.5 grams protein, 9.6 grams
carbohydrate, 2.1 grams fat (1.2 saturated),
7 milligrams cholesterol, 67 milligrams sodium,
0.9 grams fibre

helpful hints

● *White wine can be substituted for vermouth.*

● *Roasted boneless, skinless chicken breasts come ready packaged in the the supermarket. Or use rotisserie-roasted chicken breasts.*

● *Dried oregano and sage are used in this recipe. Replace dried herbs after 6 months. If they look grey and old, that's probably how they will taste.*

countdown

● *Make Italian Courgettes and Tomatoes.*

● *Make Savoury Sage Chicken.*

shopping list

DAIRY

    1 small packet grated semi-
    skimmed milk mozzarella
    cheese

MEAT

    2 X 175g (6oz) roasted
    boneless, skinless chicken
    breasts

GROCERY

    1 small bottle dry vermouth

FRUIT AND VEG

    110g (4oz) courgettes

    2 medium tomatoes

STAPLES

    Dried oregano

    Dried ground sage

    Flour

    Olive oil

    Salt

    Black peppercorns

which carbs

super speed

suppers

swordfish in spanish sofrito sauce

This meal fits the nutritional guidelines for the Which Carbs phase.

Onions, garlic, green peppers and tomatoes form the basis for a Spanish sofrito sauce. The Italian sofrito is similar using chopped celery, green peppers, onion, garlic and herbs. It's used for soups and stews. Spanish sofrito can be bought in a jar or tin in some supermarkets. If difficult to find, use a thick tomato salsa instead.

Brown rice takes about 45 minutes to cook. There are several brands of quick-cooking brown rice available. Their cooking time ranges from 10 to 30 minutes. The 10-minute rice is used in this dinner.

swordfish in spanish sofrito sauce

350g (12oz) swordfish
2 teaspoons olive oil
Salt and freshly ground black pepper
225ml (8fl oz) sofrito or thick no-sugar-added tomato salsa

Wash fish and pat dry with kitchen paper. Heat oil in a medium-sized non-stick frying pan on medium-high heat and add fish. Brown for 2 minutes. Turn and brown second side for 2 minutes. Season cooked sides with salt and pepper. Lower heat to medium, add sofrito, cover, and simmer for 5 minutes for 2.5cm (1in) thick fish, 3–4 minutes for 1.5cm (½ in) thick fish.
Makes 2 servings.

> Per serving: 308 calories, 33.6 grams protein, 0 grams carbohydrate, 12.8 grams fat (2.4 saturated), 66 milligrams cholesterol, 152 milligrams sodium, 0 grams fibre

yellow rice

300ml (11fl oz) water
300ml (11fl oz) 10-minute quick-cooking brown rice
½ teaspoon turmeric
50g (2oz) diced or sliced sweet pepper, drained
1 teaspoon olive oil

Bring water to the boil in a large saucepan over high heat. Lower heat to medium-high and add rice. Cover and cook for 5 minutes. Remove from heat and let stand for 5 minutes. Stir in pimiento and olive oil. Add salt and pepper to taste.
Makes 2 servings.

> Per serving: 196 calories, 5.0 grams protein, 36.0 grams carbohydrate, 3.9 grams fat (0.6 saturated), 0 milligrams cholesterol, 3 milligrams sodium, 2 grams fibre

helpful hints

- Any meaty fish such as halibut or tuna can be used. This meal also works well with tinned tuna.
- Saffron can be used instead of the turmeric in the rice.
- Look for: sofrito with 15 calories and 0.4 grams of fat per 25g (1oz).

countdown

- Start rice.
- Make swordfish.
- Assemble dessert.

shopping list

FISH
  350g (12oz) swordfish
GROCERY
  1 jar sofrito or thick no-sugar-added tomato salsa
  1 small jar turmeric
  1 small jar diced or sliced sweet pepper
STAPLES
  Olive oil
  10-minute quick-cooking brown rice
  Salt
  Black peppercorns

peasant country soup

This meal fits the nutritional guidelines for the Which Carbs phase.

This warm, hearty soup can be made in about 15 minutes. It keeps well. Make extra and freeze for another quick meal if you have the time.

peasant country soup

2 teaspoons olive oil
450g (1lb) sliced button mushrooms
350ml (12fl oz) pasta sauce
175ml (6fl oz) fat-free, low-sodium chicken stock
175ml (6fl oz) water
175g (6oz) cooked white haricot or cannellini beans, rinsed and drained
110g (4oz) roasted chicken strips or pieces
Salt and freshly ground black pepper

Heat olive oil in a medium-sized saucepan over high heat. Add mushrooms and sauté for 1 minute. Add pasta sauce, chicken stock, water and beans. Bring to the boil and simmer for 10 minutes. Add chicken and cook for 1 minute to warm through. Add salt and pepper to taste.
Makes 2 servings.

> Per serving: 334 calories, 29.7 grams protein, 33.6 grams carbohydrate, 8.7 grams fat (1.2 saturated), 48 milligrams cholesterol, 856 milligrams sodium, 6.2 grams fibre

herb cheese toast and salad

2 slices wholemeal bread
Olive oil spray
50g (2oz) herbed goat cheese
150g (5oz) washed, ready-to-serve salad
2 tablespoons no-sugar-added oil and vinegar dressing

Pre-heat grill. Spray wholemeal slices with olive oil spray and spread with goat cheese. Grill for 1 to 2 minutes until cheese is melted. Cut bread into 2 triangles. Place salad in a bowl and toss with dressing. Divide between 2 salad plates and place 2 toast triangles (1 slice) on the side. Serve with soup.
Makes 2 servings.

> Per serving: 237 calories, 10.7 grams protein, 12.6 grams carbohydrate, 18.0 grams fat (7.1 saturated), 22 milligrams cholesterol, 342 milligrams sodium, 3.3 grams fibre

beef teriyaki with chinese noodles

This meal fits the nutritional guidelines for the Which Carbs phase.

Juicy beef in a spicy teriyaki sauce is a traditional Japanese dish. This one can be made in minutes by buying the teriyaki sauce and the vegetables already cut for stir-fry. Some supermarkets have the meat and vegetables cut and ready to use for stir-frying in one packet. Or go to the salad bar section and buy the vegetables cut up there.

beef teriyaki

350g (12oz) sirloin steak, cut for stir-fry
1 teaspoon sesame oil
225g (8oz) sliced onion
2 garlic cloves, crushed
110g (4oz) sliced mushrooms
50ml (2fl oz) teriyaki sauce

Cut beef into strips, 7.5cm (3in) long and 0.5cm (1/4in) wide, if not already cut. Heat sesame oil in a non-stick frying pan or wok on high heat. Add onion, garlic and mushrooms. Stir-fry for 2 minutes. Add beef and stir-fry for 1 minute. Add teriyaki sauce and continue to cook for 1 minute. Makes 2 servings.

Per serving: 456 calories, 63.9 grams protein, 14.2 grams carbohydrate, 17.3 grams fat (7.6 saturated), 153 milligrams cholesterol, 755 milligrams sodium, 0 grams fibre

chinese noodles

110g (4oz) fresh Chinese noodles or dried noodles
1 teaspoon sesame oil
6 spring onions, sliced
Salt and freshly ground black pepper

Bring 2–3 litres (4–5 pints) of water to the boil in a large saucepan over high heat. Add noodles and cook for 1 minute or according to packet instructions. Drain. Add sesame oil, spring onions and salt and pepper to taste. Divide between 2 dinner plates and serve Beef Teriyaki on top.
Makes 2 servings.

Per serving: 167 calories, 5.0 grams protein, 27.6 grams carbohydrate, 4.0 grams fat (0.6 saturated), 33 milligrams cholesterol, 9 milligrams sodium, 1.1 grams fibre

helpful hints

● Look out for 'light' teriyaki sauce with 15 calories per tablespoon, 320 mg sodium and 3 grams carbohydrates.
● Rapeseed oil can be used instead of sesame oil.
● Fresh Chinese noodles can be found in the fruit and veg section of the supermarket. Or dried noodles can be used.
● Angel-hair pasta can be substituted for the Chinese noodles.
● Beef topside can be used instead of sirloin.

countdown

● Boil water for noodles.
● Make Beef Teriyaki.
● Make Chinese Noodles.

shopping list

MEAT
  350g (12oz) sirloin steak, cut for stir-fry
GROCERY
  1 small bottle sesame oil
  1 small bottle teriyaki sauce
  1 small packet fresh Chinese noodles or dried noodles
FRUIT AND VEG
  1 small packet sliced mushrooms (110g/ 4oz needed)
  1 small bunch spring onions
STAPLES
  Onion
  Garlic
  Salt
  Black peppercorns

right carbs
super speed
suppers

aromatic poached sole p204

mediterranean veal and olives   p212

parmesan sole

This meal fits the nutritional guidelines for the Right Carbs phase.

Fish is the original fast food. It takes only minutes to cook. For this quick meal, grated Parmesan cheese and breadcrumbs top the sole. This entire meal can be put together in 15 minutes.

parmesan sole

Olive oil spray
350g (12oz) sole fillet (1cm/¹/₂in thick)
2 teaspoons olive oil
2 tablespoons plain breadcrumbs
2 tablespoons freshly grated Parmesan cheese
Salt and freshly ground black pepper
2 small tomatoes, sliced

Pre-heat grill. Line a baking tray with foil and spray with olive oil spray. Rinse fish and pat dry. Place on tray and brush with 1 teaspoon olive oil. Grill for 5 minutes. Mix together breadcrumbs, Parmesan cheese, remaining oil and salt and pepper to taste. Remove sole from grill and place tomato slices over fish. Spread breadcrumb mixture evenly over fish. Grill for 2 minutes. Remove and serve.
Makes 2 servings.

Per serving: 287 calories, 38.1 grams protein, 6.8 grams carbohydrate, 11.5 grams fat (3.4 saturated), 64 milligrams cholesterol, 300 milligrams sodium, 0 grams fibre

potato cubes

350g (12oz) new potatoes
2 teaspoons olive oil
Salt and freshly ground black pepper

Wash, but do not peel, potatoes. Cut into 2.5cm (1in) cubes. Place in a microwave-safe bowl and cover with clingfilm or a plate. Microwave on high for 5 minutes. Remove and let stand, covered, for 1 minute. Remove cover carefully, because the steam will be very hot. Add olive oil and salt and pepper to taste. Toss well.
Makes 2 servings.

Per serving: 180 calories, 3.5 grams protein, 30.6 grams carbohydrate, 4.7 grams fat (0.6 saturated), 0 milligrams cholesterol, 11 milligrams sodium, 2.7 grams fibre

dessert

450g (1lb) melon cubes

Divide between 2 dessert bowls.
Makes 2 servings.

Per serving: 86 calories, 2.1 grams protein, 20.1 grams carbohydrate, 0.6 grams fat (0 saturated), 0 milligrams cholesterol, 21 milligrams sodium, 0.8 grams fibre

helpful hints

● *Any type of delicate white fish fillet can be used such as snapper or flounder.*
● *Fresh melon cubes can be found in the fruit and veg section of most supermarkets.*

countdown

● *Pre-heat grill.*
● *Make potato cubes.*
● *Make Parmesan Sole.*
● *Assemble dessert.*

shopping list

FISH
  350g (12oz) sole fillet
GROCERY
  Plain breadcrumbs
FRUIT AND VEG
  350g (12oz) new potatoes
  2 small tomatoes
  1 container melon cubes (about 450g/1lb)
STAPLES
  Olive oil spray
  Olive oil
  Parmesan cheese
  Salt
  Black peppercorns

chicken creole

This meal fits the nutritional guidelines for the Right Carbs phase.

Green pepper and onions are essential ingredients of Creole and Cajun cooking. Add some tomatoes, hot peppers and chicken and you've got a quick and easy Chicken Creole. The amount of cayenne called for in the recipe gives a mild zing to the sauce. If you like it hot, add more cayenne or serve hot pepper sauce at the table.

Brown rice takes about 45 minutes to cook. There are several brands of quick-cooking brown rice available. Their cooking time ranges from 10 to 30 minutes. The 10-minute rice is used in this recipe.

chicken creole

1 teaspoon olive oil
350g (12oz) frozen chopped onion
225g (8oz) frozen diced green
   pepper
4 garlic cloves, crushed
450g (1lb) no-sugar-added
   chopped tomatoes
2 teaspoons dried oregano
1 tablespoon Worcestershire
   sauce
1/8 teaspoon cayenne pepper
350g (12oz) roasted boneless,
   skinless chicken breast, cut into
   2.5cm (1in) cubes
Salt and freshly ground black
   pepper
Hot pepper sauce

Heat olive oil in a medium-sized non-stick frying pan on medium-high heat and add onion, green pepper and garlic. Sauté for 2 minutes. Add tomatoes, oregano, Worcestershire sauce, cayenne pepper and chicken to pan. Simmer for 3 minutes. Add salt and pepper to taste. Spoon chicken and sauce over rice and pass the hot pepper sauce.
Makes 2 servings.

Per serving: 436 calories, 59.1 grams protein, 28.1 grams carbohydrate, 10.5 grams fat (2.2 saturated), 144 milligrams cholesterol, 411 milligrams sodium, 4.6 grams fibre

helpful hints

● Look for roasted chicken breasts that have not been cooked in a honey, sugar or barbecue sauce.
● Dried oregano is used in this recipe. Replace dried herbs after 6 months. If they look grey and old, that's probably how they will taste.
● Fresh watermelon cubes can be found in the fruit and veg section of some supermarkets.

countdown

● Boil water for rice.
● Make chicken dish and cover to keep warm.
● Make rice.
● Assemble the dessert.

quick brown rice

*175g (6oz) 10-minute quick-
  cooking brown rice*
225ml (8fl oz) water
*Salt and freshly ground black
  pepper*

Bring water to the boil in a large saucepan over
high heat and add rice. Boil for 5 minutes. Cover
with a lid and let stand for 5 minutes. Or follow
packet instructions. Fluff with a fork and add salt
and pepper to taste.
Makes 2 servings.

Per serving: 128 calories, 3.8 grams protein,
26.3 grams carbohydrate, 1.3 grams fat
(0.2 saturated), 0 milligrams cholesterol, 0 milligrams
sodium, 1.5 grams fibre

dessert

275g (10oz) watermelon cubes

Divide between 2 dessert bowls.
Makes 2 servings.

Per serving: 49 calories, 1 gram protein,
11.1 grams carbohydrate, 0.7 grams fat
(0.1 saturated), 0 milligrams cholesterol,
3 milligrams sodium, 0.8 grams fibre

shopping list

MEAT
   *350g (12oz) roasted
      boneless, skinless chicken
      breast*
GROCERY
   *450g (1lb) tin no-sugar-
      added chopped tomatoes*
FRUIT AND VEG
   *275g (10oz) watermelon
      cubes*
STAPLES
   Frozen chopped onion
   Frozen diced green pepper
   Garlic
   Cayenne pepper
   Dried oregano
   Worcestershire sauce
   Hot pepper sauce
   *10-minute, quick-cooking
      brown rice*
   Olive oil
   Salt
   Black peppercorns

black bean soup with rice

helpful hints

- If you like your black bean soup thick, remove about 110g (4oz) of beans from the soup after it is cooked and purée them in a food processor. Stir the purée into the soup.
- Any type of hard grating cheese can be used.
- Brown rice takes about 45 minutes to cook. There are several brands of quick-cooking brown rice available. Their cooking time ranges from 10 to 30 minutes. Use the 10-minute rice for this dinner.

countdown

- Make rice.
- Make soup.

shopping list

DAIRY

1 small packet Manchego cheese

DELI

175g (6oz) lean gammon

STAPLES

10-minute, quick-cooking brown rice

Chilli powder

Frozen chopped onion

Frozen diced green pepper

Olive oil

Tinned black beans (225g/ 8oz needed)

Fat-free, low-sodium chicken stock

Salt

Black peppercorns

This meal fits the nutritional guidelines for the Right Carbs phase.

This hearty black bean soup makes a quick one-pot dinner. Manchego is a flavourful, semi-firm Spanish cheese made from sheep's milk.

rice

110g (4oz) 10-minute quick-cooking brown rice
150ml (5fl oz) water
Salt and freshly ground black pepper

Bring water to the boil in a large saucepan over high heat and add rice. Boil for 5 minutes. Cover with a lid and let stand for 5 minutes. Or follow packet instructions. Fluff with a fork and add salt and pepper to taste.

Makes 2 servings.

Per serving: 85 calories, 2.5 grams protein, 17.5 grams carbohydrate, 0.8 grams fat (0.2 saturated), 0 milligrams cholesterol, 0 milligrams sodium, 1 gram fibre

black bean soup

1 tablespoon olive oil
175g (6oz) lean gammon, cut into 5cm (2in) strips
225g (8oz) frozen diced green pepper
225g (8oz) frozen chopped onion
225g (8oz) rinsed and drained black beans
225ml (8fl oz) fat-free, low-sodium chicken stock
225ml (8fl oz) water
1 tablespoon chilli powder
Salt and freshly ground black pepper
50g (2oz) grated Manchego cheese

Heat olive oil in a large saucepan on medium-high heat. Add the gammon, green pepper and onion. Sauté for 1 minute. Add beans, chicken stock, water and chilli powder. Bring to a simmer and cook for 5 minutes. Add salt and pepper to taste. Sprinkle cheese on top. To serve, divide rice between 2 soup bowls and spoon soup on top.

Makes 2 servings.

Per serving: 555 calories, 41.8 grams protein, 54.0 grams carbohydrate, 19.4 grams fat (6.9 saturated), 65 milligrams cholesterol, 1100 milligrams sodium, 7.2 grams fibre

mock hungarian goulash

This meal fits the nutritional guidelines for the Right Carbs phase.

Succulent beef in a tomato sauce flavoured with onion, green pepper and paprika is the basis for Hungarian goulash. I've shortened this recipe by using good-quality, lean deli roast beef and called it Mock Hungarian Goulash. The secret to a good Hungarian goulash is good Hungarian paprika. Paprika is the Hungarian name for both sweet pepper and the powder made from it. Ordinary paprika comes in varying degrees of flavour – from pungent to virtually tasteless. True Hungarian paprika may be hot or mild and can be found in most supermarkets.

mock hungarian goulash

1 teaspoon olive oil

110g (4oz) frozen chopped onion

225g (8oz) frozen diced green pepper

40g (1½oz) sliced portobello mushrooms

1 tablespoon Hungarian paprika or 1½ tablespoons paprika

225ml (8fl oz) low-sodium, no-sugar-added tomato sauce

175g (6oz) thick sliced lean roast beef, cut into 1cm (½in) strips

Salt and freshly ground black pepper

2 tablespoons reduced-fat crème fraiche

2 medium tomatoes, cut into wedges

Heat oil in a medium-sized non-stick frying pan on medium-high heat and add onion, green pepper and mushrooms. Sauté for 1 minute. Sprinkle paprika over vegetables and sauté for 3 minutes. Add tomato sauce and simmer for 1 minute. Add roast beef and salt and pepper to taste. Remove from heat and serve over noodles. Spoon crème fraiche on top and arrange tomatoes on the side.

Makes 2 servings.

Per serving: 311 calories, 31.0 grams protein, 21.3 grams carbohydrate, 10.8 grams fat (4.0 saturated), 77 milligrams cholesterol, 100 milligrams sodium, 1.5 grams fibre

caraway noodles

110g (4oz) flat egg noodles

2 teaspoons olive oil

1 tablespoon caraway seeds

Salt and freshly ground black pepper

Bring 2–3 litres (4–5 pints) of water to the boil in a large saucepan over high heat. Add the noodles and boil for 3–4 minutes or according to packet instructions. Drain, leaving about 2 tablespoons water with the noodles. Toss with oil and caraway seeds. Add salt and pepper to taste. Divide between 2 plates and spoon goulash on top.

Makes 2 servings.

Per serving: 228 calories, 6.7 grams protein, 34.8 grams carbohydrate, 6.6 grams fat (1.0 saturated), 46 milligrams cholesterol, 10 milligrams sodium, 1.5 grams fibre

helpful hints

● Look for thinly sliced mushrooms in the fruit and veg section of the supermarket. Any type of sliced mushrooms can be used.

● If Hungarian paprika is unavailable, use regular paprika. If you have it on hand, make sure it is a fresh jar. If your paprika is older than 6 months, it's time for a fresh jar.

countdown

● Boil water for noodles.
● Make goulash.
● Make noodles.

shopping list

DAIRY

1 small pot reduced-fat crème fraiche

DELI

175g (6oz) thick-sliced lean deli roast beef

GROCERY

1 jar Hungarian paprika or ordinary paprika

1 small jar caraway seeds

110g (4oz) flat egg noodles

FRUIT AND VEG

1 small packet sliced portobello mushrooms (about 40g/1½oz needed)

2 medium tomatoes

STAPLES

Olive oil

Frozen chopped onion

Frozen diced green pepper

Low-sodium, no-sugar-added tomato sauce

Salt

Black peppercorns

weekends

By noon on Fridays, I'm already looking forward to relaxing over the weekend and spending time with my family. I also look forward to meals on which I make a little extra effort, to make them special, but I don't want to slave over the stove all day preparing them. The recipes are full of flavour and intrigue. Just who could resist the idea of Spiced Cowboy Steak with Jalapeño Rice? It puts you into a good mood for watching a great movie on Saturday night. Although the rice does take a little time to cook, it doesn't involve you in a lot of work.

How to manage a blow-out weekend? No need to worry here. Remember, balance is the key. My husband has never found it difficult, even after a deviation, to return to the low-carb lifestyle, because the menus are so appealing and varied. Seasonal eating is ever-important. You will want fresh fish and light pasta dishes and salads in summer when the supermarket shelves are filled with a huge array of saladings and vibrantly coloured peppers, squashes and sweet vine-ripened tomatoes. In winter the more robust meats and hearty cabbage dishes provide warming, comfort food to tempt you to stay with the low-carb lifestyle.

The recipes in this section are still quick and easy, but they take a few extra minutes of preparation or contain special ingredients that you may not think of for week-night dinners. I've often made dinner party menus using these dishes and been asked for the recipes!

Garlic-Stuffed Steak is a fun weekend meal that meets the guidelines for the Quick Start section. Chicken and Walnuts in Lettuce Puffs is a dinner with an Asian theme that fits the Which Carbs Menu Plan. Asian flavours are all the rage now that we travel so much more widely in countries such as Laos, Vietnam and Korea, and chefs in the West are experimenting with fusion dishes which can often be easily adapted to low-carb eating. The secret of staying with a low-carb lifestyle is to provide sufficient variation in one's diet to satisfy the taste buds. Don't get bored or you may be tempted to stray.

Pan-Seared Tuna with Mango Salsa is a delightful blend of fusion flavours and styles that fits the Right Carbs phase. There is the opportunity to mix and match, but the meals have been created to achieve the nutritional priorities of that phase in your diet. My husband and I no longer think about what is and what isn't low-carb; we simply consider it good food that fits into our busy schedules and is appreciated by our family and friends.

And of course you can have desserts. Pears with Raspberry Coulis makes a refreshing end to a great Saturday evening feast.

All of the weekend meals in this section are incorporated in the 2-week menu plans for the appropriate phase.

quick start
weekend
m e a l s

dijon chicken with crunchy couscous

The nutritional analysis for this recipes fits the Quick Start phase.

A tangy mustard sauce gently coats these chicken breasts. The couscous is made with lettuce, giving a crunchy texture to the couscous. We don't often think of cooking lettuce, but the French braise lettuce and use it to make soup.

dijon chicken

2 x 175g (6oz) boneless, skinless
  chicken breasts
Olive oil spray
Freshly ground black pepper
115ml (4fl oz) dry vermouth
2 tablespoons Dijon mustard
2 tablespoons coarse-grain
  mustard
1 tablespoon whipping cream

Place chicken between 2 pieces of greaseproof paper and flatten with a kitchen mallet or the bottom of a heavy pan to 1cm (½in) thick. Heat a medium-sized non-stick frying pan on medium-high heat and spray with olive oil spray. Brown chicken for 2 minutes, then turn and brown second side for 2 minutes. Season the cooked sides with pepper to taste. Remove chicken to a plate and add vermouth to the pan. Cook for 30 seconds, then add the two mustards and stir to blend, about 30 seconds. Return chicken to the pan and cook for 1 minute. Remove pan from heat and stir in the cream. Sprinkle over pepper to taste. Serve chicken on 2 dinner plates with the sauce spooned on top.
Makes 2 servings.

Per serving: 400 calories, 55.4 grams protein,
3.7 grams carbohydrate, 14.2 grams fat
(4.2 saturated), 155 milligrams cholesterol,
859 milligrams sodium, 0 grams fibre

crunchy couscous

225ml (8fl oz) water
110g (4oz) pre-cooked couscous
175g (6oz) shredded iceberg
  lettuce
Salt and freshly ground black
  pepper
2 tablespoons flaked almonds
Several sprigs watercress, for
  garnish

Bring water to the boil in a medium saucepan on high heat. Add couscous and lettuce. Remove from the heat, cover, and let sit for 5 minutes. Fluff couscous with a fork and add almonds and salt and pepper to taste. Arrange sprigs of watercress on the side.
Makes 2 servings.

Per serving: 146 calories, 5.8 grams protein,
18.4 grams carbohydrate, 6.2 grams fat
(0.4 saturated), 0 milligrams cholesterol,
12 milligrams sodium, 2.1 grams fibre

helpful hints

- *Four tablespoons of Dijon mustard can be used instead of the combination of Dijon and coarse-grain mustard.*

countdown

- *Make couscous.*
- *Make chicken.*

shopping list

DAIRY
  1 small pot whipping cream
MEAT
  2 x 175g (6oz) boneless,
    skinless chicken breasts
GROCERY
  1 small bottle dry vermouth
  1 small jar coarse-grain
    mustard
  1 small packet couscous
  1 small packet flaked
    almonds
FRUIT AND VEG
  1 small head iceberg lettuce
  1 bunch watercress
STAPLES
  Olive oil spray
  Dijon mustard
  Salt
  Black peppercorns

garlic-stuffed steak

The nutritional analysis for this recipes fits the Quick Start phase.
Garlic and parsley stuffed into a juicy steak make a perfect quick meal for the weekend.

The garlic cloves for this stuffing are blanched first and then chopped with fresh parsley to make a simple stuffing. Blanching gives the garlic a mild, sweet flavour. The water used for blanching the garlic has a wonderful flavour, so I add it to the water for cooking the pasta.

The asparagus is added for the last 5 minutes to the boiling pasta. This saves time and an extra pot to wash. If using fresh pasta, the cooking time will be about 3–4 minutes. Add the asparagus first and then the fresh pasta.

helpful hints

- Any type of quick-cooking steak such as sirloin or fillet can be used.
- Use the same pan for boiling pasta and garlic to save clean-up time.
- The blanched garlic and parsley can be chopped in a food processor.
- Buy good-quality Parmesan cheese and grate it yourself. Freeze extra for quick use. You can spoon out what you need and leave the rest frozen.

countdown

- Blanch garlic and then fill the pan with more water and place on heat to boil.
- Make steak.
- Make linguine and asparagus.

garlic-stuffed steak

5 garlic cloves, peeled
350g (12oz) frying steak
15g (1oz) chopped parsley
Salt and freshly ground black pepper
1 teaspoon olive oil

Place whole, peeled garlic cloves in a large saucepan and cover with cold water. Bring to the boil and scoop out garlic cloves with a strainer. Fill the saucepan with more cold water and bring to the boil for the pasta side dish.

Remove fat from steak and make slits about 2.5cm (1in) apart on top and bottom to form pockets for the stuffing. The slits should be about 1cm (½in) deep and cover the width of the steak.

Chop the garlic and parsley together. Add salt and pepper to taste. With the tip of a knife or a small spoon, stuff the slits in the steak using about half the parsley mixture. Set the rest of the stuffing aside. Heat a medium-sized non-stick frying pan on medium-high heat and add the stuffed steak. Sauté for 5 minutes. Turn and sauté 5 minutes for rare. A meat thermometer should read 60ºC/145ºF degrees. Cook 1–2 minutes longer for medium rare, or longer if you prefer your meat more well cooked. Season the cooked sides of steak. Remove from the frying pan to a chopping board and add the olive oil to the pan. Add remaining stuffing and sauté for 1–2 minutes. Cut the steak into 2.5cm (1in) slices and divide between 2 dinner plates. Spoon sautéed stuffing on top of slices.

Makes 2 servings.

Per serving: 397 calories, 61.5 grams protein,
3.6 grams carbohydrate, 17.1 grams fat
(7.5 saturated), 153 milligrams cholesterol,
119 milligrams sodium, 0 grams fibre

linguine and asparagus

50g (2oz) wholemeal linguine
110g (4oz) asparagus
2 teaspoons olive oil
*Salt and freshly ground black
    pepper*
*2 tablespoons grated Parmesan
    cheese*

Bring a large saucepan with 2–3 litres (4–5 pints) of water to the boil on high heat, using the garlic water from the stuffed steak recipe and additional water to make up the quantity. Add the pasta and boil for 5 minutes. Cut 2.5cm (1in) from bottom of asparagus end and cut the asparagus spears into 2.5cm (1in) slices. Add the asparagus to the pasta and continue to boil for 5 minutes. Remove 2 tablespoons of the water and place in a large bowl. Drain the pasta and asparagus. Add olive oil and salt and pepper to taste to the water in the bowl. Add the drained pasta and toss well. Sprinkle with Parmesan cheese.
Makes 2 servings.

Per serving: 179 calories, 8.7 grams protein,
20.4 grams carbohydrate, 7.9 grams fat
(2.5 saturated), 7 milligrams cholesterol,
180 milligrams sodium, 4.3 grams fibre

shopping list

FRUIT AND VEG
  110g (4oz) asparagus
  1 small bunch parsley
MEAT
  350g (12oz) frying steak
GROCERY
  *1 small packet wholemeal
    linguine (50g/2oz needed)*
STAPLES
  Garlic
  Olive oil
  Parmesan cheese
  Salt
  Black peppercorns

veal saltimbocca

The nutritional analysis for this recipes fits the Quick Start phase.

Saltimbocca means 'jump in mouth', which perfectly describes this dish. Fresh veal escalopes, an Italian staple, need only a few minutes cooking in a light wine sauce to flavour them.

veal saltimbocca

2 x 75g (3oz) veal escalopes
Salt and freshly ground black pepper
2 thin slices lean ham (25g/1oz)
4 small fresh sage leaves
2 teaspoons olive oil
50ml (2fl oz) dry white wine
2 tablespoons water

Place veal on chopping board and season the side facing upwards. Lay one piece of ham on each piece. Cut each sage leaf into strips and place evenly on the ham. Roll up from the narrow end and secure with a wooden cocktail stick.

Heat the oil in a medium-sized non-stick frying pan on medium-high heat. Add the veal rollups and sauté until brown on all sides, about 2 minutes per side. Add the wine, lower heat to medium, and gently simmer for 5 minutes. Remove veal to 2 dinner plates and remove the cocktail sticks. Add water to frying pan and reduce the liquid over high heat for 1 minute. Add salt and pepper to taste. Spoon sauce over veal.

Makes 2 servings.

Per serving: 263 calories, 25.2 grams protein, 0.4 grams carbohydrate, 14.3 grams fat(6.3 saturated), 82 milligrams cholesterol, 178 milligrams sodium, 0 grams fibre

parmesan courgettes

2 tablespoons grated Parmesan cheese

40g (1¹/₂oz) plain breadcrumbs

225g (8oz) courgettes, cut into 1cm (¹/₂in) slices

1 teaspoon olive oil

Salt and freshly ground black pepper

Pre-heat grill. Mix Parmesan cheese and breadcrumbs together and set aside. Place courgette slices in a shallow, microwave-safe bowl, cover, and microwave on high for 3 minutes. (Or bring a small saucepan filled with water to the boil. Add courgettes and boil for 3–4 minutes. Drain and place in shallow baking dish.) Drizzle olive oil and salt and pepper to taste over the courgettes. Sprinkle with Parmesan mixture and place under grill for 1–2 minutes or until topping is golden.
Makes 2 servings.

Per serving: 128 calories, 5.2 grams protein, 12.2 grams carbohydrate, 5.8 grams fat (2.3 saturated), 7 milligrams cholesterol, 281 milligrams sodium, 0.8 grams fibre

italian salad

150g (5oz) washed, ready-to-eat Italian-style salad leaves

2 tablespoons no-sugar-added oil and balsamic vinegar dressing

Place salad in a bowl and add dressing. Toss well.
Makes 2 servings.

Per serving: 87 calories, 0.8 grams protein, 2.3 grams carbohydrate, 8.5 grams fat (1.3 saturated), 0 milligrams cholesterol, 83 milligrams sodium, 0.4 grams fibre

shopping list

DELI

 1 small packet lean ham (25g/1oz needed)

MEAT

 2 x 75g (3oz) veal escalopes

GROCERY

 1 small bottle dry white wine

 1 small packet plain breadcrumbs

 1 bottle no-sugar-added oil and balsamic vinegar dressing

FRUIT AND VEG

 1 bag washed, ready-to-eat Italian-style salad leaves

 225g (8oz) courgettes

 1 small bunch fresh sage leaves

STAPLES

 Parmesan cheese

 Olive oil

 Salt

 Black peppercorns

which carbs
weekend
m e a l s

spiced cowboy steak

The nutritional analysis for this recipe fits the Which Carbs phase.

Texas cowboys working near the Rio Grande border loved their cowboy steaks flavoured with Mexican spices. The spice mixture forms a crisp coating over the steak, keeping the meat juicy with a burst of flavour.

Brown rice takes about 45 minutes to cook. There are several brands of quick-cooking brown rice available. Their cooking time ranges from 10 to 30 minutes. I find the 30-minute rice has more flavour, but any quick-cooking rice will work for this dinner.

spiced cowboy steak

1 teaspoon ground cumin
1 teaspoon ground ginger
1 teaspoon dried thyme
1/8 teaspoon cayenne pepper
2 medium garlic cloves, crushed
350g (12oz) sirloin steak, fat removed
Olive oil spray
Salt

Pre-heat grill. Line a baking tray with foil. Combine cumin, ginger, thyme, cayenne and garlic in a bowl. Remove fat from steak. Spoon spice mixture over both sides of steak and press in with the back of a spoon. Spray both sides of steak with olive oil spray. Leave for 15 minutes while you prepare the rice.

Place steak on baking tray under grill. Grill for 5 minutes. Turn and grill for 4–5 minutes for medium rare. A meat thermometer should read 60ºC/145ºF degrees for rare. Grill a minute longer for a steak about 2.5cm (1in) thick. Cook longer if you prefer your meat more well done. Sprinkle with salt to taste.

Makes 2 servings.

Per serving: 350 calories, 55.8 grams protein, 1.2 grams carbohydrate, 15.5 grams fat (7.2 saturated), 140 milligrams cholesterol, 104 milligrams sodium, 0 grams fibre

jalapeño rice

75g (3oz) 30-minute quick-cooking brown rice
2 tablespoons olive oil and vinegar dressing
2 medium jalapeno peppers, seeded and chopped
2 spring onions, thinly sliced
Salt and freshly ground black pepper

Bring a large saucepan with 2–3 litres (4–5 pints) water to the boil. Add rice to the saucepan, stir once or twice, and let boil for 30 minutes. Alternatively, follow the cooking instructions on the rice packet. Reserve 3 tablespoons cooking liquid and place in a serving bowl. Add the dressing to the bowl. Add peppers and spring onions. Drain rice and add to bowl. Add salt and pepper to taste. Toss well.

Makes 2 servings.

Per serving: 237 calories, 5.2 grams protein, 34.3 grams carbohydrate, 9.8 grams fat (1.5 saturated), 0 milligrams cholesterol, 80 milligrams sodium, 1.5 grams fibre

helpful hints

● Any type of frying steak can be used.

● Dried thyme is used in this recipe. Replace dried herbs after 6 months. If they look grey and old, that's probably how they will taste.

countdown

● Pre-heat grill and place foil-lined baking tray on top shelf.

● Start rice.

● Mix spices and garlic and marinate steak.

● Prepare remaining ingredients.

● Grill steak.

● Finish rice.

shopping list

MEAT
350g (12oz) sirloin steak (fillet or rump can be used)
GROCERY
Ground ginger
FRUIT AND VEG
2 medium jalapeño peppers
1 small bunch spring onions
STAPLES
Ground cumin
Dried thyme
Cayenne pepper
Garlic
Olive oil spray
30-minute quick-cooking brown rice
Olive oil and vinegar dressing
Salt
Black peppercorns

mediterranean snapper with provençal salad

The nutritional analysis for this recipes fits the Which Carbs phase.

Sunny Provence with its abundance of fresh vegetables and herbs has a cuisine that is fragrant and simple.

The snapper recipe calls for one uncommon vegetable – fennel. It has a bulbous look, with wide, celery-like stems and bright green feathery leaves. It has a very light aniseed flavour. I used the feathery leaves as a garnish.

Pernod, an aniseed-flavoured liqueur, is a perfect partner with fennel. You can buy small miniature Pernod bottles or use a dry vermouth instead.

provençal salad

1 tablespoon red wine vinegar
1 teaspoon Dijon mustard
1 teaspoon olive oil
50ml (2fl oz) non-fat natural yoghurt
small head round lettuce, washed and dried
4 radishes, sliced
1 small green pepper, sliced
6 stoned green olives
2 small wholemeal rolls

Pre-heat oven to 180ºC/350ºF/gas mark 4. Mix vinegar and mustard together in a salad bowl. Add oil and mix well. Blend in yoghurt. Add lettuce, radishes, green pepper and olives. Toss well. Warm rolls in oven while fish cooks.
Makes 2 servings.

Per serving: 145 calories, 7.9 grams protein, 20.8 grams carbohydrate, 5.2 grams fat (0.5 saturated), 1 milligram cholesterol, 493 milligrams sodium, 3.6 grams fibre

helpful hints

- *Any type of light white fish can be used. Cook the fish for 10 minutes per 2.5cm (1in) of thickness.*
- *Any type of lettuce can be used for the salad.*
- *Two tablespoons of a no-sugar-added dressing can be used for the salad instead of the dressing in recipe.*
- *Cut off fennel stalks and slice using the thin slicing blade of a food processor or mandoline.*
- *A quick way to chop the fennel leaves is to snip them off the stalk with scissors.*

countdown

- *Make dessert*
- *Pre-heat oven to warm rolls.*
- *Make salad.*
- *Heat rolls.*
- *Make fish.*

Greek Prawns with Feta p233

mediterranean snapper

350g (12oz) red snapper fillets
  (about 1cm/½ in thick)
1 small bulb fennel, sliced
2 teaspoons olive oil
2 medium garlic cloves, crushed
50ml (2fl oz) Pernod
2 tablespoons whipping cream
Salt and freshly ground black
  pepper

Rinse the fish and pat dry with kitchen paper. Remove top of fennel leaving only white bulb; wash feathery leaves and chop 2 tablespoons of leaves. Reserve some fennel ferns for garnish. Wash the fennel bulb and thinly slice. Heat the oil in a medium-sized non-stick frying pan over medium-high heat. Add fennel slices and leaves and garlic. Sauté for 3 minutes. Add fish and cook for 4 minutes per side. Remove fish to a plate and cover with foil to keep warm.
Add Pernod and reduce for 1 minute over high heat. Stir in cream and salt and pepper to taste. Spoon sauce with sliced fennel over snapper and sprinkle fennel ferns on top.
Makes 2 servings.

Per serving: 374 calories, 35.3 grams protein, 1.5 grams carbohydrate, 12.8 grams fat (4.5 saturated), 83 milligrams cholesterol, 114 milligrams sodium, 0 grams fibre

pears with raspberry coulis

110g (4oz) raspberries
Artificial sweetener equivalent to
  2 teaspoons sugar
2 medium pears

Place raspberries and sweetener in the bowl of a food processor and process until smooth. If you do not have a food processor, press berries through a sieve. Spoon sauce on to 2 dessert plates. Cut pears in half and remove core. Cut into slices and place on sauce.
Makes 2 servings.

Per serving: 129 calories, 1.3 grams protein, 32.7 grams carbohydrate, 1.1 grams fat (0 saturated), 0 milligrams cholesterol, 1 milligram sodium, 7 grams fibre

shopping list

DAIRY
  1 small pot non-fat natural
    yoghurt
  1 small pot whipping cream
FISH
  350g (12oz) red snapper
    fillets
GROCERY
  1 small container stoned
    green olives (6 needed)
  1 small pack wholemeal rolls
    (2 needed)
  1 miniature Pernod bottle
FRUIT AND VEG
  1 small bulb fennel
  1 small head round lettuce
  1 small bunch radishes
  1 small green pepper
  2 medium pears
  1 small punnet raspberries
STAPLES
  Red wine vinegar
  Dijon mustard
  Olive oil
  Garlic
  Artificial sweetener
  Salt
  Black peppercorns

chicken and walnuts in lettuce puffs

The nutritional analysis for this recipes fits the Which Carbs phase.

Stir-fried chicken, walnuts and vegetables served in lettuce puffs is one of my favourite dishes in a Chinese restaurant. Hoisin sauce spooned over crisp, cool lettuce and then topped with warm chicken and vegetables creates a taste and texture sensation.

I asked the chef at a top Chinese restaurant why cooking in a wok at home doesn't produce the same results as when food is prepared in a restaurant. Here's his advice: don't overcrowd the wok. Cook small portions. Use a wok that is about 50cm (20in) in diameter; if using a smaller wok, use even smaller portions. Heat the wok until it is almost smoking, then add the oil. Drizzle the oil around the sides, swirling to coat the wok, and wait about 5 seconds before adding the other ingredients.

helpful hints

- *Use toasted sesame oil if available in your local supermarket. It gives a smoky flavour.*
- *Chinese cabbage is also known as Chinese leaves. It has thin, crisp, pale green leaves. Any firm lettuce can be substituted.*
- *Hoisin sauce is a mixture of soya beans, garlic, chilli peppers and spices. It can be found in the Chinese section of the supermarket.*
- *Rice vinegar can be bought in the Asian section of the supermarket. Half a tablespoon of water mixed with ½ tablespoon distilled white vinegar may be used as a substitute.*

countdown

- *Prepare walnuts and chicken.*
- *While chicken marinates, prepare all other ingredients.*
- *Stir-fry Sweet and Sour Cabbage.*
- *Using same wok, stir-fry the chicken dish.*

chicken and walnuts in lettuce puffs

110g (4oz) boneless, skinless chicken breasts, cut into 1cm (½ in) pieces

1 tablespoon bottled oyster sauce

2 tablespoons walnut pieces

3 teaspoons sesame oil

1 teaspoon crushed fresh ginger or ½ teaspoon ground ginger

1 medium garlic clove, crushed

40g (1½ oz) diced carrots

50g (2oz) diced shiitake mushrooms

75g (3oz) sliced water chestnuts

½ tablespoon rice vinegar

50ml (2fl oz) hoisin sauce

8 small iceberg lettuce cups (inner leaves from lettuce that curve into a cup)

Place chicken in a bowl with the oyster sauce and leave to stand for 10 minutes. Heat wok over high heat and add walnut pieces. Toast in wok for 1–2 minutes or until slightly coloured. Remove and set aside. Heat wok over high heat. Add 1 teaspoon sesame oil. Add ginger and cook, stirring, until fragrant, about 10 seconds. Add chicken and oyster sauce and stir-fry for 1 minute. Add garlic, carrots, mushrooms and water chestnuts. Stir-fry for 2 minutes. Add remaining 2 teaspoons sesame oil and rice vinegar. Cook to heat through for a few seconds. Add walnuts and toss to coat. Remove from heat.

To serve: divide chicken, hoisin sauce and lettuce cups between 2 dinner plates. Spread a small spoonful of hoisin sauce on a lettuce cup, spoon in some of the chicken mixture, wrap in lettuce cup, and eat like a sandwich.
Makes 2 servings.

Per serving: 541 calories, 58.3 grams protein, 27.2 grams carbohydrate, 23.6 grams fat (3.6 saturated), 145 milligrams cholesterol, 797 milligrams sodium, 4.1 grams fibre

sweet and sour cabbage

Several drops hot pepper sauce
1 tablespoon hoisin sauce
2 tablespoons Chinese rice vinegar
Artificial sweetener equivalent to
  2 teaspoons sugar
¹/₂ teaspoon salt
1 teaspoon sesame oil
225g (8oz) Chinese cabbage,
  thinly sliced
1 medium red pepper, seeded and
  sliced

Mix together hot pepper sauce, hoisin sauce, Chinese rice vinegar, sweetener and salt. Heat wok to smoking and add sesame oil. When oil is smoking, add cabbage and red pepper. Stir-fry for 2 minutes. Pour in sauce. Toss well, spoon into a bowl, and leave to stand until chicken dish is ready. This can be served hot or cold. Do not wash the wok. It can be used for the chicken dish.
Makes 2 servings.

Per serving: 81 calories, 2.3 grams protein, 12.8 grams carbohydrate, 3.0 grams fat (0.4 saturated), 0 milligrams cholesterol, 691 milligrams sodium, 2.2 grams fibre

dessert

2 oranges

Slice oranges in quarters and place on 2 dessert plates.
Makes 2 servings.

Per serving: 62 calories, 1.2 grams protein, 15.4 grams carbohydrate, 0.2 grams fat (0 saturated), 0 milligrams cholesterol, 0 milligrams sodium, 3.1 grams fibre

shopping list

MEAT
  110g (4oz) boneless, skinless
    chicken breasts
GROCERY
  1 small bottle oyster sauce
  1 small bottle sesame oil
  1 small bottle hoisin sauce
  1 small tin sliced water
    chestnuts
  1 small packet walnut pieces
FRUIT AND VEG
  1 small piece fresh ginger or
    ground ginger
  1 small packet shiitake
    mushrooms (50g/2oz
    needed)
  1 small head iceberg lettuce
  1 small head Chinese
    cabbage (Chinese leaves)
  1 medium red pepper
  2 oranges
STAPLES
  Carrots
  Garlic
  Rice vinegar
  Hot pepper sauce
  Artificial sweetener
  Salt

steak in port wine

helpful hints

- *Beef fillet medallions or steaks may not be in the meat cabinet. Ask the butcher to cut two 175g (6oz) beef fillet medallions for you. Or buy a 350g (12oz) piece of beef fillet and cut it into 2 steaks at home.*
- *Haricots verts or small French green beans can be found in most supermarkets. They are pencil thin and take only a few minutes to cook. If unavailable, use fresh green beans and cut into 5cm (2in) pieces.*
- *To save washing another pan, use the same frying pan for beans and steak.*
- *Slice mushrooms and shallots in a food processor fitted with a thin slicing blade.*

countdown

- *Start rice.*
- *Make beans.*
- *Make steak.*

The nutritional analysis for this recipe fits the Which Carbs phase.

This typical French bistro dish is a delicious recipe and very simple to prepare. The shallots and mushrooms provide the base for the wine sauce.

Shallots have a milder flavour than onions. They are used in many sauces because their cellular structure allows them to melt into the sauce.

To flambé, if using gas, warm the cognac in the pan for a few seconds and then tip the pan so that the gas flame will ignite the liquid. Remove from the heat and wait for the flame to die down. If using an electric hob, throw a lighted match into the warmed cognac. When the flame dies down, remove the match. Keep a frying pan lid nearby for safety.

Brown rice takes about 45 minutes to cook. There are several brands of quick-cooking brown rice available. Their cooking time ranges from 10 to 30 minutes. I find the 30-minute rice has more flavour, but any quick-cooking rice will work for this dinner.

steak in port wine

1 teaspoon rapeseed oil
2 x 175g (6oz) beef fillet medallions
Salt and freshly ground black pepper
50ml (2fl oz) cognac
5 medium shallots, peeled and thinly sliced
110g (4oz) portobello mushrooms, thinly sliced
50ml (2fl oz) dry port wine
115ml (4fl oz) fat-free, low-sodium chicken stock
2 tablespoons single cream
2 tablespoons chopped parsley

Heat oil in a non-stick frying pan just large enough to hold the fillets in one layer over medium heat. Add the steaks and brown for 2 minutes, turn and brown 2 minutes more for a 2.5cm (1in) thick steak. Add salt and pepper to taste to the cooked sides. If steak is 5–7.5cm (2–3in) thick, lower the heat to medium and sauté the fillets 3 minutes for rare, 5–6 minutes for medium rare. Add the cognac to the steak and flambé. Remove steak to a plate and cover with another plate or foil to keep warm. Add the shallots to the pan and sauté until golden, about 2 minutes. Do not let them turn dark brown or black. Add the mushrooms and sauté for 3 minutes. Add the port. Raise the heat to high and reduce the sauce for 1 minute. Add the chicken stock and reduce the sauce by half, about 1 minute. Stir in cream, and spoon sauce over steaks. Sprinkle with parsley.
Makes 2 servings.

Per serving: 470 calories, 38.6 grams protein, 11.7 grams carbohydrate, 19.0 grams fat (7.1 saturated), 115 milligrams cholesterol, 247 milligrams sodium, 0 grams fibre

brown rice

50g (2oz) 30-minute quick cooking brown rice

Salt and freshly ground black pepper to taste

Bring a large saucepan with 2–3 litres (4–5pints) of water to the boil. Add the rice and boil for 30 minutes or according to packet instructions. Drain and add salt and pepper to taste. Divide rice between 2 plates and place steak on top. Spoon sauce over steak and rice.

Makes 2 servings.

Per serving: 85 calories, 2.5 grams protein, 17.5 grams carbohydrate, 0.8 grams fat (0.2 saturated), 0 milligrams cholesterol, 0 milligrams sodium, .0 gram fibre

french green beans

2 teaspoons rapeseed oil

1 medium garlic clove, unpeeled

225g (8oz) haricots verts (French green beans), trimmed

Salt and freshly ground black pepper

Heat oil in a non-stick frying pan on medium-high heat. Add garlic and beans and sauté for 5 minutes or until beans are tender but firm. Remove garlic clove and add salt and pepper to taste.

Makes 2 servings.

Per serving: 88 calories, 2.5 grams protein, 10.3 grams carbohydrate, 5.0 grams fat (0.6 saturated), 0 milligrams cholesterol, 4 milligrams sodium, 2.2 grams fibre

shopping list

DAIRY
  1 small pot single cream

MEAT
  2 x 175g (6oz) beef fillet medallions

GROCERY
  1 small bottle dry port wine
  1 small bottle cognac

FRUIT AND VEG
  5 medium shallots
  110g (4oz) portobello mushrooms
  1 small bunch chopped parsley
  225g (8oz) haricots verts (French green beans)

STAPLES
  Garlic
  30-minute quick-cooking brown rice
  Rapeseed oil
  Fat-free, low-sodium chicken stock
  Salt
  Black peppercorns

right carbs

weekend

meals

indian-spiced chicken

This fits the nutritional guidelines for the Right Carbs phase.

Tandoori chicken with its delicate blend of spices and intriguing aroma is cooked in a clay oven and heated by charcoal. All of the spices can be found in the supermarket.

indian-spiced chicken

350g (12oz) boneless, skinless chicken breasts
225ml (8fl oz) non-fat natural yoghurt, drained
15g (1/2oz) fresh mint leaves plus 2 tablespoons, chopped
1cm (1/2in) fresh ginger, peeled and chopped
1 teaspoon ground coriander
Pinch cayenne
Artificial sweetener equivalent to 2 teaspoons sugar
2 teaspoons rapeseed oil
225g (8oz) frozen chopped onion
2 medium garlic cloves, crushed
Salt and freshly ground black pepper

Remove fat from chicken and make 3 or 4 long slits in meat to allow marinade to penetrate. Mix yoghurt, 15g (1/2oz) chopped mint, ginger, coriander, cayenne and sweetener together. Divide in half and reserve half the marinade in a separate bowl. Add chicken to half the marinade and let marinate for 10 minutes. Turn once during this time. Heat oil in a non-stick frying pan just large enough to hold chicken in 1 layer over medium-high heat. Remove chicken from marinade and discard marinade. Add onion, garlic and chicken to the pan. Brown chicken for 3 minutes. Turn and brown for 2 minutes. Sprinkle salt and pepper to taste over cooked sides. Lower heat to medium. Spoon reserved marinade over chicken, cover, and cook for 5 minutes. A meat thermometer should read 70ºC/160ºF. Sprinkle with remaining 2 tablespoons mint and serve. *Makes 2 servings.*

Per serving: 428 calories, 60.8 grams protein, 19.5 grams carbohydrate, 12.6 grams fat (2.5 saturated), 147 milligrams cholesterol, 223 milligrams sodium, 0 grams fibre

rice and spinach pilaf

1 teaspoon rapeseed oil
225g (8oz) frozen chopped onion
150g (5oz) spinach
75g (3oz) basmati rice
225ml (8fl oz) fat-free, low-sodium chicken stock
1/2 teaspoon ground cumin
Salt and freshly ground black pepper

Heat oil in a medium-sized non-stick frying pan on medium-high heat. Add onion and spinach. Sauté for 2 minutes. Add rice and sauté for 1 minute. Add chicken stock and cumin. When liquid comes to a simmer, lower heat to medium, cover, and simmer for 15 minutes. Remove from heat, add salt and pepper to taste and serve. *Makes 2 servings.*

Per serving: 249 calories, 8.8 grams protein, 47.7 grams carbohydrate, 2.8 grams fat (0.4 saturated), 0 milligrams cholesterol, 368 milligrams sodium, 3.6 grams fibre

helpful hints

● Fresh coriander can be used instead of fresh mint. A quick way to chop mint is to snip the leaves off the stem with scissors.

countdown

● Marinate chicken.
● Start spinach and rice.
● Complete chicken.
● Complete rice.

shopping list

DAIRY
1 small pot non-fat natural yoghurt
MEAT
350g (12oz) boneless, skinless chicken breasts
GROCERY
1 small jar ground coriander
1 small packet basmati rice
FRUIT AND VEG
1 small piece fresh ginger
1 bag washed, ready-to-eat spinach (150g/5oz needed)
1 small bunch fresh mint
STAPLES
Garlic
Rapeseed oil
Fat-free, low-sodium chicken stock
Artificial sweetener
Ground cumin
Frozen chopped onion
Cayenne pepper
Salt
Black peppercorns

pan-seared tuna with mango salsa

The nutritional analysis for these recipes fits the Right Carbs phase.

Pan searing is a perfect way to cook fish. The outside becomes crisp while the inside remains tender and moist. Toasting cumin and coriander seeds in the frying pan allows their natural oils to be released for a more concentrated flavour.

Brown rice takes about 45 minutes to cook. There are several brands of quick-cooking brown rice available. Their cooking time ranges from 10 to 30 minutes. The 10-minute rice is needed for this recipe.

The Lemon Chiffon is made with jelly and needs to be made at least 2 hours in advance. For a quick dessert, serve 1 orange per person.

helpful hints

● Pan searing requires that the frying pan be very hot. Add the fish only when you see smoke rising from the pan.

● Use a non-stick frying pan that is just large enough to hold the tuna.

● Peaches or plums can be substituted for mango.

● To cube mango, slice off each side of the mango as close to the stone as possible. Take the mango half in your hand, skin side down. Score the fruit in a criss-cross pattern through to the skin. Bend the skin backwards so that the cubes pop up. Slice the cubes away from the skin. Score and slice any fruit left on the stone.

countdown

● Make dessert 2 hours ahead.

● Make Saffron Pilaf.

● Make salsa.

● Make tuna.

pan-seared tuna with mango salsa

Salsa
1 ripe mango, cut into cubes
    (about 225g/8oz)
2 tablespoons chopped red onion
1 teaspoon ground cumin
1 tablespoon balsamic vinegar
Several drops hot pepper sauce
15g (½oz) chopped fresh
    coriander
1 tablespoon cumin seeds
1 tablespoon coriander seeds
1 teaspoon olive oil
350g (12oz) tuna steak
Salt
2 wholemeal rolls

To prepare the salsa, combine mango, red onion, ground cumin, balsamic vinegar, hot pepper sauce and coriander in a bowl. Toss well. Taste for seasoning and add more cumin if needed.

To prepare the tuna, place cumin and coriander seeds in a medium non-stick frying pan over medium heat. Toss for 2 minutes and remove from heat. Place in a food processor or mini-processor and coarsely chop. Add olive oil and blend for a few seconds.

Rinse tuna and pat dry with kitchen paper. Spoon the spice mixture over both sides of the tuna, pressing the seeds into the fish with the back of the spoon. Heat the same frying pan on high. It needs to be smoking before the tuna is added. Brown tuna for 1 minute on one side and turn. Brown for another minute and lower heat to medium-high. Cook for another 3–4 minutes. Add a little salt to taste. Remove tuna to 2 plates, spoon salsa on top, and serve with rolls.
Makes 2 servings.

Per serving: 322 calories, 37.2 grams protein, 19.6 grams carbohydrate, 10.3 grams fat (2.4 saturated), 59 milligrams cholesterol, 203 milligrams sodium, 1.1 grams fibre

saffron pilaf

1 teaspoon olive oil
175g (6oz) 10-minute quick-
    cooking brown rice
225ml (8fl oz) water
1/8 teaspoon saffron
Salt and freshly ground black
    pepper

Heat olive oil in a medium non-stick frying pan over medium heat. Add rice and sauté for 1 minute. Add water and saffron. Bring to a simmer and cover. Simmer for 15 minutes. Add salt and pepper to taste.
Makes 2 servings.

Per serving: 148 calories, 3.8 grams protein, 26.3 grams carbohydrate, 3.5 grams fat (0.5 saturated), 0 milligrams cholesterol, 0 milligrams sodium, 1.5 grams fibre

lemon chiffon

125g (4 1/2 oz) sugar-free low
    calorie lemon jelly
110g (4oz) low-fat ricotta cheese

Make up jelly according to packet instructions, using 6 large ice cubes instead of cold water for a quick set. Leave to set for 1 hour. Whip with a whisk, and fold in the ricotta cheese. Spoon into 2 glass dessert bowls or dishes and leave to set for 1 hour.
Makes 2 servings.

Per serving: 174 calories, 3.6 grams protein, 19.3 grams carbohydrate, 1 gram fat (0.3 saturated), 0 milligrams cholesterol, 236 milligrams sodium, 0.6 grams fibre

shopping list

DAIRY
    1 small pot low-fat ricotta
        cheese
FISH
    350g (12oz) tuna steak
GROCERY
    2 wholemeal rolls
    1 small jar cumin seeds
    1 small jar coriander seeds
    1 small packet saffron
        threads
    1 packet sugar-free, low
        calorie lemon jelly
FRUIT AND VEG
    1 bunch fresh coriander
    1 ripe mango
STAPLES
    Red onion
    Hot pepper sauce
    Balsamic vinegar
    Ground cumin
    Olive oil
    10-minute quick-cooking
        brown rice
    Salt
    Black peppercorns

helpful hints

● *Look for unsweetened apple sauce with 100 calories, 30 grams sodium and 30 grams carbohydrates per 225ml (8fl oz).*

● *Standard pork chops can be used instead of boneless ones. Either cut the bone out before cooking or increase the cooking time for the chops by about 5 minutes.*

● *A quick way to chop chives is to snip them with scissors.*

countdown

● *Start lentils.*
● *Make pork chops and relish.*
● *Finish lentils.*
● *Make dessert.*

pork chops with apple relish

The nutritional analysis for this recipes fits the Right Carbs phase.

Sweet and tart apple relish garnishes a sautéed boneless pork chop for this quick weekend dinner. This recipe calls for a Gala apple. It's a sweet, moderately crisp, juicy apple that holds its shape well and adds just the right amount of sweetness to the relish. If you can't find Gala apples, use another type of your choice.

You can buy boneless, butterflied pork chops in the supermarket. They have very little fat and cook quickly.

Shallots have a milder flavour than onions. They are used in many sauces because their cellular structure allows them to melt into the sauce.

pork chops with apple relish

1 teaspoon rapeseed oil
2 x 175g (6oz) boneless loin pork
    chops
Salt and freshly ground black
    pepper
1 medium Gala apple, cored and
    coarsely chopped
1 medium shallot, chopped
2 tablespoons apple cider vinegar
Artificial sweetener equivalent to
    2 teaspoons sugar

Heat rapeseed oil in a small non-stick frying pan over medium-high heat. Add pork chops and brown for 2 minutes. Turn and brown second side for 2 minutes. Season the cooked sides to taste with salt and pepper. Reduce heat to medium and cook for 4 minutes. A meat thermometer should read 70ºC/160ºF.

While pork chops cook, mix apple, shallot, apple cider vinegar and sweetener together in a small bowl. Add salt and pepper to taste.

Place pork chops on individual dinner plates and spoon apple relish on top.
Makes 2 servings.

Per serving: 325 calories, 45.5 grams protein, 12.7 grams carbohydrate, 10.1 grams fat (3.0 saturated), 146 milligrams cholesterol, 106 milligrams sodium, 1.9 grams fibre

toasted walnut lentils

225ml (8fl oz) fat-free, low-sodium chicken stock
225ml (8fl oz) water
110g (4oz) dried lentils
2 tablespoons walnut pieces
Salt and freshly ground black pepper
15g (1/2oz) snipped chives

Bring chicken stock and water to a rolling boil in a medium-sized saucepan over high heat. Slowly add lentils so that the water continues to boil. Reduce the heat to medium-low, cover with a lid and simmer for 20 minutes. Meanwhile place walnuts on a foil-lined baking tray and toast in a toaster oven or under a grill for several minutes. Watch them carefully. They burn easily. Remove lid and continue to cook lentils over high heat, until any remaining liquid has been absorbed. Season with salt and pepper to taste. Toss with walnuts and chives.
Makes 2 servings.

Per serving: 245 calories, 16.8 grams protein, 29.7 grams carbohydrate, 7.9 grams fat (0.7 saturated), 0 milligrams cholesterol, 285 milligrams sodium, 15.4 grams fibre

cranberry apple sauce

450ml (16fl oz) unsweetened apple sauce
2 tablespoons dried cranberries
50ml (2fl oz) water

Divide apple sauce between 2 dessert bowls. Microwave cranberries with water for 1 minute. Drain cranberries, divide in half and stir into the apple sauce.
Makes 2 servings.

Per serving: 145 calories, 0.4 grams protein, 42.1 grams carbohydrate, 0.2 grams fat (0.1 saturated), 0 milligrams cholesterol, 31 milligrams sodium, 4 grams fibre

shopping list

MEAT
  2 x 175g (6oz) boneless loin pork chops
GROCERY
  1 small bottle apple cider vinegar
  1 small packet dried lentils
  1 small packet walnut pieces
  1 small jar unsweetened apple sauce
  1 small packet dried cranberries
FRUIT AND VEG
  1 medium Gala apple
  1 medium shallot
  1 small bunch chives
STAPLES
  Rapeseed oil
  Fat-free, low-sodium chicken stock
  Artificial sweetener
  Salt
  Black peppercorns

entertaining

This section is geared to making parties that don't take all day to prepare. I love to have friends over, but find it hard to spend days shopping and cooking. I also want to serve food that's fun to eat and won't break the calorie bank. These parties let you splurge a little and still keep within the overall guidelines of the low-carbohydrate lifestyle.

These menus are designed for eight people to show you dishes you can prepare to follow a theme and create an atmosphere. The foods and quantities fit within the guidelines for the phase indicated at the top of each menu. You may want to make more and have some leftovers rather than run short (some of your guests may want to take more of a dish they prefer and less of another).

Every detail of these parties has been planned for you, including:
- A shopping list with the amounts you will need
- A countdown for the days prior to and the day of the party itself
- The countdown indicates when to buy the ingredients, when to prepare each dish, and how to store and reheat or prepare them for serving.

Most of the recipes need very little preparation and many can be made ahead. There's almost no last-minute preparation.

Choose from the different party styles to best suit your occasion
- The Buffet for Friends is perfect for football or other sports-related parties, picnics or those times when you have a group over for a Sunday brunch after a family event.
- Prepare the Italian Supper for Friends for simple gatherings or casual Saturday nights. It is perfect for any season of the year.
- The Barbecue Party is easy to assemble, set up outside or in, and creates a fun atmosphere for your entertaining.
- It seems that a majority of guests always want to hang out in the kitchen. So, serve the Casual Soup Supper right in the kitchen with the soup in a large

pot on the stove and the sandwiches and salad on the kitchen work surfaces.

● For the times you want an elegant dinner, the Dinner Party for Eight is your answer. Much of it can be made ahead and there are exact instructions for preparing the dishes so that you don't have to spend the evening in the kitchen.

Here are some general guidelines for drinks that will fit any of these parties:

● To keep within the low-carb guidelines, count 1 glass of alcohol or wine per person and choose from this list some other interesting drinks for them to try.

● Make a jug of strong-flavoured coffee, such as hazelnut or amaretto, and cool in the refrigerator. Serve over ice in tall attractive glasses. Be sure to place ice in the jug just before serving or serve the ice in a bucket on the side.

● Stay away from flavoured syrups for coffee. They usually are made with a sugar syrup base.

● Make a jug of flavoured iced tea such as peach, berry or apple cinnamon. Or make a mixture of peach and apple cinnamon tea together. Set out glasses with a slice of the particular type of fruit in each glass.

● Serve no-sugar-added, flavoured sparkling water with a twist of lemon or lime.

● Serve unusual-flavoured diet soft drinks.

Decorate your table for the occasion. Let your table set the atmosphere and create a warm, welcoming feeling. A TV lifestyle expert gave me some tips on how to make my buffet table look attractive.

Decorate around the theme of the meal by using

● Italian pottery and colours for an Italian meal

● The colours of the teams playing for a sports party

● Colours from your garden flowers for an outdoor or barbecue party

● A tone-on-tone theme (for example, different shades of white and cream) for an elegant party.

Fill the buffet table with enticing objects. Take your coloured napkins and go around the house looking for objects that go with them. Gather them together and see what looks best on the table. These can be pottery, vases, candlesticks, garden baskets, flowerpots, an old child's toy or a miniature wooden wheelbarrow. Select pieces that go with your theme or colours and set them on the table. Remove those that don't look right until you have an attractive display. Use these objects as bases for flower arrangements, napkin and cutlery holders, or just as a design element on the table. This will make your table fun and inviting without having to spend hours preparing a groaning display of food.

italian supper for friends

This party fits the guidelines for the Which Carbs section.

This Italian meal is perfect for a casual buffet. Most of the recipes can be made ahead, leaving just a few things to do on the day.

menu

Garden Crudités and Dips

Chicken Tonnato

Lentil and Rice Salad

String Beans with Crumbled Gorgonzola

White Chocolate Whip

countdown

Two days ahead

- *Shop for ingredients.*

One day ahead

- *Poach chicken and make sauce.*
- *Cut courgette for crudités, and store in plastic bags in the refrigerator.*
- *Make Lentil and Rice Salad and place in attractive bowl. Wrap and refrigerate.*
- *Blanch green beans, place in plastic bag, and refrigerate.*

Morning of the party

- *Make dessert, place in dessert glasses or dishes, and refrigerate.*
- *Slice fennel, arrange crudités platter, wrap and refrigerate. Make dip.*
- *Arrange string beans on a platter, wrap and refrigerate.*
- *Arrange chicken on platter with sauce, peppers, capers and olives. Wrap and refrigerate.*

One hour before guests arrive

- *Remove finished dishes from refrigerator to bring to room temperature.*
- *Drizzle dressing on green beans and sprinkle cheese on top.*

shopping list

Buy 2 days ahead of party

DAIRY
1 large pot non-fat natural
    yoghurt
825g (30oz) low-fat ricotta
    cheese
1 packet crumbled
    Gorgonzola
MEAT
8 x 175g (6oz) boneless,
    skinless chicken breasts
GROCERY
1 small jar honey
1 small packet dried lentils
1 small packet basmati rice
1 small container saffron
    threads
1 packet pine nuts
1 small jar ground coriander
1 small bottle dry white wine
1 small tin anchovy fillets
1 jar sweet peppers
1 jar capers
1 container stoned black
    olives (18 needed)
2 packets instant fat-free,
    sugar-free, white
    chocolate pudding mix
    (75g/3oz needed)
1 small packet semi-sweet
    chocolate

FRUIT AND VEG
225g (8oz) broccoli florets
675g (1½lb) haricots vert
1 small courgette
2 medium fennel bulbs
STAPLES
Staples
Olive oil spray
Red onions
Garlic
Dijon mustard
Fat-free, low-sodium chicken
    stock
Reduced-fat mayonnaise
Olive oil and vinegar dressing
Olive oil
Salt
Black peppercorns
Tinned tuna packed in water

Garlic-Stuffed Steak   **p250**

Veal Saltimbocca **p252**

garden crudités

225g (8oz) broccoli florets,
    washed and cut in half, if large
1 small courgette, washed and
    sliced diagonally in 0.5cm (¹/₂in)
    slices
2 medium bulbs fennel, sliced
115ml (4fl oz) non-fat natural
    yoghurt
2 tablespoons honey
2 tablespoons Dijon mustard

Arrange the vegetables on a platter or plate. Mix yoghurt, honey and mustard together and place in a small bowl. Or slice the top off a small red cabbage and hollow out the inside. Spoon the dressing into the cabbage and serve near the crudités. Makes 8 servings.

Per serving: 56 calories, 2.2 grams protein, 9.1 grams carbohydrate, 0.4 grams fat (0 saturated), 0 milligrams cholesterol, 110 milligrams sodium, 0.8 grams fibre

helpful hints

● If you can find one, use a yellow courgette for extra colour.

● Any type of pre-cut vegetables can be added.

● Use cut vegetables from the salad bar. Pick and choose the vegetables that are in season.

● To slice fennel, cut off stem and leaves and slice the bulb only.

chicken tonnato

This is a traditional summer Italian dish that is perfect for buffets. The secret to keeping the chicken moist is to gently poach it and let it cool in the poaching liquid.

8 x 175g (6oz) boneless, skinless chicken breasts
115ml (4fl oz) dry white wine
225ml (8fl oz) fat-free, low-sodium chicken stock
Salt and freshly ground black pepper
6 anchovy fillets
250g (9oz) tinned tuna, packed in water
150ml (5fl oz) reduced-fat mayonnaise
150ml (5fl oz) non-fat natural yoghurt
1½ teaspoons lemon juice
2 large peppers, thinly sliced
6 tablespoons capers, drained and rinsed
18 stoned black olives, halved

Remove fat from chicken. Add wine and chicken stock to a large saucepan. Bring to the boil on medium-high heat. Add chicken and then enough warm water to make sure all of the chicken is covered by liquid. Bring to a simmer, lower heat to medium-low and gently simmer, uncovered, for 5 minutes. Do not boil the chicken. Remove from heat and let chicken cool in the liquid for 15 minutes (reserve 115ml/ 4fl oz of the poaching liquid). Sprinkle chicken with salt and pepper to taste.

While chicken cools, make the sauce. Rinse anchovy fillets and place in the bowl of a food processor with tuna, mayonnaise and yoghurt. Process until smooth. Add poaching liquid and continue to process. Add lemon juice and process to blend into sauce.

To serve, remove chicken from liquid and place on serving platter. Spoon enough sauce over chicken to coat. Serve remaining sauce on the side. Lay pimiento strips across chicken. Sprinkle capers over chicken and arrange the olives attractively. Cover and refrigerate until needed. Bring to room temperature before serving.

Per serving: 412 calories, 59.9 grams protein, 6.8 grams carbohydrate, 17.2 grams fat (3.4 saturated), 153 milligrams cholesterol, 1057 milligrams sodium, 0.7 grams fibre

lentil and rice salad

450ml (16fl oz) fat-free, low-sodium chicken stock

450ml (16fl oz) water

225g (8oz) lentils, rinsed to remove stones

110g (4oz) basmati rice, rinsed

½ teaspoon saffron threads

Salt and freshly ground black pepper

50g (2oz) pinenuts

350g (12oz) sliced red onion

6 garlic cloves, crushed

½ teaspoon ground coriander

2 tablespoons plus 2 teaspoons olive oil

Bring chicken stock and 225ml (8fl oz) water to the boil in a non-stick pan on medium-high heat. Add the lentils slowly so that the stock continues to boil. Lower heat to medium. Cover with a lid and simmer for 5 minutes. Add rice, saffron and remaining water to the lentils. Bring back to a simmer, cover, and simmer for 15 minutes. The liquid will be absorbed and the lentils cooked through, but firm. Add salt and pepper to taste. While lentils and rice cook, heat a non-stick frying pan on medium-high heat and add the pinenuts. Sauté pinenuts for 1–2 minutes or until golden. Be careful because the nuts burn easily. Remove and set aside. Heat 2 teaspoons olive oil in the same pan and add the onion. Sauté, without browning, for 5 minutes. Add the garlic and continue to sauté for another 5 minutes.

Place lentils, rice and onion in a large bowl and add the remaining 2 tablespoons oil, coriander and salt and pepper to taste. Toss well. Taste for seasoning and add more salt and pepper, if needed. Sprinkle toasted pinenuts on top and serve.

Makes 8 servings.

Per serving: 231 calories, 9.2 grams protein, 29.6 grams carbohydrate, 5.1 grams fat (0.7 saturated), 0 milligrams cholesterol, 144 milligrams sodium, 7.3 grams fibre

helpful hint

- *Turmeric can be substituted for the saffron.*

string beans with crumbled gorgonzola

helpful hints

● A quick way to trim beans is to line them up with the ends together and slice off the tips. Turn bunch around the other way, line them up again, and slice off the tips.

● Large green beans can be used. Cut them into 10cm (4in) lengths before blanching.

● Any type of blue veined cheese can be used.

675g ($1^3/4$lb) haricots verts (small green beans)

3 tablespoons olive oil and vinegar dressing ·

Salt and freshly ground black pepper

110g (4oz) crumbled Gorgonzola

Bring a medium-sized saucepan of water to the boil. Trim beans and add to boiling water. As soon as the water comes back to the boil, drain and plunge beans into a bowl of iced water. Drain. Place on platter, drizzle dressing over the top and toss. Add salt and pepper to taste. Sprinkle cheese on top.

Makes 8 servings.

Per serving: 64 calories, 3.5 grams protein, 5.1 grams carbohydrate, 3.6 grams fat (2.1 saturated), 10 milligrams cholesterol, 194 milligrams sodium, 1.1 grams fibre

white chocolate whip

825g (30oz) low-fat ricotta cheese
450ml (16fl oz) water
75g (3oz) fat-free, sugar-free
  instant white chocolate pudding
  powder
4 teaspoons grated semi-sweet
  chocolate

Whisk ricotta cheese and water together until smooth. Add the white chocolate pudding powder and whisk until smooth. Divide between 8 dessert bowls. Sprinkle ½ teaspoon grated chocolate on top of each dish.
Makes 8 servings.

Per serving: 114 calories, 0.1 grams protein, 4.9 grams carbohydrate, 0.2 grams fat (0.1 saturated), 0 milligrams cholesterol, 272 milligrams sodium, 0 grams fibre

helpful hint

● *For speed, use a food processor to whip up this dessert.*

dinner party
for eight

dinner party for eight

This dinner party fits the nutritional guidelines for the Which Carbs phase.

There's no need to spend all day making an elegant dinner party. These recipes are easy to make and you and your guests can enjoy the evening without worrying about the calories and carbs.

menu

Bruschetta

Guinea Fowl in Red Wine

Brown Rice with Toasted Pinenuts

Roasted Asparagus with Red Pepper

Radicchio, Chicory and Watercress Salad

Berry Cups with Almond Sauce

countdown

Two days ahead

- Shop for ingredients.

One day ahead

- Make Guinea Fowl in Red Wine. Place in ovenproof casserole or dish in their sauce. Cover and refrigerate.
- Make Brown Rice with Toasted Pinenuts. Place in an oven-to-table dish, cover and refrigerate.
- Make Almond Sauce for dessert. Cover and refrigerate.

Morning of the party

- Assemble berry cups without sauce and wrap and refrigerate.
- Prepare asparagus ready for the oven. Cut off the woody ends, place on baking trays, roll in olive oil, and place in refrigerator.
- Wash watercress, radicchio and chicory; dry and place in salad bowl. Cover with clingfilm and refrigerate.
- Make bruschetta topping and refrigerate.

One hour before guests arrive

- Remove guinea fowl, rice, asparagus, berries and sauce from refrigerator.

Thirty minutes before guests arrive

- Pre-heat oven to 150°C/300°F/gas mark 2.
- Place guinea fowl in their sauce and rice in oven for 30 minutes to warm through.
- Remove salad from refrigerator and toss with dressing.
- Spoon topping for bruschetta on toasts and arrange on serving tray.

Before dessert

- Spoon sauce over berries just before serving.

shopping list

Buy 2 days ahead of party

DAIRY
  1 pot reduced-fat crème
     fraiche (225ml/8fl oz
     needed)
MEAT
  4 guinea fowl, about 900g
     (2lb) each
GROCERY
  1 jar sweet peppers
     (450g/16oz needed)
  1 packet flaked almonds
  1 packet pinenuts
  1 bottle almond essence
  1 bottle red wine (Beaujolais
     or Burgundy)
FRUIT AND VEG
  1 medium tomato
  1 medium head radicchio
  2 medium heads chicory
  1 bunch watercress
  900g (2lb) asparagus
  350g (12oz) button
     mushrooms
  1 packet broccoli florets
     (275g/10oz needed)
  Mixture of raspberries,
     strawberries and
     blueberries (1.1kg/2½lb
     berries needed)

STAPLES
  30-minute quick-cooking
     brown rice
  Olive oil spray
  Red onion
  Yellow onion
  Carrots
  Garlic
  Wholemeal bread
  Fat-free, low-sodium chicken
     stock
  Olive oil
  Balsamic vinegar
  Olive oil and vinegar dressing
  Artificial sweetener
  Salt
  Black peppercorns

bruschetta

Olive oil spray
225g (8oz) sliced red onion
2 garlic cloves, crushed
1 medium tomato, diced
½ tablespoon olive oil
1 teaspoon balsamic vinegar
Salt and freshly ground black
  pepper
4 slices of wholemeal toast, cut
  into squares

Heat a non-stick frying pan on medium-high heat. Spray with olive oil spray and add onion and garlic. Sauté for 10 minutes. The onion should be golden. Remove from heat and toss with tomatoes. Add olive oil, balsamic vinegar and salt and pepper to taste. Place in a bowl and refrigerate until needed.

To serve, spoon tomato mixture on to toast and place on serving platter.

Per serving: 56 calories, 1.6 grams protein, 7.9 grams carbohydrate, 1.9 grams fat (0.4 saturated), 0 milligrams cholesterol, 39 milligrams sodium, 0.5 grams fibre

helpful hint

● Chicory should not be placed in water to clean. The leaves will turn brown. Just remove any damaged outer leaves and then wipe with damp kitchen paper.

radicchio, chicory and watercress salad

1 medium head radicchio
1 bunch watercress
2 medium heads chicory
5 tablespoons olive oil and vinegar
  dressing

Wash radicchio and watercress and dry. Cut about 2.5cm (1in) off flat end of chicory and remove any torn or brown outer leaves. Wipe chicory with damp kitchen paper. Tear radicchio leaves into bite-sized pieces. Break large stems off watercress. Slice chicory into 2.5cm (1in) circles. When salad is dry, place in a salad bowl, cover with clingfilm, and refrigerate. Just before serving, toss with the dressing.

Makes 8 servings.

Per serving: 56 calories, 0.7 grams protein, 1.9 grams carbohydrate, 5.4 grams fat (1.9 saturated), 0 milligrams cholesterol, 59 milligrams sodium, 0.2 grams fibre

guinea fowl in red wine

4 guinea fowl, each about 900g (2lb)

Olive oil spray

450g (16oz) diced yellow onion

2 medium carrots, diced

4 medium garlic cloves, crushed

300ml (12fl oz) red wine (Beaujolais or Burgundy)

300ml (12fl oz) fat-free, low-sodium chicken stock

350g (12oz) sliced button mushrooms

Salt and freshly ground black pepper

Remove the fat from the cavity of the guinea fowl and split them in half. Heat 2 large non-stick frying pans just large enough to hold the halves in 1 layer over medium-high heat. Spray with olive oil spray. Brown the birds on both sides, about 5 minutes. Remove to a plate and pour off any excess fat. Add the diced onion, carrots and garlic to the pan. Sauté until the vegetables start to shrivel, about 5 minutes. Return guinea fowl halves to the pan, lower the heat to medium, and cover with a lid. Leave to cook until the guinea fowl are cooked through, about 20 minutes. A meat thermometer should read 80ºC/170ºF for white meat and 85ºC/180ºF for dark meat. Remove birds to a dish and cover with foil to keep warm. Pour off any remaining fat, add wine, and scrape the brown bits from the bottom of the pan while the wine simmers for about 2 minutes. Add the chicken stock and mushrooms. Simmer for 2 more minutes. Remove skin from guinea fowl and add salt and pepper to taste. If serving immediately, return the birds to the pan and let cook to warm through. Or place in an ovenproof serving platter and spoon sauce and vegetables on top. Cover and refrigerate. Remove from refrigerator and allow to come to room temperature, about 30 minutes. Place, covered with foil or a lid, in a 150ºC/300ºF/gas mark 2 oven for 20–30 minutes or until warmed through.

Makes 8 servings.

Per serving: 260 calories, 35.2 grams protein, 7.0 grams carbohydrate, 6.3 grams fat (1.6 saturated), 153 milligrams cholesterol, 215 milligrams sodium, 0.2 grams fibre

brown rice with toasted pinenuts

1 cup 30-minute quick-cooking brown rice
275g (10oz) broccoli florets
3 tablespoons pinenuts
1 tablespoon olive oil
Salt and freshly ground black pepper

Fill a large saucepan with 2–3 litres (4–5 pints) cold water. Add rice, cover with a lid and bring to a boil over high heat. When water comes to the boil, remove the lid, lower heat to medium-low and boil for 25 minutes. Add broccoli and continue to boil for 5 minutes. While rice boils, place pinenuts on a foil-lined baking tray and toast under a grill for 2–3 minutes or until golden.

When rice is cooked through, drain and toss with oil and salt and pepper to taste. Place in a serving bowl and sprinkle pinenuts on top.

Recipe may be made ahead until this point. Place rice in oven-to-tableware dish and store in the refrigerator. Before serving, bring to room temperature and place in pre-heated oven with guinea fowl for 30 minutes. Remove from oven and serve.

Makes 8 servings.

Per serving: 104 calories, 3.2 grams protein, 15.5 grams carbohydrate, 2.6 grams fat (0.4 saturated), 0 milligrams cholesterol, 10 milligrams sodium, 1.4 grams fibre

helpful hint

● *Watch the pinenuts carefully as they burn easily.*

roasted asparagus with red peppers

$\frac{1}{2}$ *tablespoon olive oil*
Salt and freshly ground black pepper
900g (2lb) asparagus
450g (16oz) peppers

Pre-heat oven to 200ºC/400ºF/gas mark 6. Line a baking tray with foil and spoon oil on to foil. Add salt and pepper to taste. Add asparagus and roll in oil, making sure all spears are coated with oil and salt and pepper. Spread asparagus out to form 1 layer and roast in oven for 5 minutes. Remove asparagus and turn. Roast 10 more minutes for thick spears, 5 more minutes for thin ones. Remove from oven and arrange spears in straight rows on an oval serving platter. Cut peppers into thin strips and sprinkle over top.
Makes 8 servings.

Per serving: 33 calories, 2.0 grams protein, 5.0 grams carbohydrate, 1.1 grams fat
(0.2 saturated), 0 milligrams cholesterol, 8 milligrams sodium, 2.4 grams fibre

berry cups with almond sauce

1.1kg (2¹/₂lb) berries (mixture of raspberries, blueberries and strawberries)

2 teaspoons almond essence

Artificial sweetener equivalent to 2 teaspoons sugar

225ml (8fl oz) reduced-fat crème fraiche

3 tablespoons flaked almonds

Place berries in 8 small ramekins. Mix almond essence and sweetener into crème fraiche and spoon or dollop sauce on top of each one. Sauté almonds in a frying pan until just turning golden. Be careful toasting the almonds as they burn easily. Sprinkle almonds on top of sauce.
Makes 8 servings.

Per serving: 134 calories, 3 grams protein, 17.3 grams carbohydrate, 6.8 grams fat (2.7 saturated), 15 milligrams cholesterol, 20 milligrams sodium, 6.3 grams fibre

helpful hint

● *Watch the almonds carefully as they burn easily.*

casual soup
supper

casual soup supper

This meal fits the nutritional guidelines for the Right Carbs phase.

Whenever we have friends over, it seems that everyone ends up standing around the kitchen. I planned this party so that the kitchen is part of the fun. I make the soup and leave it in a large, colourful saucepan on the stove with a ladle in the soup. The bowls are nearby and people can help themselves. The sandwiches and salad are placed on the work surface. Everyone can help themselves on their way to finding a seat at the table.

menu

Creamy Wild Mushroom Soup

Grilled Halibut Sandwich

Three Bean Salad

Mango Fool

countdown

Two days ahead

● Shop for most ingredients except the fish.

One day ahead

● Make soup, cover and refrigerate.

Morning of the party

● Buy fish.

● Make Mango Fool, place in attractive glass, and refrigerate.

● Make salad. Place in serving bowl. Cover and refrigerate.

One hour ahead

● Prepare ingredients for halibut sandwich.

● Remove salad from refrigerator.

● Remove soup from refrigerator.

Fifteen minutes before guests arrive

● Marinate fish.

When guests arrive

● Place soup on stove and heat. When soup is hot, lower heat to extra low and leave until served.

● Make halibut sandwich just before serving.

● Remove dessert from refrigerator.

● Spoon sauce over berries just before serving.

shopping list

Buy 2 days ahead of party except the fish

DAIRY

1 small pot double cream (115ml/4fl oz needed)

4 pots non-fat, sugar-free mango or tropical fruit yoghurt (900ml/32fl oz needed)

GROCERY

1 small packet dried ceps (mushrooms)

FISH

8 X 175g (6oz) halibut fillets (purchase on the day of the party)

FRUIT AND VEG

1 bunch fresh dill

1 bunch spring onions (6 needed)

350g (12oz) sliced portobello mushrooms

2 medium tomatoes

1 medium Spanish onion

225g (8oz) green beans

225g (8oz) yellow beans

2 medium ripe mangoes (450g/1lb)

1 bunch fresh mint

STAPLES

Red kidney beans (500g/ 18oz needed)

Yellow onion

Olive oil spray

Balsamic vinegar

Olive oil and vinegar dressing

Flour

Grated nutmeg

Multi-grain bread

Fat-free, low-sodium chicken stock

Mayonnaise

Lemons

Salt

Black peppercorns

Dinner Party for Eight   p278-285

creamy wild mushroom soup

Many 'wild' mushrooms are cultivated and don't have a strong flavour of the woods. Dried ceps (called porcini in Italy) that have been gathered in the woods add a depth of flavour to this soup.

The secret to this soup is cooking the onion until it is sweet. Grated nutmeg gives the soup an intriguing flavour.

40g (1½oz) dried cep mushrooms
1.2 litres (40fl oz) hot water
Olive oil spray
1 large yellow onion, sliced
350g (12oz) sliced portobello
    mushrooms
1 tablespoon flour
900ml (32fl oz) fat-free, low-
    sodium chicken stock
8 tablespoons double cream
¼ teaspoon grated nutmeg
Salt and freshly ground black
    pepper

Add dried ceps to 225ml (8fl oz) hot water and leave to stand for 5 minutes. Drain, reserving the liquid, and slice. Strain liquid 2 to 3 times to remove sand.

Heat a large saucepan over medium-high heat and spray with olive oil spray. Add the onion and sauté for 2 minutes. Reduce heat to medium and continue to cook onion until golden, about 5 minutes. Do not brown onion. Add the portobello mushrooms and sauté for 2 minutes, stirring 1 or 2 times. Sprinkle flour on top and stir until absorbed, about 1 minute. Add chicken stock and remaining water. Lift reconstituted mushrooms from the hot water with a slotted spoon and add to the soup. Place a piece of kitchen towel in a sieve and strain the mushroom liquid into the soup. Bring to a boil. Simmer for 10 minutes. Add nutmeg and salt and pepper to taste.

Remove 225ml (8fl oz) soup to a blender or food processor and purée. Return to the soup. Spoon cream into soup and mix well. Taste for seasoning, adding more if necessary.
Makes 8 servings.

Per serving: 102 calories, 2.9 grams protein, 5.4 grams carbohydrate, 7.4 grams fat (3.8 saturated), 21 milligrams cholesterol, 288 milligrams sodium, 0 grams fibre

helpful hints

● *Slice onion and mushrooms in a food processor fitted with a 0.5cm (¼in) slicing blade.*
● *Cook the onion until it is transparent, but not brown, to give the soup a sweet flavour.*
● *Morel mushrooms can be substituted.*
● *The soup can be made a day in advance. It will thicken on standing. Stir in a little stock when reheating.*

grilled halibut sandwich

helpful hints

● *Ask for the skin to be removed when you buy the fish.*
● *A quick way to chop dill is to snip the leaves with scissors.*
● *Make sure the grill bars are clean and spray them with vegetable cooking spray before grilling the fish.*
Any type of firm, white, non-oily fish fillet can be used.

Grilling fish gives great flavour. Grill on a barbecue, use your kitchen grill or simply sauté the fish in a frying pan. A renowned fish chef once showed me this method for grilling fish in advance. Sear the fish on the grill about 1 hour before needed and then place in a 140ºC/275ºF/gas mark 1 oven to finish cooking for about 30 minutes. For a 2.5cm (1in) thick fillet, sear 2 minutes per side and then place in oven.

8 x 175g (6oz) halibut fillets
450ml (16fl oz) balsamic vinegar
115ml (4fl oz) mayonnaise
2 tablespoons lemon juice
75g (3oz) snipped fresh dill
Salt and freshly ground black pepper
16 slices multi-grain bread
8 slices Spanish onion
8 slices tomato

Pre-heat grill. Rinse fish fillets and pat dry with kitchen paper. Place in a self-seal plastic bag and add balsamic vinegar. Marinate for 15 minutes. Meanwhile, mix mayonnaise with lemon juice and fold in 50g (2oz) dill, reserving the rest for garnish. Add salt and pepper to taste.

Remove fish from bag and pat dry with kitchen paper. Place on a barbecue grill 10cm (4in) from heat or under pre-heated kitchen grill. Grill for 2 minutes per side. Season cooked sides. While fish is cooking, toast the bread.

To serve, spread each slice of toast with a layer of mayonnaise. Place a fish fillet on each slice. Place onion slices on the fish and finish with tomato slices. Sprinkle with reserved dill. Serve as open sandwiches.

Makes 8 servings.

Per serving: 455 calories, 36.8 grams protein, 38.9 grams carbohydrate, 14.7 grams fat (2.5 saturated), 62 milligrams cholesterol, 570 milligrams sodium, 1.2 grams fibre

three bean salad

225g (8oz) green beans, trimmed
    and cut into 2.5cm (1in) pieces
225g (8oz) yellow beans, trimmed
    and cut into 2.5cm (1in) pieces
500g (18oz) cooked red kidney
    beans, rinsed and drained
6 spring onions, sliced
6 tablespoons olive oil and vinegar
    dressing
Salt and freshly ground black
    pepper

Bring a large saucepan filled with water to the
boil. Add the green and yellow beans. As soon
as the water returns to the boil, drain and refresh
under ice cold water. Place in a large serving
bowl and add the kidney beans, spring onions
and dressing. Toss well. Add salt and pepper to
taste. Toss once more.
Makes 8 servings.

Per serving: 141 calories, 4.4 grams protein,
17.1 grams carbohydrate, 6.7 grams fat
(1.0 saturated), 0 milligrams cholesterol, 61 milligrams
sodium, 2.2 grams fibre

mango fool

*I was introduced to luscious, creamy fruit fools when I first moved to England. They are rich
desserts, often made with tart green gooseberries. I have adapted this idea using fresh
mangos and yoghurt.*

900ml (32fl oz) non-fat, sugar-free
    fruit yoghurt, such as apricot/
    mango or mango/tropical fruit
2 ripe mangos, cubed (about
    450g/1lb)
8 small mint sprigs

Fold the mango cubes into the yoghurt and
spoon into 8 attractive martini glasses or dessert
bowls. Arrange a mint sprig in each glass.
Refrigerate until 15 minutes before needed. Let
come to room temperature before serving.
Makes 8 servings.

Per serving: 104 calories, 5.8 grams protein,
20.3 grams carbohydrate, 0.2 grams fat (0 saturated),
3 milligrams cholesterol, 96 milligrams sodium,
0.6 grams fibre

helpful hints

● *To blanch the beans and
set their colour, they need to
be plunged into iced water
after they are drained. Fill a
roasting tin with water and
ice cubes and place near the
sink. As soon as the beans
are drained, plunge them
into the iced water. When
they are cold, drain.*

● *To cube a mango, slice off
each side as close to the
stone as possible. Cut a
2.5cm (1in) piece from one
half. Remove the skin from
the slice and cut into thin
strips for a garnish. Take the
mango half in your hand,
skin side down. Score the
fruit in a criss-cross pattern
through to the skin. Bend the
skin backwards so that the
cubes pop up. Slice the
cubes away from the skin.
Repeat with the other half.
Score and slice any fruit left
on the stone.*

buffet for
friends

buffet for friends

This meal fits the nutritional guidelines for the Right Carbs phase.

Informal family gatherings, brunch with friends, or 'open-house' parties all call for grazing foods that, when placed on a table, invite everyone to help themselves. This party needs very little attention during the festivities, leaving you to join in the fun.

menu

Prawns in Lime-Mustard Sauce

Roasted Meat Platter with Horseradish and Honey Mustard Dressing

Tomato Platter

Pasta Salad

Frozen Yoghurt Berry Cup

countdown

Two days ahead

- *Shop for ingredients.*

One day ahead

- *Arrange meat platter, wrap and refrigerate.*
- *Make sauces for meats. Cover and refrigerate.*
- *Make sauce for prawns.*
- *Poach prawns. Cover and refrigerate.*

Morning of the party

- *Arrange prawns on serving platter, wrap and refrigerate.*
- *Measure frozen yoghurt and place in dessert bowls. Place in freezer. Sprinkle berries around yoghurt just before serving.*
- *Slice tomatoes and assemble tomato platter.*
- *Make pasta salad.*

One hour before guests arrive

- *Remove prawns, meat and sauces from refrigerator and set on buffet table. Place prawn sauce near prawns and meat sauces near meat platter. Drizzle tomatoes with Honey Mustard Dressing. Place bread for meat platter in basket.*
- *Remove yoghurt bowls from freezer and sprinkle with berries 15 minutes before serving dessert.*

shopping list

Buy 2 days ahead of party

DAIRY
   1 pot non-fat natural yoghurt
      (275ml/10fl oz needed)
DELI
   350g (12oz) sliced lean deli
      roast beef
   350g (12oz) sliced roast
      turkey breast
   350g (12oz) lean sliced ham
      (not honey-baked or
      glazed)
SEAFOOD
   675g (1³/₄lb) prawns, peeled
      and deveined
GROCERY
   1 bottle horseradish
   1 jar honey-flavoured mustard
   225g (8oz) wholemeal penne
      or other wholemeal short-
      cut pasta
   1 carton low-fat, frozen
      strawberry yoghurt
      (900ml/32fl oz needed)
   2 packets thin-sliced rye bread
      (32 slices needed)

FRUIT AND VEG
   2 limes
   ½ head red-leaf lettuce
   1 bunch chives
   1 bunch watercress
   2 large red tomatoes
   2 large yellow tomatoes
   2 lemons
   1 bunch dill
   150g (5oz) broccoli florets
   1 medium cucumber
   2 medium red peppers
   1.1kg (2½lb) fresh raspberries
STAPLES
   Mayonnaise
   Dijon mustard
   Reduced-fat mayonnaise
   Salt
   Black peppercorns

prawns in lime-mustard sauce

675g (1³/₄lb) prawns, cooked, peeled and deveined
6 tablespoons mayonnaise
2 teaspoons Dijon mustard
1¹/₂ tablespoons lime juice

Arrange prawns in a circle, tails pointed out, on a serving platter. Mix mayonnaise, mustard and lime juice together in a small bowl. Place the bowl in the centre of the platter.
Makes 8 servings.

Per serving: 148 calories, 3.8 grams protein, 26.3 grams carbohydrate, 3.5 grams fat (0.5 saturated), 0 milligrams cholesterol, 0 milligrams sodium, 1.5 grams fibre

helpful hints

● *Shelled prawns are available at most supermarket seafood counters. The slightly higher cost is worth the time saved.*
● *If you're pressed for time, buy ready-cooked prawns from the seafood department of the supermarket.*
● *You can substitute lemon juice for the lime juice.*

helpful hint

● *To keep the informal atmosphere, place bread in a basket near the meat for people to make their own sandwiches.*

roasted meat platter with horseradish and honey mustard dressing

1/2 head red-leaf lettuce

350g (12oz) sliced lean deli roast beef

350g (12oz) sliced roast turkey breast

350g (12oz) lean sliced ham (no honey-baked or glazed)

50ml (2fl oz) reduced-fat mayonnaise

275ml (10fl oz) non-fat natural yoghurt

1/2 tablespoons horseradish

15g (1/2oz) snipped chives

1/2 tablespoons honey-flavoured mustard

32 slices thin-sliced rye bread (or 16 slices medium-sliced rye bread)

To prepare the meat platter, line a serving platter with lettuce leaves. Place meat in radiating rows from the centre of the platter to the edge, folding the slices in half and overlapping them. The folded edge should show.

To prepare the horseradish sauce, mix the mayonnaise, 115ml (4fl oz) yoghurt, horseradish and chives together and place in a small bowl. Serve with meat platter.

To prepare the Honey Mustard Dressing, mix the remaining yoghurt and honey-flavoured mustard together and place in a small bowl. Serve with the meat platter and the bread.

Makes 8 servings.

Per serving: 453 calories, 39.1 grams protein, 43.8 grams carbohydrate, 12.3 grams fat (2.9 saturated), 87 milligrams cholesterol, 1091 milligrams sodium, 2.1 grams fibre

tomato platter

2 large red tomatoes
2 large yellow tomatoes
1–2 tablespoons Honey Mustard
    Dressing from the Roasted
    Meat Platter
1 bunch watercress, for garnish

Slice tomatoes and alternate coloured slices on a serving platter. Drizzle 1–2 tablespoons Honey Mustard Sauce over. Place sprigs of watercress on the side for a garnish.
Makes 8 servings.

Per serving: 46 calories, 2.4 grams protein, 7.6 grams carbohydrate, 0.4 grams fat (0 saturated), 1.0 milligrams cholesterol, 29 milligrams sodium, 0 grams fibre

pasta salad

helpful hint

● *Enhance the display of your buffet by covering the table with a colourful cloth or napkins.*

50ml (2fl oz) reduced-fat mayonnaise

2 tablespoons freshly squeezed lemon juice

15g (¹/₂oz) snipped fresh dill

225g (8oz) uncooked wholemeal penne or other wholemeal short-cut pasta

150g (5oz) small broccoli florets

1 medium cucumber, peeled, seeded and cubed

2 medium red peppers, cubed

Salt and freshly ground black pepper to taste

Place a large saucepan with 2–3 litres (4–5 pints) water to boil. Mix mayonnaise, lemon juice and dill together in a large serving bowl. Add pasta to boiling water and cook for 5 minutes. Add broccoli and continue to cook for 4 minutes or until pasta is cooked but still firm. Drain and add to serving bowl. Add cucumber, red pepper and salt and pepper to taste.

Makes 8 servings.

Per serving: 123 calories, 4.7 grams protein, 21.4 grams carbohydrate, 3.0 grams fat (0.6 saturated), 3 milligrams cholesterol, 66 milligrams sodium, 3.3 grams fibre

frozen yoghurt berry cup

900ml (32fl oz) low-fat, frozen strawberry yoghurt
1.1kg (2¹/₂lb) fresh raspberries

Spoon yoghurt into 8 dessert bowls and sprinkle berries on top.
Makes 8 servings.

Per serving: 151 calories, 3.6 grams protein, 27.1 grams carbohydrate, 3.4 grams fat (1.5 saturated), 10 milligrams cholesterol, 80 milligrams sodium, 2.9 grams fibre

helpful hints

● *Any fresh berries can be used.*

● *The frozen yoghurt can be spooned into dessert bowls and placed in the freezer in the morning. They only need to be removed and sprinkled with berries just before serving. They will also hold for about 30 minutes out of the freezer this way.*

barbecue
party

barbecue party

The meal fits the nutritional guidelines for the Right Carbs phase.

'Let's have a barbecue' is an invitation that brings smiles to everyone. Grilled food is popular year-round and the idea of cooking outside brings sunny thoughts to most of us, even in the winter months.

Most barbecued foods are coated with sugary sauces that have a lot of carbs. This simple barbecue party captures the flavours of the grill without the carbohydrates.

It's easiest to serve this meal buffet-style.

menu

Spicy Tuna Spread

No-Fuss Salad Bar

Lime Barbecued Chicken with Black Bean Sauce

Green Bean and Orzo Salad

Melon with Marinated Strawberries

countdown

Two days ahead

● *Shop for ingredients.*

One day ahead

● *Make Spicy Tuna Spread.*

● *Make black bean sauce for chicken. Cover and refrigerate.*

● *Prepare and blanch onion and red pepper for chicken recipe. Cover and refrigerate.*

● *Make strawberry sauce and place in a bowl. Cover and refrigerate.*

Morning of the party

● *Place ingredients for salad bar in attractive bowls. Cover and refrigerate.*

● *Make Green Bean and Orzo Salad. Wrap and refrigerate.*

● *Cut melon into slices and place in bowl. Cover and refrigerate.*

● *Cut cucumber slices for tuna spread. Wrap and refrigerate.*

One hour before guests arrive

● *Marinate chicken, covered, in refrigerator.*

● *Light barbecue, if using charcoal.*

● *Remove tuna spread, black bean sauce, red pepper and onion, orzo salad and strawberry sauce from the refrigerator.*

● *Arrange melon on individual dessert plates. Cover with clingfilm and set aside.*

● *Set up salad bar on buffet table.*

shopping list

Buy 2 days ahead of party

DAIRY
  1 small piece Parmesan
    cheese (25g/1oz
    needed for Parmesan
    curls)
MEAT
  8 x 175g (6oz) boneless
    skinless chicken breasts
GROCERY
  1 small container stoned
    green or black olives
    (8 olives needed)
  1 small jar horseradish
  1 small packet orzo
  1 small container orange
    juice
  1 small packet icing sugar
  1 packet almond-
    flavoured or other
    biscuits

Fifteen minutes before guests arrive

● *Place black bean sauce in a saucepan over low heat to heat through.*

● *Spread tuna on cucumber slices and place on serving platter.*

● *Pre-heat gas barbecue.*

● *While guests are having drinks and hors d'oeuvres, grill chicken and place on platter in low oven to keep warm.*

To serve meal

● *Spoon half the black bean sauce on to a serving platter, place chicken on top and sprinkle with blanched onion and red pepper. Serve the remaining sauce in a bowl next to the chicken platter. Place on buffet table.*

● *Place orzo salad on buffet table.*

To serve dessert

● *Pre-heat oven and place biscuits in oven while main dishes are being cleared.*

● *Spoon strawberry sauce over melon and place biscuits on side.*

spicy tuna spread

8 stoned green or black olives

175g (6oz) tin tuna packed in water

2 tablespoons mayonnaise

3 tablespoons horseradish

15g (¹/₂oz) fresh basil leaves, washed and dried

2 medium cucumbers, peeled and sliced on the diagonal

Place olives, tuna, mayonnaise, horseradish and basil in a food processor and process until smooth. Taste for seasoning, adding more horseradish if necessary. Just before serving, spread on cucumber slices, and place on serving platter.

Makes 8 servings.

Per serving: 49 calories, 6.3 grams protein, 3.8 grams carbohydrate, 1.3 grams fat (0.1 saturated), 9 milligrams cholesterol, 199 milligrams sodium, 0.6 grams fibre

shopping list (continued)

FRUIT AND VEG

1 bunch basil leaves

1 small bunch parsley

1 small bunch coriander

2 medium cucumbers

2 bags washed, ready-to-eat lettuce

1 bag grated, washed, ready-to-eat carrots

2 bags shredded, washed, ready-to-eat red cabbage

2 bags washed, ready-to-eat celery sticks

2 red peppers

900g (2lb) fresh green beans

1kg (2¹/₂lb) cherry tomatoes

3 limes

2 lemons

1 honeydew melon

1.1kg (2¹/₂lb) fresh strawberries

STAPLES

175g (6oz) tin tuna packed in water

Red onion

Garlic

Cayenne pepper

Mayonnaise

No-sugar-added salad dressings

Tinned black beans (450g/16oz needed)

Olive oil

Balsamic vinegar

Salt

Black peppercorns

no-fuss salad bar

A colourful salad bar makes a pretty display and is easy to assemble. Here are some tips on how you can put one together without any washing or cutting. Buy a selection of these items from your supermarket: pre-washed lettuce, grated carrots, sliced red cabbage, celery sticks.

2 bags washed, ready-to-eat lettuce

1 bag grated carrots

2 bags shredded red cabbage

2 bags celery sticks

1kg (2¹/₂lb) cherry tomatoes

8 tablespoons no-sugar-added salad dressing

All you need to do is open the bags and place the vegetables in attractive bowls. Add a bowl of rinsed cherry tomatoes. I have given you guidelines, but you can choose whatever vegetables you like. The secret is to make a colourful display. I like to use different sizes and shapes of bowls for the vegetables and dressing. For a party it's nice to fill bowls with the dressings. For nutritional values, plan for 1 tablespoon dressing per person.

Buy 2 different types of dressings. Look for dressings that have no sugar added and are made with olive or rapeseed oil.

Per serving: 201 calories, 15G protein, 12G carbohydrate, 11G fat (3G saturated), 426MG cholestorol, 511MG sodium, 3G fibre

Buffet for Friends   p292-299

Buffet for Friends p292-29

lime-barbecued chicken with black bean sauce

115ml (4fl oz) fresh lime juice
225ml (8fl oz) olive oil
1 teaspoon cayenne pepper
4 garlic cloves, crushed
8 x 175g (6oz) boneless, skinless chicken breasts
50g (2oz) chopped red onion
2 red peppers, diced
50ml (2fl oz) balsamic vinegar
115ml (4fl oz) orange juice
450g(16oz) drained and rinsed cooked tinnned black beans
Salt and freshly ground black pepper
Several sprigs fresh coriander or parsley, for garnish

To prepare the chicken, mix lime juice, oil, cayenne pepper and 2 cloves crushed garlic together and pour into plastic bag or bowl. Add the chicken breasts and marinate overnight or about 8 hours. Remove from refrigerator, drain, and bring to room temperature. Seal the juices in the chicken by browning each piece on both sides, about 2 minutes per side. Move chicken to a cooler area of barbecue to finish cooking without burning, about 5 minutes.

To prepare for Black Bean Sauce, mix vinegar, orange juice, remaining 2 cloves garlic, and black beans together and purée in a blender or food processor. Add salt and pepper to taste. Warm in a microwave or in a saucepan. To blanch the onion and red pepper, bring a pot of water to the boil and add the onion and red pepper. As soon as the water returns to the boil, drain and rinse under cold water. Or place in a microwave-safe bowl and microwave on high for 3 minutes.

To serve, spoon a little Black Bean Sauce on a serving platter and place the chicken over the sauce. Sprinkle the top with the onion and red pepper. Garnish the platter with coriander or parsley. Serve the remaining sauce on the side. *Makes 2 servings.*

Per serving: 353 calories, 54.0 grams protein, 15.2 grams carbohydrate, 9.3 grams fat (1.9 saturated), 132 milligrams cholesterol, 117 milligrams sodium, 1.8 grams fibre

helpful hints

● *Make sure the grill bars on your barbecue are clean. Spray with vegetable oil spray. If using charcoal, heat the barbecue for about 45 minutes before use or 15 minutes if using gas. The coals should be glowing and the bars hot.*

● *If you do not have a barbecue, then brown the chicken in a very hot sauté pan.*

● *An easy way to marinate the chicken is to place it and the marinade in a self-seal plastic bag. It takes up less space in the refrigerator than a bowl and can be easily flipped over to make sure all sides of the chicken are marinated.*

green bean and orzo salad

225g (8oz) orzo

900g (2lb) fresh green beans, trimmed and cut into 2.5cm (1in) pieces

50ml (2fl oz) olive oil and vinegar dressing

Salt and freshly ground black pepper

25g (1oz) Parmesan cheese

Bring a large saucepan with 3–4 litres (5–7 pints) of water to the boil over high heat. Add the orzo and boil for 5 minutes. Add the beans and continue to boil for 5 minutes more. Drain. Place in a serving bowl and drizzle the dressing on top and toss well. Add salt and pepper to taste. Make Parmesan curls by thinly slicing the Parmesan with a potato peeler. Place the curls on top of the salad.

Makes 8 servings.

Per serving: 224 calories, 7.2 grams protein, 30.0 grams carbohydrate, 10.1 grams fat (2.6 saturated), 3 milligrams cholesterol, 108 milligrams sodium, 3.4 grams fibre

melon with marinated strawberries

1 honeydew melon, sliced

1.1kg (2¹/₂lb) fresh strawberries

3 tablespoons icing sugar, sifted

2 tablespoons freshly squeezed lemon juice

8 almond-flavoured or other bought biscuits

Wash, hull and slice strawberries. Blend in sugar and lemon juice. Leave to marinate for 3–4 hours.

Place 2 slices melon on each dessert plate and spoon strawberry sauce on top. Serve 1 biscuit on the side of each plate.

Makes 8 servings.

Per serving: 126 calories, 2.3 grams protein, 30.2 grams carbohydrate, 1 gram fat (0 saturated), 0 milligrams cholesterol, 16 milligrams sodium, 3.3 grams fibre

helpful hint

● *Any type of berry can be used, such as blueberries, raspberries or blackberries.*

desserts

introduction

With this chapter to hand, there's no need to abandon your healthy eating lifestyle when you want a special treat or have guests for dinner.

Most regular desserts, unfortunately, are laden with carbohydrates. I created these recipes for those occasions when you want something sweet at the end of a meal, without straying outside the guidelines of a low-carb lifestyle.

Desserts have not been included as part of the Quick Start section, but the Strawberry Pecan Whip and Coffee Latte Whip are two desserts that you can enjoy during the Quick Start phase (and subsequent phases). They make a satisfying end to a meal and have limited carbohydrate content. A few desserts are included in the Which Carbs section because they fit the nutritional guidelines for that menu. But most desserts have been included with the Right Carbs meals.

Here I have created some additional temptations as alternatives to a simple fruit or low-fat yoghurt dessert. The Mocha Fudge Soufflé and the Raspberry Parfait are winners with my family, and can be served to guests with pride.

dessert index

mocha fudge soufflé

Melting the chocolate in a microwave takes only minutes.

mocha fudge soufflé

50g (2oz) bittersweet or plain chocolate

1 tablespoon strong, decaffeinated, black coffee

2g (¹⁄₁₆oz) artificial sweetener

4 egg whites

Preheat the oven to 180°C/350°F/gas mark 4. Place the chocolate in a microwave-safe bowl and microwave on high for 2 minutes to melt. Stir in the coffee and sweetener.

Beat the egg whites until stiff peaks form. Fold into the chocolate mixture. Spoon into 2 soufflé dishes 4cm (1½in) high and 10cm (4in) in diameter, or a single Pyrex bowl 8cm (3in) high and 15cm (6in) in diameter. Bake in the oven for 8 minutes and serve warm.

Makes 2 servings.

One serving: 169 calories, 11g protein, 9g carbohydrate, 15g fat (9g saturated), 0mg cholesterol, 111mg sodium, 0g fibre

helpful hints

- *Buy high-quality chocolate for best results.*
- *Instant coffee can be used.*

countdown

- *Preheat oven to 180°C/350°F/gas mark 4.*
- *Melt chocolate.*
- *Whip egg whites.*
- *Complete recipe.*

shopping list

GROCERY

50g (2oz) bittersweet or plain chocolate

STAPLES

Eggs

Decaffeinated coffee

Artificial sweetener

strawberry pecan whip

'Whipped Jell-O' was a favourite of mine when I was young. Here is an updated version that fits perfectly into a low-carb lifestyle – and can be eaten in Quick Start, Which Carbs and Right Carbs.

strawberry pecan whip

125g (4½oz) sugar-free, low-calorie strawberry jelly

225ml (8fl oz) boiling water

225ml (8fl oz) cold water

1 teaspoon vanilla essence

2 tablespoons pecan pieces, toasted

50ml (2fl oz) semi-skimmed ricotta cheese

Dissolve the jelly in boiling water, stirring for 2 minutes. Add the cold water and place in the refrigerator to set for 1½ hours. Stir the vanilla essence and pecans into the ricotta cheese. Whip into the partially set jelly with an electric beater. Divide between 4 dessert bowls. Refrigerate to set once more before serving. *Makes 4 servings.*

One serving: 147 calories, 8g protein, 3g carbohydrate, 11g fat (3g saturated), 15mg cholesterol, 45mg sodium, 1g fibre

helpful hints

● *Any fruit-flavoured, sugar-free jelly can be used.*
● *Be careful toasting pecans, as they burn easily.*

countdown

● *Set water to boil.*
● *Make recipe.*

shopping list

DAIRY
1 small pot semi-skimmed ricotta cheese
GROCERY
1 packet sugar-free, low-calorie strawberry jelly
1 small packet pecan pieces
STAPLES
Vanilla essence

apricot almond custard

Good quality dried apricots add more flavour to this dish. Once reconstituted, they should look like fresh apricots. This dessert can be eaten during Right Carbs.

apricot almond custard

6 dried apricots
125ml (4fl oz) skimmed milk
2g (¹/₁₆oz) artificial sweetener
¼ teaspoon almond essence
1 egg
1 tablespoon flaked almonds

Preheat the oven to 180°C/350°F/gas mark 4. Bring a small saucepan of water to the boil and add the apricots. Boil for 3–4 minutes to reconstitute, then drain and coarsely chop. Combine the apricots, milk, sweetener, almond essence and egg in a small bowl. Divide between 2 ovenproof ramekins or a bowl 8 x 4.5cm (3 x 1¾ in) deep. Sprinkle the almonds on top. Bake for 30 minutes, or until the custard is firm.
Makes 2 servings.

One serving: 143 calories, 8g protein, 17g carbohydrate, 6g fat (1g saturated), 108mg cholesterol, 64mg sodium, 3g fibre

countdown

- Preheat oven to 180°C/350°F/gas mark 4.
- Set a small saucepan of water to boil.
- Complete recipe.

shopping list

GROCERY
  1 packet dried apricots (6 needed)
  1 small bottle almond essence
  1 small packet flaked almonds (about 10g/½oz needed)
STAPLES
  Skimmed milk
  Artificial sweetener
  Egg

coffee latte whip

This recipe was created for the Quick Start phase but can be used during any phase.

coffee latte whip

helpful hint
- Instant decaffeinated coffee can be used.

countdown
- Prepare ingredients.
- Make recipe.

shopping list

DAIRY
   1 small pot whipping cream
GROCERY
   1 packet gelatine (7g/¼oz envelope needed)
   1 container unsweetened cocoa powder
STAPLES:
   Artificial sweetener
   Decaffeinated coffee

1 tablespoon gelatine (7g/¼oz)
50ml (2fl oz) cold water
115ml (4fl oz) boiling water
4g (⅛oz) artificial sweetener

½ tablespoon unsweetened cocoa powder
50ml (2fl oz) strong, decaffeinated, black coffee
2 tablespoons whipping cream

Soak the gelatine in the cold water for 5 minutes. Pour the boiling water into the cold water-gelatine mixture to dissolve the gelatine. Stir in the sweetener, cocoa powder and coffee. Pour into a bowl and refrigerate for 1 hour to set. Remove the gelatine from the refrigerator and whip with an electric beater. Add the whipping cream and continue to whip until fluffy. Pour into 2 dessert dishes and refrigerate to set, about 15 minutes.

Makes 2 servings.

One serving: 74 calories, 4g protein, 3g carbohydrate, 6g fat (4g saturated), 21mg cholesterol, 12mg sodium, 0.5g fibre

acknowledgements

Many, many thanks go to my husband, Harold. He has been the main force behind this book. Since his decision nine years ago to adopt a low-carb lifestyle, he has stood by my work and by my side. He encouraged me to create the recipes, helped to test and taste them and edited every word.

I'd like to thank my assistant, Jackie Murrill, for her patience and help in testing these recipes. She spent hours on her feet working with me – and always with a smile.

Lisa Ekus has been my trusted friend for many years and as my agent was a wonderful help in bringing my ideas to the page. Many thanks, Lisa.

I'd also like to thank my family who have always supported my projects and encouraged me every step of the way. My son James, his wife Patty and their sons Zachary and Jacob, who all helped taste these recipes; my son Charles and his wife Lori who tested recipes via e-mail. My son John, his wife Jill and their children Jeffrey and Joanna, who cheered me on; my sister Roberta and brother-in-law Robert, who helped to edit my thoughts and words.

Thanks too go to Kathy Martin, my editor at the *Miami Herald*, who has been a friend and booster for my columns and books.

Producing and hosting a weekly radio show has been a delight as well as a vast amount of work. Thanks to the management and staff at WLRN 91.3 FM, public radio for South Florida, for their friendship and help.

I'd like to thank the many readers and students who correspond with me from all over the US to say how much they enjoy the recipes and how much better they feel. This kind of encouragement makes the lonely time in front of the computer worthwhile.

Most importantly, I'd like to thank all of you who read this book and prepare the meals. I hope you enjoy them and reap the benefits as much as I've enjoyed creating the recipes and watching the wonderful results.

index

notes